Determinants
of Infant Behaviour

Contributing Authors

JOHN BOWLBY

HELEN BLAUVELT

JOSEPH MCKENNA

MAVIS GUNTHER

H. F. R. PRECHTL

JAY S. ROSENBLATT

GERALD TURKEWITZ

T. C. SCHNEIRLA

HARRY F. HARLOW

GENEVIÈVE APPELL

MYRIAM DAVID

HARRIET L. RHEINGOLD

J. A. AMBROSE

R. A. HINDE

JACOB L. GEWIRTZ

DETERMINANTS
OF INFANT BEHAVIOUR

Proceedings of a Tavistock study group
on mother-infant interaction
held in
the house of the CIBA Foundation
London, September 1959

EDITED BY

B. M. FOSS

with a Foreword by
JOHN BOWLBY

LONDON· METHUEN & CO LTD
NEW YORK: JOHN WILEY & SONS INC

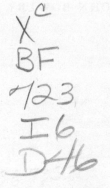

Contents

Contents

Plates

Members of the CIBA Seminar

DR J. A. AMBROSE, Senior Psychologist, Tavistock Child Development Research Unit, London

MLLE G. APPELL, Psychologist, Association pour le Développement de l'Assistance aux Malades, Montrouge, Paris

MRS M. BERNSTEIN, Assistant Psychologist, Tavistock Child Development Research Unit, London

DR H. BLAUVELT, Assistant Professor, Department of Pediatrics, Syracuse Memorial Hospital, New York

DR J. BOWLBY, Consultant Psychiatrist, Director of the Tavistock Child Development Research Unit, Director of the Department for Children and Parents, Tavistock Clinic, London

DR M. DAVID, Child Psychiatrist, Paris

MR B. M. FOSS, Lecturer, Department of Psychology, Birkbeck College, University of London

DR J. L. GEWIRTZ,[1] Professor of Psychology, Hebrew University, Jerusalem, Israel

DR M. GUNTHER, Obstetrician, Infant Welfare and Children's Department, University College Hospital, London

DR H. F. HARLOW, Professor of Psychology, University of Wisconsin, Madison, U.S.A.

DR R. A. HINDE, Zoologist, Department of Zoology, University of Cambridge

DR H. D. HUNTER, Consultant Psychiatrist, Department of Children and Parents, Tavistock Clinic, London

DR E. P. G. MICHELL, Consultant Psychiatrist, Department for Children and Parents, Tavistock Clinic, London

DR H. F. R. PRECHTL, Zoologist, Neurologische Kliniek, Academisch Ziekenhuis, Groningen, Holland

DR H. L. RHEINGOLD, Clinical Psychologist, Laboratory of Psychology, National Institute of Mental Health, Bethesda, Maryland, U.S.A.

[1] previously at National Institute of Mental Health, Bethesda, Maryland, U.S.A.

CIBA Seminar, 1959

MR J. ROBERTSON, Psychoanalyst, Senior Project Officer, Tavistock Child Development Research Unit, London

DR J. S. ROSENBLATT, Psychologist, The American Museum of Natural History, New York

DR T. ROWELL, Zoologist, Department of Zoology, University of Cambridge

DR J. D. SUTHERLAND, Consultant Psychiatrist, Director of the Tavistock Clinic, London

MISS R. THOMAS, Psychoanalyst, Hampstead Child-Therapy Clinic, London

Editor's Note

This study group was built around seven prepared papers, presented by Ambrose, Blauvelt, David, Gewirtz, Harlow, Rheingold and Rosenblatt. These are here published in full, though in most cases the scripts have been revised since the meetings were held. This is particularly so for the paper by Gewirtz. The group heard only a small part of his paper, and the discussion of it which is printed here will not appear to do justice to it. Since the extended form of the paper mentions Bowlby's work several times, I asked Bowlby to write a short reply, which is included.

During the course of the meeting, there were extended but improvised contributions from Gunther, Hinde and Prechtl. These are also included in revised form, with the discussions that followed them. Further discussion followed the showing of the film 'Maternal Deprivation in Young Children' by Appell. The central character of the film is a girl called Monique, and here we are printing some case notes about her. These illustrate the points raised in the discussion.

The discussions were recorded, transcribed and rigorously edited, with the result that the views of the speakers may be misrepresented on occasion. For this I take responsibility. Also there were two accidents – after Rheingold's paper the recording apparatus was found to be out of order, so that the discussion following her paper has had to be reconstructed from notes; and the exigencies of the time-table prevented a proper discussion of the paper presented by Rosenblatt.

For purposes of presentation in printed form the Proceedings have been divided into four parts, which reflect the dominant interests of the group. Part I – Neonate Behaviour – which includes the contributions from Blauvelt, Gunther and Prechtl, is concerned with responses showing in the human infant at birth or immediately afterwards. Part II – Animal Experiments – contains the papers presented by Rosenblatt and Harlow. The first is concerned largely with suckling in kittens, and might have been included in Part I; the second reports a study of the responses of baby rhesus monkeys to parent surrogates, and might equally well have been included in Part III – Social Behaviour. This has the contributions from Appell, David, Rheingold and Ambrose, and centres on the human infant's responding or failing to respond to adults. It also includes the short contribution from Hinde, which is largely theoretical, but arises mainly from the paper by Ambrose. Part IV – A Theoretical Approach – consists of the paper by Gewirtz, with discussion and Bowlby's reply.

The members of the group have been exemplary in making things easy for the editor, not only by being efficient, but very positively by their encouragement. I have been helped throughout by members of the Tavistock Child Development Research Unit, and particularly by Audrey Sanders, who undertook the arduous task of recording and transcribing the discussions, and by Janice Edmunds, who bore the brunt of the secretarial work; and for advice I have always been able to call on Tony Ambrose and Jimmy Robertson; and especially John Bowlby, who has been a constant support. My thanks go to all of them.

Members of the group will wish me to thank John Bowlby for convening the meetings, and for acting throughout as the most efficient yet benevolent of chairmen.

BRIAN FOSS

Foreword

Over the past fifty years it has become abundantly clear that the beginnings of both mental health and ill-health are to be found in the experience of the infant and young child in relation to his mother. The range of ill-health which can be understood as stemming from this relation and the extent of its significance for the whole problem of mental illness remain of course unknown and controversial. This does not affect the research worker, however. So long as there are grounds for believing that the nature of the relation is of any consequence for mental ill-health, it demands systematic attention.

Until recent years most of the knowledge available about mother-infant interaction in humans was either anecdotal or else a result of reconstructions based on data derived from older subjects. In the past decade, however, enquiries have been begun which have as their aim the systematic descriptive and causal study of what actually occurs during a baby's interaction with the humans who care for him. I believe this to herald a great advance in knowledge. Since both an improvement of research techniques in this field and an expansion of research is urgent, there was a strong case for bringing together a small group of interested workers. Thanks to a fertile proposal by Helen Blauvelt and the generous assistance of the Ciba Foundation a first meeting of a study group was convened and met in September 1959.

The constitution of the Group was designed to mix together three main groups of worker, each of whom seemed to have a specific contribution to make. First, we wished to have as many as we could of that small number who were already engaged in first-hand studies of the behaviour of infants and young children in a social setting. Secondly, we wished for representatives of the more numerous band of those making similar studies in animals, particularly mammals. Thirdly, we wished for a number of clinicians who could contribute from their experience of what seems pathologically and therapeutically relevant. The fact that with only one or two exceptions all those invited responded enthusiastically suggests that the time was ripe for a gathering of the kind envisaged.

The programme was structured to give about half the time available to invited presentations and to leave the other half free for such discussions and additional presentations as the Study Group itself determined. Anxiety that as a result there might be time hanging on our hands was swiftly dispelled. Instead the Chairman was faced with the difficult task of deciding which of the many topics clamouring for inclusion could be found a place.

In the belief that problems of method and theoretical interpretation are best approached from a firm base in empirical data, those invited to give papers were asked to concentrate on the findings of their empirical investigations. These papers and the discussions arising therefrom make up the bulk of the proceedings. They provide also the base that we sought from which discussion of theory could be fruitful.

In the event the Study Group found itself spending most of its time on the very young infant, human and sub-human, so that, apart from the film presentation by Geneviève Appell, the child of over twelve months was rather neglected. Moreover, considering it was intended to be a Study Group on mother-infant interaction, material on the behaviour of human mothers and their interactions with their infants was noticeably absent. No doubt there are reasons for this imbalance. It reflects perhaps the youth and complexity of the research topic. Methods of studying interaction are little developed as yet and there is much to be said as a first step for trying to elucidate some of the factors governing the behaviour used in the interaction process by one partner at a time. That the infant rather than the mother should have been the partner first to be selected need hardly surprise us. Not only is the infant in his cot a convenient captive subject but his behaviour repertoire is relatively limited – although complex enough. Neither the toddler nor his mother are quite so readily studied. If the Study Group has done no more than point both to the complexity of the problem and the distance still to be travelled, it has served a purpose.

On behalf of the Tavistock Child Development Research Unit which convened the Study Group I wish to record our deep gratitude to the Ciba Foundation for giving hospitality to participants and providing unrivalled facilities for a meeting of this kind; and

Foreword

to Brian Foss for undertaking the task of editing the proceedings.

We are grateful also to those bodies which support the work of the Unit. These are – The National Health Service, The Josiah Macy Jr. Foundation, the Foundations Fund for Research in Psychiatry and the Ford Foundation.

JOHN BOWLBY

PART I

Neonate Behaviour

Mother-Neonate Interaction : Capacity of the Human Newborn for Orientation[1]

HELEN BLAUVELT and JOSEPH McKENNA[2]

It is customary in a zoological study of behavior to precede experiment with a report of observation: a description of mother-neonate interaction. It has seemed wise to reverse this process. The form and tempo of any action of the human newborn may be the passive result of movement of a mother who supports it against the force of gravity.

Before attempting to study the interactions of the newborn with adults, it is necessary to know the capacity of babies for responses in the environment provided by the mother, and in the pre-feeding phase of the digestive cycle when babies in this study are routinely taken to their mothers.

Therefore, the description takes the form of hypotheses suggested by systematic observation.

Hypotheses suggested by Observation

From direct observation and study of the film grew the hypothesis that the newborn has capacity to respond to the stimulation of its mother with activity which orients the baby to its mother, stimulates her, and gives her information about the infant's capacities. The baby was not only manipulated by its mother but responded to her stimulation with active movement toward her, with her, and away from her. The effective movements of orientation, of prehension and opposition, which the newborn appeared to give to specific stimulation, often seemed to the observer to control the interrelationship.

It is possible that the great range of comfort and efficiency of this

[1] This study is supported by a grant from the Ford Foundation.

[2] Mr McKenna is at the Department of Industrial Engineering, Syracuse University, Syracuse, New York.

3

interaction sometimes is due to the rapid and vigorous movement of the baby, with or in opposition to, the activity of its mother. Often the investigator could see stimulation of the baby known to be associated with reflex responses. These may explain the mode and timing of the infant's active movement. This often included active manipulation of its mother by the baby. These movements could be seen by the observer, but not defined. At any moment, gravity or the mother's own action might be moving the baby and thereby be responsible for its movement.

Our observations suggest that mothers orient to their babies during the first day postpartum. Either the ventral surface of the baby is held against the mother's body where head movements of the baby may be felt, or the mother maintains a face-to-face orientation in which she can see the median ventral line of the baby's head, the median line of its face. If proximity is added to this orientation there is considerable opportunity for stimulation of a number of reflex responses which might serve to orient the neonate in the human environment offered by its mother. Where proximity occurred there was stimulation for the directional response to perioral tactile stimulation, the so-called rooting reflex. It is suggested here that the precise repetitive responses of the neonate to this stimulation, and its mother's constant orientation to her baby, form early interactions. These observations led to the basic hypothesis that the human mother and infant possess capacity for mutual orientation post-partum. Two experiments were then set up to determine whether the directional response to perioral tactile stimulation served to orient the baby to the type of stimulus observed in mother-infant contacts. Clearly this is an example of contact behavior which can serve an orienting function.

The Reflex Response of the Neonate

The movements of the baby's head in response to touch on the cheek and lips form the most mature of the newborn's behavioral responses. They are present in the eight and one-half week old fetus, in contra-lateral form (Hooker, 1952). There is evidence that the movements of the head lead in activity of the newborn, other body parts relating reflexly to the head's position (Gesell, 1938).

This reflex has been recently reviewed in a stimulating behavioral

4

study (Prechtl, 1958). Early development of the sense organs in the reflexogenous zone (Merkel discs; Golgi-Mazzoni corpuscles; Meissner's corpuscles and free nerve endings) are described by Hogg, 1941. The mandibular and maxillary branches of the trigeminal nerve innervate the reflexogenous zone. Through the afferent fibers of these nerves, impulses reach the spinal trigeminal complex (Olszewski, 1950), and are mediated via internuncial neurons and the spinal trigeminal tract (Humphrey, 1952) to the first five cervical segments. The efferent fibers of these nerves innervate the executive muscles, principally sternomastoid and the upper part of trapezius. This system has connections with higher centers through dorsal and ventral ascending tracts.

This response is reported as a reflex in the first twenty weeks of life (Gesell, 1941).

Plates 1 and 2 are instances illustrating a few of the many forms of stimulation of this reflex. This baby is two weeks old. In Plate 1 the baby is turning his median ventral line toward his mother's face in response to her touch on his left cheek.

Plate 2 shows the same baby. Here his mother's face turns and makes contact with his right cheek as her shoulder supports the left side of his head. Stimulated on both sides he will come to rest with his face against her neck.

Procedure for Observations

Since it was desirable not to change any aspect of the hospital environment for purposes of sampling, the investigator entered the hospital at a time chosen at random and worked with the next family to enter the hospital. This removed bias from the selection of the individuals studied, the hospital staff who cared for this baby and mother, and the part of the hospital in which the baby and mother lived.

The first two years of this study were concerned with a 'field study' in a three hundred and forty-two bed hospital which has accommodation for fifty-four babies and their mothers. Overt interactions of baby and mother were observed during:

A 1. The postpartum period in the delivery room; and during a fifteen minute period when mother, father, and baby were together after the mother and her baby left the delivery room.

2. The first feeding period, usually twenty-four hours after delivery.

3. Further periods when mother and baby had contact during the four or five day stay in the hospital.

B 1. Periods when infants were cared for by the nursing staff. The interaction of a baby and mother was compared with that of baby and nurse.

The movement of babies in the inanimate environment of the nursery crib was also studied. This included a preliminary analysis of the interrelationship of head and extremity movements.

The investigator joined the room-to-room staff tour made during periods when mothers and babies are together. The purpose of the tour is to offer assistance to mothers and to check the safety of the babies. The orientation and posture of mothers and their babies were recorded immediately after leaving each room.

Some instances of these interactions were recorded on film for more detailed study. Twenty families chosen at random, agreed to the filming of any of the baby's movement during its stay in the hospital. The film was taken with the knowledge and consent of the mother, who, however, never knew when a sample interaction was to be filmed. No further interference with hospital routine was made. This procedure enabled us to record 1,400 feet of filmed mother-infant relationship.

Experimental Procedure

In order to detect the movements of the child and relate them to the movements of the stimulation, techniques were needed which would provide for (1) slow-motion analysis of the movements in question, (2) precise measurements of the time relationships involved, (3) possibility of reviewing the original motion sequences at any time. These requirements suggested the use of micro-motion study developed by F. B. Gilbreth (Barnes, 1948) and first made public in 1912.[1] Micro-motion study makes use of motion pictures taken at constant and known speeds so that the time lapse between frames is uniform

[1] A motion picture, though valuable in itself, should not be confused with a micromotion study. The latter requires, in addition to the picture of the operation, a very accurate timing device and a full analysis of the motions used. (Barnes, 1948, p. 94.)

and known. Thus, the filmstrip itself constitutes a time sequence of activity.

The film samples were taken at the 2 a.m. feeding. The four-hour period from the end of evening visiting from 10 p.m. to 2 a.m. is the time when hospital routine gave the babies least stimulation. The infants were allowed to wake spontaneously. The same nursing staff, two registered nurses, assisted throughout the study.

The children in this nursery were dressed in fresh shirt and diapers before feeding. As their clothes were removed they were rolled in their own cribs a few feet from the camera and for six seconds gently stimulated, as we had observed their mothers stimulate them. The sample was recorded on moving picture film.

Equipment

A 16-mm. moving picture camera with a wide-angle lens, mounted on a tripod. No artificial light was used, fast film making possible

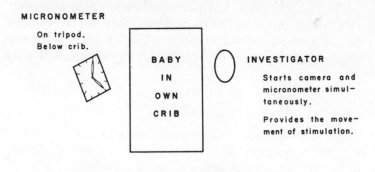

MICRONOMETER

On tripod.
Below crib.

BABY IN OWN CRIB

INVESTIGATOR

Starts camera and micronometer simul-taneously.

Provides the move-ment of stimulation.

CAMERA

On tripod. Pointing down at an angle of 45°.

Records micronometer readings and the movements of stimulation and response.

FIG. 1

Schematic diagram of method of recording the movements of stimulation and of response the recording in the normal soft light of the nursery. The level of illumination was indicated by a Weston meter reading of 1·5, the light of the nursery. Figure 1 gives a diagram of the equipment. A typical frame is shown in Plate 3.

Subjects

The subjects are all the babies in the hospital nursery on the days samples were collected. Each infant was examined by a pediatrician and reported a normal, full-term infant.

The Form of the Stimulus

This sequence, often observed, suggested the form of the stimulus. As a baby's face is turned towards its mother, the stimulation of her supporting arm may move from the baby's ear along its cheek to the region of the lips. The baby's lips may move to meet such stimulation. When the mother moves the baby's head away from her this stimulation may be reversed, moving from the baby's lips towards the ear. The baby's lips may move to overtake this stimulation, following after it.

The Samples

The sample is divided into three periods. Period 1 is 0·160 minute before tactile stimulation. This period serves as a control period. Period 2 is the experimental period of tactile stimulation.

With the child lying on its left side, contact is made on the right cheek at the ear with the ball of the forefinger which proceeds in a clockwise direction following an oval pattern from a point near the lobe of the ear to the oral area and back again with light pressure between the finger and the cheek. This movement repeated three times in 0·160 minute ±0·030 minute constitutes the experimental stimulus. The time stimulation takes, in traveling from ear to lips or lips to ear, is defined as an interval. Each interval of Period 2 is matched with a comparable interval of time in Period 1. Period 3 is the 0·160 minute immediately following tactile stimulation.

These three periods recorded on film constitute the sample.

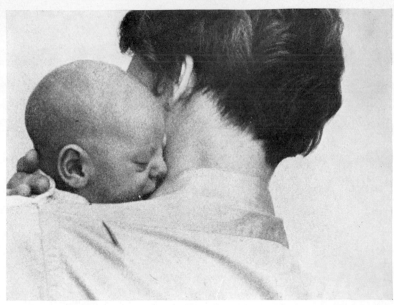

Plate 1

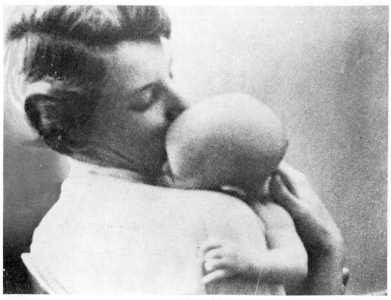

Plate 2

PLATES 1 and 2. Stimulation of the orienting reflex as a mother holds her two-week old baby.

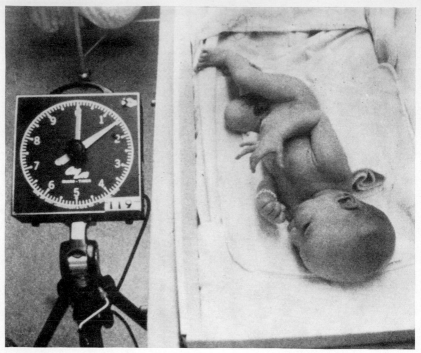

PLATE 3. Typical frame from sample film

Samples not used in this Study

Before samples were collected, it was planned to set aside those in which movement of the baby was of such speed or amplitude that the stimulus was sub-standard.

There are forty-six babies in Experiment 1. One sample was recorded from each baby. Nine samples were set aside as sub-standard.

There are seventeen babies in Experiment 2. One sample was recorded from each baby – one each of the first four days of life, making sixty-eight samples. In thirteen of these it was not possible to get a standard sample, so they were set aside.

The Predicted Movement

In the first Experiment it was apparent from the charts that the movement to the right most often occurred in 0·3 of an interval before and after the finger crossed the midline of the lips. It was predicted that any movement in this period would be a right movement or a right movement followed by a left movement. Movement to the left occurred most consistently in the 0·3 interval before and after the finger passed the ear. It was predicted that any movement in this period would be a left movement or a left movement followed by a right.

(Experiment 1 is a completed experiment. Experiment 2 is incomplete. For this symposium, the four samples on each child, one on each of the first four days, are added so that we can see how they compare with Experiment 1. The responses of these four days are quite possibly not independent.)

Analysis of the Film

The data are taken from the film by an analysis in terms of functioning movements. Interrelationships become systematically apparent. The film is analyzed on one of the Time and Motion Study projectors developed for micro-motion study. The speed is calibrated so that the analyst controls and is always aware of the 'Magnification' of time attained.

In this way the interrelationship of the movements of stimulation and the movements of response can be plotted in time and their

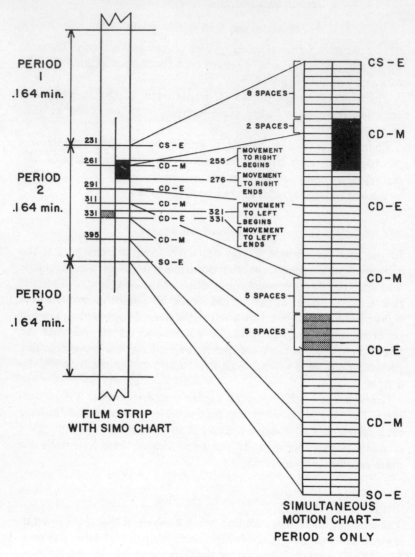

FIG. 2

Film analysis and proportioning of data

10

coordination assessed with precision. One-thousandth of a minute was chosen as the unit of measurement. This meant that movements and rest periods between movements of less than 0·001 minute were eliminated from consideration.

The result of the film analysis is a vertical time scale on which is recorded at the proper points in time; the contact of the stimulus; the point at which the stimulus ceases contact; the various changing directions of the stimulus; and the time of the beginning and end of each movement of the child's head to the right or left. This permits us to summate the frequencies of the movements in the population and relate them to the stimulation with precision. Barnes (1948) gives a detailed description of the method.

Proportioning of the Data

The great precision of this method made minute differences in the non-mechanical stimulus apparent. It was necessary to proportion the analysis charts in order to make them directly comparable. This proportioning requires that each of the periods within the stimulus period be equal for all of the film sequences. The desired result was accomplished by setting up a chart having standard proportions (Figure 2). In this chart the stimulus and the control periods were each divided into six intervals of ten units in length. The analysis of each sample was adjusted to conform to this standard chart. Where a period had to be lengthened, the motions within it were lengthened in the same proportion, and wherever a period had to be shortened in order to conform with the standard length of period, the motions within it were shortened proportionally also.

After each motion sequence had been modified to conform to these standard motion charts, it was possible to place all of these charts side by side, and by adding horizontally, determine the number of movements to either right or left which appeared in any horizontal line.

Method for the Comparison of Responses to the Same Stimulation near the Lips and near the Ear

Figure 3 illustrates schematically the path of the movement of experimental stimulation as well as the two responses to stimulation

11

near the lips. From the tragus of the ear to the median line of the lips is an interval which can be divided into ten equal parts by the pace of the moving stimulus. From the lips to the ear is another interval.

To compare responses near the ear and near the lips while stimulation is moving from the ear to the lips, we compare responses in the first 0·3 of this interval near the ear with response in the last 0·3 of it near the lips. Similarly, to compare responses near the ear with

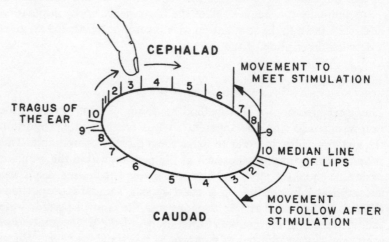

FIG. 3

The path of stimulation and movements of response

those near the lips when stimulation moves from the lips to the ear, we compare response in the first 0·3 of this interval near the lips with response in the last 0·3 near the ear.

The film of Experiment 1 was analyzed by two investigators; that of Experiment 2 by three. One sample in every ten was chosen at random and analyzed by each worker for reliability. Workers disagreed on time of beginning and end of movements, and the presence of pauses in long movements, but disagreement as to the presence of a movement was rare. The film was analyzed frame by frame so that one could locate the frame on which action began or at least find the last frame before movement began, and the first one after it began.

12

Helen Blauvelt and Joseph McKenna

The movements of the newborn, analyzed at this level, are seen to be a series of movements and pauses rather than the smooth continuous motion of adult movement. It is possible that the muscles and their antagonists are not yet adequately coordinated for smooth motion. Some criteria must be set up to define these pauses. We chose to ignore pauses of 0·004 minute or less in a movement. Movements of less than 0·001 minute are not included.

TABLE I

Reliability

Agreement as to Frequency of Movement	
Experiment	% Agreement
1	100
2	98

Specific Hypotheses

1. We suggest that the response movements at the lips will coordinate repetitively with the movements of stimulation both in direction and in time, with precision necessary to maintain orientation.

It is of interest to know whether such capacity is specific or generalized. Hence –

2. We suggest there will be a difference in the orientation of movements evoked by tactile stimulation of two regions of the face: the perioral region and the region mesad of the tragus of the ear.

Results

Will babies move in response to this stimulus with such precision that the movements of response will coordinate with the movements of stimulation? Can the neonate orient in time and space to rapid repetitive stimulation? Will the median line move to meet this stimulation, and follow after it as well?

The results in Experiment 2 for both these responses are illustrated in Figure 4. The left side of this graph shows the direction of movements in the stimulus period as stimulation approaches the median line of the lips: the right side of the graph shows the direction of

13

movements in the stimulus period as stimulation leaves the lips. The results at the first, second and third repetitive stimulations are shown. The direction of movement in comparable periods of time in the pre-stimulus control period is shown above; and comparable periods of time in the post-stimulus period are shown below.

Orientation during repetitive tactile stimulation near the lips[1]

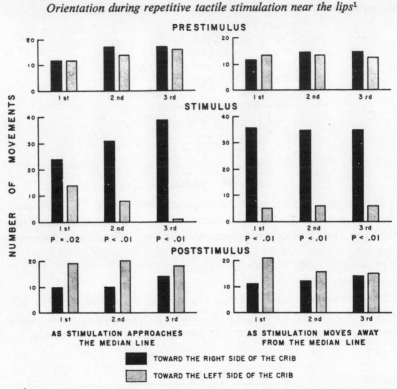

[1] 0.3 of the area between the tragus of the ear and the median line of the lips as measured by the moving stimulus

FIG. 4

We see fairly even numbers of movements to the left and to the right in the pre-stimulus periods in each stimulation, in both experiments. The incidence of movement to the right goes up. General motility of the babies increased during the pre-stimulus period, probably in response to the sound of the camera and clock. In the

14

Helen Blauvelt and Joseph McKenna

stimulus periods the movement becomes sharply patterned with movement to the right much greater than movement to the left. Both, as stimulation approaches from the right, and as it moves away toward the right, the median line of the lips orient to it. The movement in the post-stimulus periods returns again to a more random appearance. Movements to the right are active movements. Movements toward the left are both active and passive. Therefore, we may expect more movement to the left than to the right.

The data for these responses in both Experiments are shown in Tables II and III.

TABLE II

Movement to Meet Repetitive Stimulation Approaching the Lips

Movement	EXPERIMENT I			EXPERIMENT II		
	To Meet	Other	N	To Meet	Other	N
First Stimulation:						
Experimental	19	18	37	24	31	55
Control	4	33	37	12	43	55
N	23	51	74	36	74	110
	$\chi^2 = 14 \cdot 19$ $P < \cdot 01$			$\chi^2 = 5 \cdot 95$ $P < \cdot 05$		
Second Stimulation:						
Experimental	18	19	37	31	24	55
Control	11	26	37	17	38	55
N	29	45	74	48	62	110
	$\chi^2 = 2 \cdot 78$ $P < \cdot 05$			$\chi^2 = 7 \cdot 24$ $P < \cdot 01$		
Third Stimulation:						
Experimental	19	18	37	39	16	55
Control	9	28	37	17	38	55
N	28	46	74	56	54	110
	$\chi^2 = 5 \cdot 75$ $P < \cdot 01$			$\chi^2 = 17 \cdot 606$ $P < \cdot 01$		

Stimulation in the 0·3 of an interval nearest the lips. An interval is the distance from the tragus of the ear to the median line of the lips as measured by the moving stimulation. If the expected frequency falls below 5, Fisher's exact test is used (Fisher, 1950).

15

TABLE III

The Movement to Follow after Repetitive Stimulation Leaving the Lips

Movement	EXPERIMENT I			EXPERIMENT II		
	To Meet	Other	N	To Meet	Other	N
First Stimulation:						
Experimental	22	15	37	36	19	55
Control	2	35	37	12	43	55
N	24	50	74	48	62	110
	$\chi^2 = 24{\cdot}67$		$P < {\cdot}01$	$\chi^2 = 19{\cdot}93$		$P < {\cdot}01$
Second Stimulation:						
Experimental	23	14	37	35	20	55
Control	8	29	37	15	40	55
N	31	43	74	50	60	110
	$\chi^2 = 12{\cdot}49$		$P < {\cdot}01$	$\chi^2 = 14{\cdot}67$		$P < {\cdot}01$
Third Stimulation:						
Experimental	21	16	37	35	20	55
Control	12	25	37	15	40	55
N	33	41	74	50	60	110
	$\chi^2 = 4{\cdot}43$		$P < {\cdot}01$	$\chi^2 = 14{\cdot}67$		$P < {\cdot}01$

Stimulation in the 0·3 of an interval nearest the lips. An interval is the distance from the tragus of the ear to the median line of the lips as measured by the moving stimulation. If the expected frequency falls below 5, Fisher's exact test is used (Fisher, 1950).

The control for non-experimental stimulation from the environment is of importance in these experiments undertaken in the normal living quarters of these infants.

In this control the experiment is repeated except that the 'stimulating' finger moves without making contact with the baby. In other words, the only difference between these samples is the tactile stimulation of the baby. Table IV indicates that the frequency of response with tactile stimulation (Experimental) was greater than the frequency of response without tactile stimulation (Control).

TABLE IV

Control for Non-Experimental Stimulation in the Environment

Movement to meet stimulation approaching the lips.

Stimulation Number	FIRST			SECOND			THIRD		
Movement	To Meet	Other	N	To Meet	Other	N	To Meet	Other	N
Experimental	24	31	55	31	24	55	39	16	55
Control	14	41	55	15	40	55	16	39	55
N	38	72	110	46	64	110	55	55	110

$$\chi^2 = 4\cdot02 \quad P < \cdot05 \qquad \chi^2 = 9\cdot57 \quad P < \cdot01 \qquad \chi^2 = 19\cdot24 \quad P < \cdot01$$

Movement to follow after stimulation leaving the lips.

Stimulation Number	FIRST			SECOND			THIRD		
Movement	To Meet	Other	N	To Meet	Other	N	To Meet	Other	N
Experimental	36	19	55	35	20	55	35	20	55
Control	19	36	55	14	41	55	20	35	55
N	55	55	110	49	61	110	55	55	110

$$\chi^2 = 10\cdot51 \quad P < \cdot01 \qquad \chi^2 = 16\cdot23 \quad P < \cdot01 \qquad \chi^2 = 8\cdot18 \quad P < \cdot01$$

Stimulation in the 0·3 of an interval nearest the lips. An interval is the distance from the tragus of the ear to the median line of the lips as measured by the moving stimulation. If the expected frequency falls below 5, Fisher's exact test is used (Fisher, 1950).

The orientation of movement when stimulation approaches and leaves the ear is illustrated in Figure 5. In the pre-stimulus period the movement appears unpatterned. In the stimulus periods, both as stimulation approaches and moves away from the tragus of the ear, the movement becomes strongly patterned, movements to the left increasing in frequency as compared with such movements in the pre-stimulus control periods, and in the post-stimulus periods.

The meaning of these movements to the left is not clear. In these experiments there is no control for the force of gravity in movements to the left. Such movement may be active or passive. In the stimulus period, movements to the right may be followed by movement to the left as stimulation leaves the reflexogenous region near the lips. This is suggested in the data of Tables V and VI. Here the

Movement of the head [1] during repetitive tactile stimulation near the ear

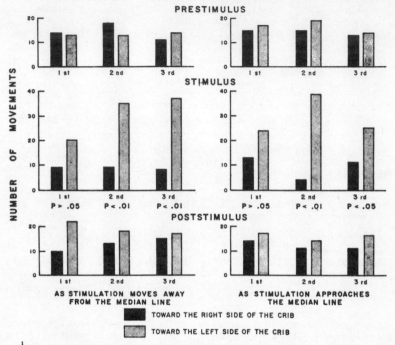

[1] 0.3· of the area between the tragus of the ear and the median line of the lips as measured by the moving stimulus

FIG. 5

TABLE V

Head Movement as Repetitive Stimulation Approaches the Ear

	EXPERIMENT I			EXPERIMENT II		
Movement	Toward the left	Other	N	Toward the left	Other	N
First Stimulation:						
Experimental	16	21	37	24	31	55
Control	7	30	37	17	38	55
N	23	51	74	41	69	110
	$\chi^2 = ·2762$ $P > ·05$			$\chi^2 = 1·91$ $P > ·05$		

18

Second Stimulation:						
Experimental	15	22	37	39	16	55
Control	10	27	37	19	36	55
N	25	49	74	58	52	110

$\chi^2 = 1.5102$ P > ·05 $\chi^2 = 14.59$ P < ·01

Third Stimulation:						
Experimental	18	19	37	25	30	55
Control	9	28	37	14	41	55
N	27	47	74	39	71	110

$\chi^2 = 4.7233$ P < ·05 $\chi^2 = 4.81$ P < ·05

Stimulation in the 0·3 of an interval nearest the ear.

TABLE VI
Head Movement as Repetitive Stimulation Leaves the Ear

	EXPERIMENT I			EXPERIMENT II		
Movement	Toward the left	Other	N	Toward the left	Other	N
First Stimulation:						
Experimental	8	29	37	20	35	55
Control	7	30	37	13	42	55
N	15	59	74	33	77	110

$\chi^2 = ·0083$ P > ·05 $\chi^2 = 2.12$ P > ·05

Second Stimulation:						
Experimental	21	16	37	35	20	55
Control	7	30	37	13	42	55
N	28	46	74	48	62	110

$\chi^2 = 11.2609$ P < ·01 $\chi^2 = 17.89$ P < ·01

Third Stimulation:						
Experimental	19	18	37	37	18	55
Control	9	28	37	14	41	55
N	28	46	74	51	59	110

$\chi^2 = 5.7453$ P < ·05 $\chi^2 = 19.34$ P < ·01

Stimulation in the 0·3 of an interval nearest the ear.

expected movement is a movement to the left during the same stimulation which drew right movements in response near the lips. 'Other'

19

movement includes movement to the right and samples in which no movement occurs. In the first two stimulations approaching the ear and in the first stimulation leaving the ear, the difference between experimental and control samples is not significant. Only later, when the movement to the right in response to stimulation near the lips is high, does this movement to the left become significantly patterned.

Essential to the infant's capacity to coordinate with its mother's movement is specificity of response in certain regions of the body. It was predicted that movement would differ when the same tactile stimulation was applied near the lips and near the ear. The method of making this comparison is described on page 12. Tables VII and VIII present the data.

TABLE VII

A Difference in Response to the Same Stimulation Near the Ear and Near the Lips
(Stimulation Moving from the Ear to the Lips)

Movement	EXPERIMENT I			EXPERIMENT II		
	To the right	To the left	N	To the right	To the left	N
First Stimulation:						
Near the ear	7	8	15	9	20	29
Near the lips	19	4	23	24	14	38
N	26	12	38	33	34	67
	$\chi^2 = 5\cdot43$ P < ·05			$\chi^2 = 6\cdot79$ P < ·01		
Second Stimulation:						
Near the ear	5	21	26	9	37	46
Near the lips	18	5	23	31	8	39
N	23	26	49	40	45	85
	$\chi^2 = 17\cdot07$ P < ·01			$\chi^2 = 30\cdot42$ P < ·01		
Third Stimulation:						
Near the ear	3	19	22	8	37	45
Near the lips	19	6	25	39	1	40
N	22	25	47	47	38	85
	$\chi^2 = 18\cdot28$ P < ·01			$\chi^2 = 54\cdot45$ P < ·01		

If expected frequencies fall below 5, Fisher's exact test is used (Fisher, 1950, p. 96). Stimulation in the 0·3 of an interval nearest the ear and lips respectively.

TABLE VIII

A Difference in Response to the Same Stimulation Near the Ear and Near the Lips
(Stimulation moving from the Lips to the Ear)

Movement	EXPERIMENT I			EXPERIMENT II		
	To the right	To the left	N	To the right	To the left	N
First Stimulation:						
Near the ear	10	16	26	13	24	37
Near the lips	22	2	24	35	6	41
N	32	18	50	48	30	78
	$\chi^2 = 15\cdot33$ $P < \cdot01$			$\chi^2 = 20\cdot73$ $P < \cdot01$		
Second Stimulation:						
Near the ear	4	15	19	4	39	43
Near the lips	23	5	28	35	6	41
N	27	20	47	39	45	84
	$\chi^2 = 17\cdot28$ $P < \cdot01$			$\chi^2 = 48\cdot8$ $P < \cdot01$		
Third Stimulation:						
Near the ear	6	18	24	11	25	36
Near the lips	21	3	24	35	6	41
N	27	21	48	46	31	77
	$\chi^2 = 19\cdot05$ $P < \cdot01$			$\chi^2 = 23\cdot94$ $P < \cdot01$		

Stimulation in the 0·3 of an interval nearest the lips and the ear, respectively. An interval is the distance from the tragus of the ear to the median line of the lips as measured by the moving stimulation. If the expected frequency falls below 5, Fisher's exact test is used (Fisher, 1950, p. 96).

The Reflex Response

It is of interest to note what is the reflex response to this stimulation before it is divided into its behavioral components of movement to meet and movement to follow after. This is illustrated for Experiment 2 in Figure 6. The data for both experiments are given in Table IX. Table VII shows the difference in frequency of right and left movements as stimulation moves mesad, from the ear to the lips. Table VIII gives similar data as stimulation moves laterad from the lips to the ear. In both tables a difference in the direction of movement when stimulation is near the ear and when it is near the lips is apparent at each stimulation in both experiments.

21

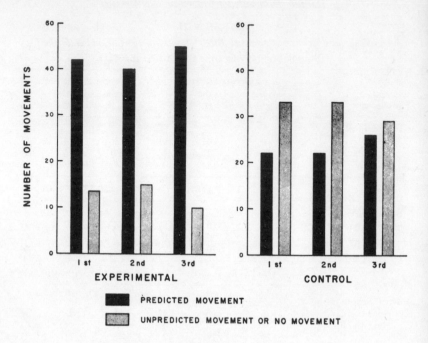

FIG. 6

Reflex response to tactile stimulation in oral area

TABLE IX

The Response as a Reflex

Movement	EXPERIMENT I			EXPERIMENT II		
	Reflex	Other	N	Reflex	Other	N
First Stimulation:						
Experimental	24	13	37	42	13	55
Control	10	27	37	22	33	55
N	34	40	74	64	46	110
		$\chi^2 = 10 \cdot 66$	$P < \cdot 01$		$\chi^2 = 14 \cdot 945$	$P < \cdot 01$
Second Stimulation:						
Experimental	26	11	37	40	15	55
Control	14	23	37	22	33	55
N	40	34	74	62	48	110
		$\chi^2 = 7 \cdot 83$	$P < \cdot 01$		$\chi^2 = 11 \cdot 98$	$P < \cdot 01$

Third Stimulation:						
Experimental	26	11	37	45	10	55
Control	16	21	37	26	29	55
N	42	32	74	71	39	110

$$\chi^2 = 5\cdot51 \quad P < \cdot01 \qquad \chi^2 = 14\cdot34 \quad P < \cdot01$$

Discussion

In this biological study, it is appropriate to consider such interaction in other primates. Since its selective value may be considerable at this taxonomic level, the manner and timing of primate mother and neonate interaction may help to define interactions for which human babies and their mothers possess potentialities.

Mother-Neonate Interaction in Other Primates

There is a considerable literature giving field descriptions of observed primate maternal-neonate interaction in both primitive and highly specialized groups.[1] A few studies of animals in captivity add information. The different genera of primates vary in the posture and precise position in which the neonate is carried and protected. Common for all groups for which we have field data, however, is an orientation of mother and newborn in which the ventral surface of the young opposes the ventral surface of the mother after birth. The newborn grasps her fur with hands and feet (tail prehension does not develop until later).

The mother tolerates this contact, and in some groups she is seen to facilitate it and to support the newborn with her arms when she does not require them for locomotion or other activities. A fine series of photographs by Spiegel (1954) shows the birth and first mother-infant interaction in the Javanese Macaque, *iris*. The mother appears to reach behind to support the infant's head as its body emerges, and moves the infant to her ventral surface where she holds

[1] Bingham, 1932; Bolwig, 1959; Carpenter, 1934a, 1934b, 1935, 1938, 1940; Haddow, 1952; Harms, 1956; Meyer-Holzapfel, 1949, 1956; Nissen, 1931; Nolte, 1958, 1959; Pocock, 1906; Robinson, 1925; Rand, 1935; Schultz, 1926; Schiller. 1952: Spiegel, 1954; Yerkes, 1935.

23

it against herself. Ventral flexion of the mother's body around her newborn provides shelter and protection when they are at rest. During locomotion of the mother, the newborn may maintain the contact unaided. We may speculate that the primate neonate has capacity for sustained orientation to its mother and for making contact with her as it lies against her, its hands and feet grasping her fur. It is possible that the postpartum physiological state of the mother is associated with her tolerance of the newborn. Specific stimulation by the newborn itself may initiate the specific overt action by which its mother supports it.

We may speculate whether the human newborn also possesses capacity to respond to its mother in this way. Would this response be associated with her mode of handling the baby?

The experimental study of the development of behavioral responses and their mechanism in phylogenetically related groups is of interest as stated by Gavin de Beer (1954): 'Since phylogeny is but the result of modified ontogeny, there is the possibility of a causal analytic study of present evolution in an experimental study of the variability and genetics of ontogenetic processes.'

Since the mechanisms underlying such behavior result from the phylogenetic history of each organism, these responses require study in each taxonomic group.

In a provocative paper published in 1935, Konrad Lorenz listed characteristic responses of parent and young animals which mediated the social relationship between them. He suggested that the responses he describes are not purposive, but are physiologically potentiated and represent genetic adaptations. Recently he rephrased this early theory: 'The organism receives information from the internal and external environment, from its ontogeny (personal experience), and from the phylogenetic stream' (Lorenz, 1958).

Bowlby (1958) suggests this as a rewarding approach for the study of the human infant and its mother. He suggests that sucking, clinging, crying, smiling and following may release the behavior which functions as maternal care.

Sensitive and well-documented anthropological studies have informed us of the differences in the human environment offered the young in different human societies (Mead and MacGregor, 1951). The stimulation offered the neonate and the capacities of babies to respond may have different meaning in different populations. This paper offers a method for the measurement of some of these differences.

The demonstration of the infant's response to specific stimulation makes possible the study of the mutual action of mother and baby. The continued orientation to their baby's face, observed in many parents, suggests that all or some of them sense and respond to this early response of their infants. At the level appropriate to his phase of development, the neonate possesses capacity for such an interaction.

Acknowledgements

The tempo of the stimulus and the interesting importance of establishing a difference in response at the lips and at the ear were suggestions contributed by Earle Lipton, M.D. The adaptation of micromotion analysis, and the method of proportioning the data are the work of Joseph McKenna. The senior author takes responsibility for the experiments and their interpretation.

REFERENCES

BARNES, R. M. (1948) 'Motion and Time Study', Chap. 8 in *Micromotion Study*. John Wiley and Sons, Inc., New York

BINGHAM, H. C. (1932) 'Gorillas in a Native Habitat' *Carnegie Inst. Wash. Pub.* No. 426, 66

BOLWIG, NIELS (1959) 'A Study of the Behavior of the Chacma Baboon (Papio ursinus)' *Behaviour*, **14**, 136

BOWLBY, JOHN (1958) 'The Nature of the Child's Tie to His Mother' *Int. J. Psycho-Anal.* **39** (5), 1-24

CARPENTER, C. R. (1934a) 'Behavior & Social Relations of Howling Monkeys' *Comp. Psychol. Monogr.* **10**, 127

CARPENTER, C. R. (1934b) 'Sexual Behavior of Free Ranging Rhesus Monkeys' *J. comp. Physiol.* **33**, 133-162

CARPENTER, C. R. (1935) 'Behavior of Red Spider Monkeys in Panama' *J. Mammal.* **16**, 171

CARPENTER, C. R. (1938) 'A Survey of Wild Life Conditions in Atjeh, North Sumatra, with Special Reference to the Orangutan' *Communications No. 12 of the Netherlands Committee for International Nature Protection*, 1-34

CARPENTER, C. R. (1940) 'A Field Study in Siam of the Behavior and Social Relations of the Gibbon (Hylobates Lar)' *Comp. Psychol. Monogr.* Vol. 16, No. 5, 212

CROSBY, E. C., & YOSS, R. E. (1954) 'The Phylogenetic Continuity of Neural Mechanisms as illustrated by the Spinal Tract of V and its Nucleus' *Res. Publ. Ass. nerv. ment. Dis.* 33, 174-208

DE BEER, GAVIN (1954) *Embryos and Ancestors* Oxford U. Press, London

FISHER, R. A. (1935) *The Design of Experiments* Hafner Pub. Co., New York

FISHER, R. A. (1950) *Statistical Methods for Research Workers* Hafner Pub. Co., New York

GESELL, ARNOLD (1938) 'The Tonic Neck Reflex in the Human Infant: Its Morphogenetic and Clinical Significance' *J.Pediat.* 13, 455-464

GESELL, ARNOLD, & ARMATRUDA, CATHERINE (1941) *Developmental Diagnosis* Hoeber, New York

GRAHAM, F. K. (1956) 'Behavioral Differences Between Normal and Traumatized Newborns: The Test Procedures' *Psychol. Monogr.* 70 (20), 1-16

GRAHAM, F. K., MATARAZZO, RUTH G., & CALDWELL, BETTYE M. (1956) 'Behavioral Differences Between Normal and Traumatized Newborns II: Standardization, Reliability and Validity' *Psychol. Monogr.* 70 (21), 17-33

GUNTHER, MAVIS (1955) 'Instinct and the Nursing Couple' *The Lancet*, 575-578

HADDOW, A. J. (1952) 'Field and Laboratory Studies on an African Monkey, Cercopithecus ascanius schmidti. Matschie' *Proc. zool. Soc. London*, 122, 297-394

HARMS, SCHWANGERSCHAFT, & GEBURT in H. HOFER, A. H. SCHULTZ, & D. STARCH (1956) *Primatologia*, S. Karger, Basel

HOGG, I. D. (1941) 'Sensory nerves and associated structures in the skin of human fetuses of 8 to 14 weeks of menstrual age correlated with functional capability' *J. comp. Neurol.* 75, 371-410

HOOKER, DAVENPORT (1939) 'Fetal Behavior' *Res. Publ. Ass. Res. nerv. ment. Dis.* 19, 237-243

HOOKER, DAVENPORT (1942) 'Fetal Reflexes and Instinctual Processes' *Psychosom. Med.* 4, 199-205

HOOKER, DAVENPORT (1943) 'Reflex Activities in the Human Fetus' in *Child Behav. and Develop.* ed. by Barker, Kounin and Wright, McGraw-Hill, New York. Chap 2, 17-28

HOOKER, DAVENPORT (1952) *The Prenatal Origins of Behavior* U. of Kansas Press, Kansas, 62-82

HOOKER, DAVENPORT (1954) 'Early Fetal Behavior with a Preliminary Note on Double Simultaneous Fetal Stimulation' *Proc. Ass. Res. nerv. Dis.* 33, 98-113

HOOKER, DAVENPORT, & HUMPHREY, T. (1954) 'Some Results and Deductions from a Study of the Development of Human Fetal Activity' *Gazety Medico Portuguesa*, 7, 189-197

HUBER, E. (1931) *Pre-Evolution of Facial Musculature and Facial Expression* Johns Hopkins Press

HUMPHREY, TRYPHENA (1951) 'The Caudal Extent of the Descending Root of the Trigeminal Nerve during the Period of Early Human Fetal Activity (8 to 8·5 weeks of menstrual age)' *Anat. Rec.* 109, 306-307

HUMPHREY, T. (1954) 'The Trigeminal Nerve in Relation to Early Human Fetal Activity' *Proc. Ass. Res. nerv. Dis.* 33, 127-154

INGRAM, W. R. (1952) 'Brain Stem Mechanisms in Behavior' *Electroenceph. clin. Neurophysiol.* 4, 397-406

LORENZ K. (1935) 'Der Kumpan in der Umwelt des Vogels' *Jour. Ornithol.* 83, 137-213, 289-413

LORENZ, K. (1958) In Proceedings of the International Congress of Ethology, Cambridge

MAGNUS, R. (1924) *Korpersteilung* Julius Springer, Berlin, 12, 740

MEAD, M., & MACGREGOR, F. (1951) *Growth and Culture* C. P. Putnam & Sons, New York

MEYER-HOLZAPFEL, MONIKA (1949) 'Die Beziehungen zwischen den Trieben Junger und Erwachsener Tiere' *Schweiz. Z. Psychol.* 8, 32-60

MEYER-HOLZAPFEL, MONIKA (1956) 'Das Speil bei Säugetieren' *Kükenthals Handb. Zool*, 8, part 10, 11-36

MINKOWSKI, M. (1920a) 'Reflexes et mouvements de la tête, du tronc et des extrémités du foetus humain, pendant la première moitié de la grossesse' *C. R. d.1. Soc. Biol.* 83, 1202-1204

MINKOWSKI, M. (1920b) 'Movimientos y reflejos del feto humano durante la primera mitad del embrazo' *Trabajos* (Madrid), 18, 269-273

MINKOWSKI, M. (1920c) 'Uber Bewegungen und Reflexe des menschlichen Foetus während der ersten Hälfte seiner Entwicklung' *Schweiz. Arch. Neurol. Psychiat.* **7**, 148-151

MINKOWSKI, M. (1922) 'Uber frühzeitige Bewegungen, Reflexe und muskuläre Reaktionen beim menschlichen Foetus und ihre Beziehungen zum foetalen Nerven und Muskelsystem' *Schweiz. med. Wschr.* **3**, 721-724, 751-755

MINKOWSKI, M. (1928) 'Neurobiologische Studien am menschlichen Foetus' *Abdernaldene Handbuch d. biologischen Arbeitsmethoden*, Lief 253, 511-618

MINKOWSKI, M. (1936) 'Cervical and Labyrinthine Reflexes in the Human Fetus' (Original in Russian) *Symp. on Problems of Nervous Physiology and Behavior, In honor of Prof. J. S. Beritoff* USSR Acad. Sci., Georgian Br., 249-258

NISSEN, H. W. (1931) 'A Field Study of the Chimpanzee' *Comp. psychol. Monog.* **8**, 1, 122

NOLTE, A. (1958) 'Beobachtungen über das Instinktverhalten von Kapuzineraffen (Cebus apella L.) in der Gefangerschaft' *Behaviour*, **12** (3), 183 and 330

NOLTE, A. & DUCKER, GERTI (1959) 'Jugendentwicklung eines Kapuzineraffen (Cebus appella L.) mit besonderer Berücksichtigung des Wechselseitigen Verhaltens von Mutter und Kind' *Behaviour*, **14**, 335-373

OLSZEWSKI, J. (1950) 'On the Anatomical and Functional Organization of the Spinal Trigeminal Nucleus' *J. comp. Neurol.* **92**, 401-409

POCOCK, R. (1906) 'Notes upon Menstruation and Parturition of some Monkeys that have lived in the Society's Gardens' *Proc. zool. Soc. London*, 558-570

PRECHTL, H. F. R. (1958) 'The Directed Head Turning Response and Allied Movements of the Human Baby' *Behaviour*, **13**, 212-242

ROBINSON, S. M. (1925) 'Birth of a White-handed Gibbon (Hylobates Lar) in Captivity' *J. Bombay Nat. Hist. Soc.* **30**, 456-458

RAND, A. L. (1935) 'On the Habits of some Madagascar Mammals – Lemoridea' *J. Mammal.* **16**, 89, 95-103

RUCH, T. C. (1944) *Bibliographica Primatologica. A Classified Bibliography of Primates Other than Man.* Part I. Anatomy, Embryology, and Quantitative Morphology, Physiology, Phylogeny and Miscellanea. Springfield

SCHULTZ, A. H. (1926) 'Studies in the Variability of Platyrrhine Monkeys' *J. Mammal.* **7**, 286-305

SHERRINGTON, C. S. (1946) *The Integrative Action of the Nervous System* Yale Univ. Press, New Haven, Conn.

SCHILLER, P. H. (1952) 'Innate Constituents of Complex Responses in Primates' *Psychol. Rev.* 177-191

SPIEGEL, A. (1954) 'Beobachtungen und Untersuchgungen an Java-makaken' *Zool. Garten*, **20**, 227-270

YERKES, R. M. & TOMILIN, M. L. (1935) 'Mother-Infant Relations in the Chimpanzee' *J. comp. Psychol.* **20**, 321-359

Discussion following Paper by Dr Blauvelt

HARLOW *Could you give us some idea how the responses you have described change with the age of the baby?*

BLAUVELT *This is a fascinating question. Other studies have shown changes in infant behaviour in the first four days of life. The objective record of our film has not indicated a significant change in the incidence of this response during the first four days in this population of nursery babies. The four-day-old infant often shows greater amplitude of movement, particularly against gravity, than he did on his first day. Hence, his action appears more varied and vigorous. It is entirely possible as we analyse other aspects of this response and the movements which are thought to accompany it, that we will find daily differences. This may occur in babies who live with their mothers in the 'rooming-in' programme. Since there is opportunity for this stimulation when the baby is fed, early conditioning would seem probable. However, since the baby has limited capacity to support his head against gravity, he often gives himself this stimulation in the crib environment when he lies prone or on his side, and by movements which bring his hands to touch the oral area.*

HARLOW *Are there any babies that fail to show the responses on day one?*

BLAUVELT *Yes, there are some who fail to show it in the sample we have. But no more fail to show it on day one, than on days two, three and four. My impression is that the response is seen most reliably immediately after birth, unless the medication of the mother has*

29

been so great that the baby is affected. Babies are usually very active in this period.

PRECHTL *It does depend very much on the medication of the mother. After barbiturate medication you often find that the baby will not show the response for the first two days. Because of this we always wait two days before giving babies a neurological examination – whether or not the mothers have been medicated. This is partly because we are looking for other responses, too, which cannot always be seen clearly on the first two days.*

HARLOW *In neonate monkeys the head-turning response is more strongly elicited by stimulating the upper, rather than the lower, lip. Do you find this, too?*

BLAUVELT *We did not test for this exactly. In an early pilot study, we found that if the lower lip was stimulated before the upper one in our experimental stimulus, the incidence of the response was not as great. The action which follows tactile stimulation in the oral area is such that one may speculate about the pressures of natural selection. Maybe the population which we have available for study today is the one whose ancestors had capacity for the action which brings the mouth to the stimulating object, and forms part of the eating pattern in the neonate? This action can occur with a movement of the jaw when stimulation is on the lower lip, but must be a head movement when the upper lip is stimulated. In our neonate kids and lambs, stimulation to the upper lip initiates the thrusting movements which occur as the young animal finds the teat. As they stand under the mother, it is the upper lip which is stimulated when the little animal lifts its head.*

GEWIRTZ *With the babies, to what extent could the extra effectiveness of upper-lip stimulation have been the result of learning? What I mean is, does this effectiveness change after their first few feeds?*

BLAUVELT *A change in the incidence of the response is not indicated by the data during the four-day stay in the hospital. The first-day babies had not fed. There are six feedings a day for each of the three following days.*

GUNTHER *I have found quite definitely that the baby's behaviour changes very much before and after the first feed. In particular, it is the first feed which makes it pick up its head.*

BLAUVELT *It would be interesting to compare our American babies with your English ones. We have few breast-fed babies, and the mothers of these are frequently without the help and advice available to women in a population where breast feeding is the rule. Although it is the intent of the nursing and clinical staffs to offer every assistance, breast feeding is not the fashion and early phases of it may be difficult for both baby and mother. When I visited the large London hospital to see the programme under Dr Gunther's skilled direction, every mother but one breast-fed her baby successfully.*

ROWELL *To what extent can you control the stimulation which you are giving a baby?*

BLAUVELT *It is always gentle, but not standard, in the laboratory definition of this term. We can control it fairly well, though the baby sometimes foils us by its own movements. I think the intensity of the response varies considerably with the pressure, and this pressure probably varies considerably as I move my finger across the baby's cheek, especially when the baby moves, too. This, of course, is what happens when the baby moves with its mother, and this is the kind of stimulation we wanted to reproduce.*

ROWELL *The reason why I asked this is that the significance of the stimulus to the baby may change with the strength of the stimulus. I think it was Lorenz who said that breathing hard on the face of a puppy by its mother is taken by the puppy to be punishment, a sign of rejection as it were.*

BLAUVELT *This is interesting. I have never seen the equivalent of 'breathing hard' on the face of a neonate animal or human. We have observed both animal and human mothers breathe on their babies' faces. The human mothers in our study often talk to their babies with their face close to that of the baby. The animal mother (ewe or goat) has no hands or arms to hold and move her young one. These animals use the muzzle area of their heads for contact with their newborn, cleaning the neonate, usually starting with the head, of amniotic membranes and fluid with the tongue. There is certainly much breathing on the 'face' and head of the young in this process. This licking is thought to be a stimulation pertinent to viability in the young animal. The so-called 'greeting' of goats is a nose-to-nose contact. This is often the first postpartum contact of our ungulates and their young, one of a number of interactions suggesting that the sense of smell may be an important means of identification between mother and young.*

31

FOSS *I noticed in your film that when you stimulated a baby on day one, it immediately brought up its hand to its mouth. This seemed to me to have two possible interpretations. Either it was going to suck its fingers as a nipple-substitute, and so complete the chain of behaviour which you had started; or it was attempting to brush off a source of unpleasant stimulation.*

BLAUVELT *May I suggest a third interpretation. It is easy to read that purpose or meaning into the baby's movements which the action we see suggests. We notice the position of the baby's hands when they touch or hold something, but do not see it as readily when they move over the face in the control period. There has been much discussion about how and why babies' hands get to their mouths. The action of the joints of the human arm is such that they can hardly do otherwise. The principal movements of the upper extremities of the neonate are extension and flexion. One or more joints may be involved. If you flex your shoulder, the hand moves toward the median line as well as ventral. Next, flex your elbow, your hand moves to the median line and somewhere near the oral area. A result of this position of the hands near the median line is that the babies' hands grasp anything near the mouth or nose. With movements which simulate purposive action, the baby may 'hold the bottle' if the baby is bottle fed, or move so that they grasp and manipulate the clothing or hand or breast of the mother holding her baby against herself in breast feeding. These same movements may result in the baby's hands being 'in the way' if the mother does not coordinate her movements with those of her baby. I do not believe that these movements of the baby are purposive in any sense of this word. It is interesting to speculate whether their occurrence in the population we have for study is related to evolutionary history of* Homo sapiens. *We sometimes forget that in the past, and in most of the world today, neonates must feed at the breast to live. The head orientation of the neonate, his mouth movements and the action of his hands can function together easily and effectively in the feeding sequence to position the baby for feeding and hold him there. His mother holding him often provides the environment in which this is stimulated and does occur. Adaptation per se does not exist, but must be adaptation to something. We may speculate whether the capacities of the baby represent adaptation in the environment of its mother at this phase of development. Such*

Discussion

speculations, however plausible, are not evidence of the genetic history of the population.

ROSENBLATT *I would agree with Dr Blauvelt's point about the chance nature of arm movements at this early stage of development. In the film there were very frequently interesting sequences in which it was clear that turning of the head accompanies arm movements. This suggests a basic mechanism by which vision may gradually be coordinated with other sensory systems in the control of arm movements, reaching and grasping. There may therefore be a sequence in development in which at first the arm is extended or flexed in* response to *stimulation but not* in relation to *the stimulus. Later, extension or flexion of the arm may be directed toward a stimulus that has been contacted, and still later vision may come to control both the arousal and the control of reaching and grasping. It would therefore be wise to restrict the term reaching to a specific phase of arm movement and to describe earlier arm movements as extension, flexion, etc.*

BLAUVELT *I think that the babies' movements are completely without purpose in any sense of this word, and that they participate in an orderly interaction of baby and mother. These two statements are not paradoxical.*

In the past and in some parts of the world today most infants who cannot feed from their mothers will perish. It is possible that the interplay of organism and environment during this important phase of the reproductive cycle offers an opportunity for natural selection to act upon the population. This seems the most reasonable explanation for the adaptedness[1] of the baby's natural movements to the environment which his mother may offer him. Our experiment makes reasonable the assumption that the neonate turns its face towards its mother at her touch. The evidence is that his hand reaches toward her, too. This is not inevitable, as the experiment indicates, but is the behavior one may predict at this pre-feeding time for the brief ·150 of a minute of our test. The mother holding her baby offers him the environment (indeed she is the environment) rich in opportunity for this stimulation, and his responses are modified by it so that the final result appears purposeful. Also there is evidence

---

[1] Weiss, Paul (1944), 'The Biological Basis of Adaptation' in Romano, John, *Adaptation*, p. 3, Cornell University Press, Ithaca.

that he may communicate information to her by the tone and tempo of his responsiveness to her.

RHEINGOLD *Perhaps this is mainly due to the mother's responses. It struck me while watching your film that the mothers seemed to follow the actual movements of the child. When the child's mouth opens, she opens hers; and when the child bent back, she did the same.*

BLAUVELT *Very probably this is so. The sustained attention the mothers cooperating in our study give their babies makes this plausible. Unless she is holding the baby to her so that head movements are felt, the new mother orients almost continuously so that she may see the median line of the baby's face. This means her head moves with every considerable movement of the baby's head. Some of this coordination of movement is due to the reflex responses of the baby which are stimulated by the handling its mother gives it. The orientation she gives her baby to herself means that the ventral movements of infant head and hands will be directed toward herself, often toward her face. These movements toward the mother are often seen as the baby moves from the so-called 'position of comfort', the posture* in utero, *which is often held by the neonate at rest. It may be that these are responses she can easily sense and respond to. It is also possible that the mothers of another culture would stimulate and respond to their babies quite differently. Many mothers in our study hold their baby with minimal touch at first. This leaves the baby free to move, and perhaps she gets more experience of the baby's capacities. Then, a few days later, she holds the baby with full contact and appears to anticipate what the infant will do next.*

AMBROSE *You showed us a still picture of a baby crying. I am interested in the onset of this. Does it occur if you simply go on giving the same stimulation.*

BLAUVELT *We have not studied crying. Older babies (four days) often wake at the feeding hour crying. The stimulation of this test usually quiets them. I suspect any change in the environment would do so temporarily.*

I think the too long continued application of any stimulation to a neonate might result in crying. I have not tried this. But one sees the mother who is unsuccessfully trying to feed, stimulate the baby repeatedly and this is often followed by crying, with a characteristic

Discussion

posture: dorsal flexion of the trunk and head, with arm and hand movements of opposition rather than prehension so that the total impression is that the baby is resenting contact.

BOWLBY *This is a real practical problem, the conditions under which babies 'fight'. Could you say more about them?*

BLAUVELT *With the neonate I might suggest that it is when the babies are not ready, not in an appropriate state of responsiveness, and that their mothers may learn to recognize this quickly. But I believe Dr Prechtl has evidence that this oppositional behavior may result simply from repeated stimulation of the 'approach' response – it changes its sign with repetition.*

ROSENBLATT *I think the implication is that the orientation response depends not only on the stimulus but also on the state of the infant. The orientation is not only a motor action, it is also an internal condition.*

BLAUVELT *As this response occurs naturally, I think it depends on the internal state of baby and mother, and the external environment in which they interact.*

Infant Behaviour at the Breast

Contribution by MAVIS GUNTHER

My job for some years has been to observe mothers feeding their babies from the breast. While watching them it became apparent that the total number of patterns of babies' responses was limited. First I noticed that one can predict from the shape of the breast whether the baby would feed easily or not. The prediction was not simply whether the baby would obtain milk or not but whether he would be vigorous or not when taking. The shape of the breast was so effective that where the breast was marginal in design the baby could be positioned better so that he got a better hold and from then on he would feed vigorously. Sometimes this moment of first feeding vigorously had not been reached until the second or third day when I had come to help the baby's position. The mothers would often say to me, 'My baby has always known how to feed since you came.' For the first years I thought this was flattery, but after a while the inference of it came to me and I became certain that it was true. I then measured breasts to see what length of hold they gave and predicted their effectiveness in inducing feeding from that. The correlation between shape and effectiveness was complete. What I thought was occurring in a Lorenzian way was that the shape of the nipple and the tissues drawn with it into the mouth was acting as a sign release stimulus evoking instinctive feeding behaviour in the baby. The ordinary concept that the baby feeds because it is thirsty does not hold. If you put an empty bottle teat into a baby's mouth, even immediately after birth, the baby is driven to try to feed. This is in marked contrast to a teaspoonful of milk which merely seeps away at the back of the mouth.

Having watched this response to oral stimulation for a long time, I wanted to describe it in a film. There was every difficulty in making it. Eventually we shot it with paired mothers over several days, the babies conforming entirely, but unfortunately the shutter had not worked. So what you are now going to see is what we snatched with one length of film[1] on an August Bank Holiday afternoon. Even with these limiting conditions it was possible so to predict the babies' behaviour that the film shows the expected responses, and nothing has been cut from the film. In its hundred-per-cent-ness is the confirmation of what we were trying to record. We were trying to show not only this vigour of feeding built up by the experience of having one feed, but to show two other things. One was the extraordinary apathy of a baby if it is put to the breast but does not get the whole feeling in its mouth. If it has not got the right pattern of the stimulus on its soft palate, tongue and oral cavity, it will stay apathetic, and where we denied these babies bottle feeds, they stayed apathetic right through. I am afraid one of the mothers came back recently and said that her baby, now five, has never been a proper feeder from that day to this. So there is an apathy response where the breast won't go in. The third thing we wanted to show was a quite separate line of thought, a common behaviour of a baby in which it fights the mother. It does this with its fists. This is a typical action of a baby when it is in anoxia. These babies protest as soon as you put them to the breast – once they have experienced something – and this one experience seems to be obstruction of the airway either by the upper lip going up over the nostrils or by the breast covering the nostrils. The curious thing is that no mother or nurse apparently looks to see what this part of the lip is doing or to notice if it blocks the airway; so when a baby who has experienced nasal obstruction is put to the breast, it cries and boxes itself off. Then the attendant midwife shoves a bit harder to get the baby on and it boxes even more. You have only got to have this fight two or three times and from then on the baby cries as you turn it towards the mother. I have even known babies reach a stage by the fifth day, so that if you turn them on their side they start crying from the expectation that they will be put on the breast. Usually the whole thing has developed by the second or third day; you can sometimes get them out of it up to the fourth day, but generally speaking this is a situation which no mother can endure. It is literally frightful for the mother. Mothers who have endured it lose all wish to feed the baby because they cannot bear being so rejected by the baby.

I can only show you three babies, and I have to apologize that I

[1] Photographed by Anthony Bligh.

have had to mix up what you see because of the circumstances of the making of the film. You will see first a newborn baby. We measured the breast because it was part of our research to show that it was the design which makes it easily taken and desirable to the baby. We then brought the baby to the mother. The baby was born eight hours before the film was taken. The mother was a primipara and the baby had not been given anything in the mouth before. We tried to stimulate it round its mouth and it was only doing what I call innate automatous movement and little movements of its head. I did not film it for the first two or three minutes when the baby first went on the breast, because one does want the mother to have her first experience of feeding without feeling the eye of the camera, so we just left this tiny gap. Then you see the baby going two or three times to the breast in the following minutes, so the whole filming is all over in ten minutes from the first moment when the baby is unresponsive to the moment when it picks its head up and is practically taking the breast of its own accord. This change of behaviour lasts, once it has happened, indefinitely. This first baby shows you the first sequence. Immediately following on that you will see a typical fighting baby. We have a technique for getting them out of the fighting by giving them oral satisfaction with an empty bottle teat, and while it is confident with the bottle teat, the baby is turned towards the mother and allowed to accept that situation and then it is slipped on to the breast. The occasion of this particular recording was the first time that that baby, already five days old, had ever been on the breast at all and you can see it go tranquil for a moment at the breast instead of fighting as it had done before. Then the third baby shows you a mother with a difficult breast where the baby does not get on at all easily and the camera caught the up-going lip; the situation of the up-going lip and the anoxia and the fighting as a sequence are all dependent on a poorly shaped breast. Where the baby does not go on easily the mother's, the midwife's or the baby's attempt to give the baby a hold shoves the lip up. You will see in the film the upper lip riding up over the nostrils. After that you will see the baby at the breast but able to breathe easily and the film runs out with the baby officially taking the breast but with no urge to feed at all because the breast is the wrong shape to drive the baby who just stays accepting it but not actively.

Discussion following the Contribution
by Dr Gunther

RHEINGOLD *Do you differentiate the shape of the nipple from the shape of the breast?*

GUNTHER *When the baby takes the breast, it takes the nipple as a centering knob. I always teach that the nipple is like a cherry on a stalk. There are two positions for a cherry, one near the teeth, the other at the back of the mouth. The nipple should go to the back. The tissues beneath the areola should be soft and protractile and the total length of the nipple and areola, not in the position of rest, but when in the mouth, should go into the baby's mouth as far as the bottle teat does. The baby can only feed properly when the areola is sufficiently protractile.*

MICHELL *And you are able to predict this antenatally?*

GUNTHER *Yes. It was known that you get on better with a well-shaped breast, but it was not known what it was that was good. People always talked about the nipple, but the designs of nipple are very various.*

The breast has three parts: the breast itself, a nipple, and an areola; and when we test whether a breast is good or not we put our fingers on the areola and measure the protractility. The tissues are so soft and yielding at the end of pregnancy that the fingers and thumb will meet to within half a centimetre and the nipple will pull forward. When we were first trying to do this investigation we needed to know the size of a baby's jaw gap. We used sterilized petri dishes and put them over experienced babies' mouths. The baby thought it was the breast and tried to feed. One could look through the dish and mark with chalk on the other side the width of the jaw gap. We discovered the average gap when a baby opens its mouth is about two centimetres and the breast has got to be pulled through this size of gap. Now pregnancy does a lot to make these tissues soft and yielding and two pregnancies are usually completely successful. But very often at the end of the first pregnancy the breast is quite inadequate.

GEWIRTZ *You can't treat that during the first pregnancy?*

Discussion

GUNTHER *Oh yes we can. We first see mothers at twenty weeks of pregnancy and anyone about whom there is any doubt at all is fitted with a glass appliance called a Woolwich shield. It works by trapping the breast between the chest wall and the shield. The shield has to have its force exerted by the brassière; part of the fitting is to have a good bra. The breast is lifted up so that it is facing horizontally out and then trapped between ribs and the flat surface of the shell. Then with the repeated small pressures of the woman working round the house, if she wears the appliance for a few hours a day, the tissues become soft and yielding. (Funnily enough, another thing that we found was that difficulty in feeding is linked with the colour of hair. Very few black-haired people have trouble but many fair-haired and red-haired do.)*

RHEINGOLD *May I ask about this third baby we saw in the film? Would this baby begin to lose weight so that the mother would be unhappy because she would think that the baby was sleeping at the breast and she would report that to the doctor?*

GUNTHER *Yes, they simply can't take it.*

RHEINGOLD *Then the doctor would ordinarily advise bottle feeding?*

GUNTHER *That particular breast is a marginal one and with positioning it might be possible to get that baby to feed from it. But if you feed that baby with a bottle teat while the breast is treated, the baby is likely to get imprinted with the bottle teat – it falls in love with it. The baby's mouth action will be completely different if it has had a bottle within two days of life.*

RHEINGOLD *Wouldn't it be similar to what it would be on a good natural mother's nipple?*

GUNTHER *Well the main difference is that in accepting the bottle teat, since the teat is always stiff, as they receive it they put their tongue up much higher; and the nurses usual comment is 'Dr Gunther, this baby has a funny trick of putting its tongue up.' You then know that the baby has had difficulty in getting on the breast and the nurses have fed it with a bottle and the situation is either solvable immediately, within a day or two, or else it is hopeless. The speed of change in the mother is so rapid – it is as quick as in the baby at this stage. If she is rejected either by the fighting or by the apathy, she cannot take it at all, and she says, 'I want it to be on the bottle. It always takes the bottle so well.' Of course it does! The bottle*

41

teat has been evolved empirically and is extraordinarily effective in making the baby feed.

RHEINGOLD *This film is the earliest record we have of learning in the human infant. I want to stand up and cheer.*

GUNTHER *As far as I know it is also of the first neurosis of life where there is competition between the urge to breathe and the urge to feed. Is that a fair comment?*

PRECHTL *Can I ask a question about the first baby in the film. Was it fighting?*

GUNTHER *No, the first baby was not fighting.*

PRECHTL *There were arm movements, with closing and opening of the hand. It did this three or four times. You see this in many cases in prematures, lying on the back in the incubator, when they show quite regular rhythmic movements similar to these. We interpreted this as 'climbing' movements.*

BLAUVELT *You do get opposition of the baby's hands in just this situation. It does occur I am sure.*

GUNTHER *I wouldn't say the movements were strong enough in this case to be clearly fighting. Can I ask you one thing back? I personally often have difficulty in breathing while I am talking to an audience while I am watching the film of the fighting baby. Would any of you tell me whether you felt your breathing affected by watching a baby fight like that?*

BOWLBY *I find myself very restless.*

ROSENBLATT *I suppose the mothers get the same sort of reaction?*

GUNTHER *They go into a sweat all over and you can almost warm your hands by them.*

ROSENBLATT *Do you find then that changes that might occur, if nursing were continued normally, are inhibited in the mother as a result of the physical or structural deficiencies in the breast, and the difficulties which these cause in the initial interaction of mother and infant?*

GUNTHER *I think that is too difficult for me. But if it is a dud breast, the behaviour of baby and mother come to disaster quite rapidly.*

ROSENBLATT *Is there evidence of rapid conditioning of the secretion of her hormone that influences the letting down of milk?*

GUNTHER *Well, yes, but you see the total secretion is usually very scanty until the fourth day. Until the fourth day the total yield is about five ounces; on the third day it is only two or three and that* amount is milkable almost without the let-down working very strongly.

BOWLBY *This precedes the time let down is operative?*

GUNTHER *Well in the primipara, Waller used to say that the let down did not get going until fourteen days. I don't think that is true myself but the reflex isn't so firmly established and isn't nearly so vigorous in action until after a few days of experience.*

ROSENBLATT *There is evidence in studies on the rabbit that disturbance will inhibit lactation, chiefly milk let-down. Conversely, there is evidence in women that lactation may be facilitated by external stimuli and may even be conditioned to previously neutral stimuli. These studies, though only introductory, indicate one pathway by which reactions to the young of a disturbing nature or a pleasant nature affect the mother in her further care of the newborn.*

GUNTHER *If you have a mother with a premature baby, she will use her hands and milk herself for say six weeks until the baby is big enough to be put to the breast; she is then so scared of the baby and her conditioned reflexes are so used to the hand that in some instances she cannot feed the baby at all.*

AMBROSE *Of course this is another instance where the reinforcing stimulus is the same as the eliciting: in so far as there isn't very much milk but it is simply the shape of the breast which does the eliciting in the first place.*

HINDE *The head-turning reflex was very weak. Did I understand you to say that it becomes stronger after one experience of feeding? Does it become strong after one experience of an empty bottle?*

GUNTHER *Curiously the baby expects the bottle teat to be thrust into its mouth and it does not do so much looking for it. I cannot answer your question because I do not know how many bottle feeds you have to have for orienting to occur.*

HINDE *Is the reinforcement the milk or the sucking?*

GUNTHER *Oh, I am quite certain that it is the shape and the sucking, because they seem to be quite unaware of the quantity of milk.*

ROWELL *What would have happened when there was no alternative bottle feeding in a baby whose mother did not happen to have the right breast?*

GUNTHER *Wet-nursing usually. But I have seen African mothers who have a fascinating way. The mother holds the baby and puts her finger into the baby's mouth to make it swallow and then tips in a creamy mess with the palm of the hand at the same time. I do not know how universal it is.*

GEWIRTZ *Have you ever fed babies by cup?*

GUNTHER *It would be most tedious. You cannot get the ounces in. That applies to a teaspoon too.*

GEWIRTZ *What do you think then of the work[1] of Dr Robert Fredeen of Kansas, who has reported that he has fed babies by cup for years, with no adverse effects?*

GUNTHER *I personally would start with a prejudice, because I believe that bones are made best when the whole limb is used: I like to see a baby use its jaw a lot. I think it makes a better face.*

HARLOW *We have used cup feeding on young monkeys, and my impression is that the cup doesn't get far enough into the mouth to stimulate the essential receptor system which produces the normal sucking and ingesting responses.*

RHEINGOLD *Would you care to say anything about the function of the baby's hand movements during feeding?*

GUNTHER *The baby doesn't do much holding, except by chance. But the movements are very stimulating to the mother. Unfortunately very often the baby is presented to the mother so wrapped up that it sometimes can't move its chin, let alone its arms. It cannot then be put to the breast properly so that it finds itself in danger of anoxia, and at the same time the mother is deprived of an important source of stimulation.*

---

[1] Fredeen, R. C. (1948) 'Cup feeding of newborn infants' *Pediatrics*, **2**, 544.

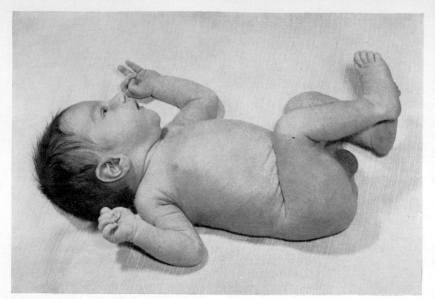

PLATE 4. In a normal newborn, the response to a symmetrically applied pinprick in the soles of the feet is a flexion of both legs. Age: 7 days

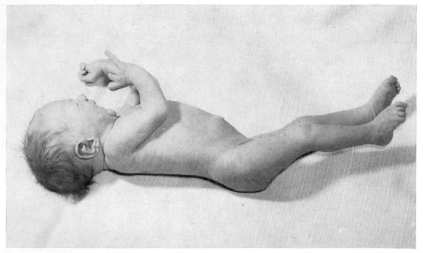

PLATE. 5. In a baby born in breech presentation with extended legs, the flexion response of the leg is converted to an extension. Age: 8 days

Neurological Sequelae of Prenatal and Paranatal Complications

Contribution by H. F. R. PRECHTL

The motor and behaviour patterns of the human neonate are sometimes grossly disturbed because of injuries to the central nervous system which are caused by prenatal and paranatal complications. I would like to demonstrate in a film a series of babies with different syndromes of such neurological abnormalities.[1]

In babies born in breech presentation we found a change of the flexion and extension reflexes of the leg (see Plates 4 and 5).[2] In normal babies born in the vertex position one can elicit a flexion of the hip, knee and foot by stimulating the sole of the foot with a pinprick. On the other hand an extension of the leg can be elicited by the application of a mild pressure against the sole of the foot (magnet reflex of Rademaker). In the breech presentation with extended legs, an extension instead of a flexion occurred after a pinprick. This was not due to peripheral mechanical factors, since the babies were able to flex the legs completely if the legs were relaxed. In the breech-foot presentation and foot presentation the flexion reflex was increased, and the extension reflex decreased or could not be elicited, although a maximal extension of the leg was possible. We are not yet sure about the underlying causal mechanism, but the correlation between the position of the legs (as well as the duration in which the breech position was present *in utero*) with the type of the abnormal response after birth is striking. In every case a simple reflex is influenced and modified by external factors.

Another neurological abnormality which we called the 'hyperexcitability syndrome' might have more serious consequences for

[1] Prechtl, H. F. R. *Neurological sequelae of birth trauma in the newborn infant.* 16-mm. film, black and white, University, Groningen.

[2] Prechtl, H. F. R., & Knol, A. R. (1958) 'Der Einfluss der Beckenendlage, auf die Fuszsohlenreflexe beim neugeorenen Kind' *Arch. Psychiat. ges. Neurol.* **196**, 542-553.

child-mother interaction.[1] After complications (which probably included disturbances in the oxygen supply of the nervous system of the foetus or the newborn) we very often found the baby hyperactive, easily startled, and with a very low threshold of the Moro-response; and as the most impressive symptom, a tremor of low frequency (4-6/sec.) and high amplitude, which was superimposed on the spontaneous movements as well as on the elicited responses (e.g. the Moro). Mothers who do not know that their baby is neurologically abnormal think he is very easily frightened. As we know now from a follow-up study, most of these babies show a choreaformic diskinesia a few years later.[2] Other symptoms in these infants and children are: a very short concentration span; hypermotility; an instability of mood; and some degree of learning difficulty, especially in reading, writing and arithmetic. In other words, they sometimes have severe behaviour problems.

There is another pathological state seen in the newborn baby which is in a way the opposite of the hyperexcitability syndrome. These babies are hypokinetic, somnolent, hypotonic; and if a response is elicited, the movements are very slow and weak. In our experience this syndrome indicates that the nervous pathology is more severe.

These three types of abnormalities will be illustrated in the film.

Discussion following Dr Prechtl's Film

PRECHTL *We look again at the children with histories of complication when they are three or four years old; and we have a control group of neurologically non-pathological babies of the same age. In the control normal group we found 20 per cent behaviour problems and in the experimental group 70 per cent.*

HINDE *How long do the neurological symptoms in breech babies persist?*

[1] Prechtl, H. F. R., & Dijkstra, J. (1959), 'Neurological diagnosis of cerebral injury in the newborn' *Proc.* '*Symposium on Prenatal Care*' Noordhoff, Groningen.
[2] Prechtl, H. F. R., & Stemmer, C. J. (1959) 'Ein choreatiformes Syndrom bei Kindern' *Wien. med. Wschr.* **109**, 461-463.

Discussion

PRECHTL *It depends on the intensity of the change of the reflexes. For some weeks or months, as far as I know.*

HINDE *And then the response becomes normal?*

PRECHTL *I don't know exactly.*

BOWLBY *May I ask, supposing a clinician were to see these children at two, three, four years of age, would he be able to distinguish the two groups, the neuro-pathological and the non-pathological neonates from a clinical examination?*

PRECHTL *We also have a neurological examination in the follow-up study at 2-4 years. Of the neonatal normals there were 8 per cent with neurological symptoms and in the pathological group there were 68 per cent who were neurologically abnormal.*

GUNTHER *Would your pathological group have been separated from their mothers by admission into hospital in the intervening time?*

PRECHTL *No.*

MICHELL *Did they spend a longer time before they went to the breast than the normal group?*

PRECHTL *No. All of them went to the mother at the sixth day.*

ROSENBLATT *You have said that 70 per cent of the pathological group showed behaviour problems when they were 3-4 years old. Were you implying that the neurological damage was more extensive than was seen originally in the specific symptoms and that it underlies these behaviour problems, or were you suggesting that the relationship with the mother had become disturbed as a result of the original behavioural difficulties and that this initial disturbance continued to exert its effects?*

PRECHTL *It was yesterday during Dr Blauvelt's presentation that I realized this second possibility: that it might be (in addition to the brain damage effects) also due to a disturbance of interaction with the mother resulting from the baby's abnormal motor patterns. These might influence the behaviour of the mothers.*

ROWELL *Is the baby born with its legs stuck out straight because it has extension responses* in utero?

PRECHTL *No. I am sure it is not so because it depends on the position of the foetus. In the first case of breech presentation, you saw that there was a difference in position of the two legs and also a difference in responses.*

ROWELL *Is it not possible that the leg had an extension* in utero *and therefore the baby was born with its leg stuck out? Or do you feel that it is a central lesion that caused this extension?*

PRECHTL *No, I cannot believe that it is a central lesion but I found it striking that foetal position during the last part of pregnancy has such an influence.*

BOWLBY *But can you rule out Thelma Rowell's alternative hypothesis that it is because of the state of the reflexes that the leg is stuck out* in utero?

MICHELL *It quickly rights itself in the first two or three weeks of life.*

PRECHTL *If the state of the reflex is the cause of the breech presentation, you would expect all breech presentations to have this response, but it depends completely on the position of the legs at the breech presentation what type of reflex alteration will be present after birth.*

BOWLBY *But a particular position might be due to the reflex state of the infant.*

HINDE *Except that in that case you would not expect the reflex to become normal so quickly would you?*

MICHELL *Occasionally you have breech presentation with extended legs in which you see a really stiff joint, and I think in that case there must be some primary trouble in the foetus.*

PRECHTL *In those cases the effects can be long lasting. We saw some cases that had been breech presentations walking very stiffly and two of them were treated for congential hipluxation.*

ROWELL *But there is no anatomical thing to which you can point and say 'that is the cause of the position'?*

PRECHTL *Nobody knows exactly what the cause of breech presentation is.*

HINDE *I don't think the argument that it usually corrects itself after birth is a very forceful one, is it? I mean, so many of the developmental processes are self-regulating in a sense, and the fact that when the baby gets into a different environment outside the uterus it becomes normal does not seem to me necessarily to imply that the reflexes were responsible or not. It does not seem to distinguish cause and effect* in utero.

PART II

Animal Experiments

D

Early Socialization in the Domestic Cat as based on Feeding and Other Relationships between Female and Young[1]

JAY S. ROSENBLATT,
GERALD TURKEWITZ,
and T. C. SCHNEIRLA

Among the mammals, suckling is one of the first specific responses to appear after birth. As a major reaction to tactual, thermal and other stimuli afforded by the female, suckling forms the basis in the newborn for the earliest attachment to the mother.

In the domestic cat, suckling often appears in the first-born before all of the litter has been delivered, and thereafter until weaning is a recurring and changing response. Then, as the processes of weaning begin in the fifth week, suckling declines and is gradually replaced by self-feeding, which as a rule is established by the eighth week.

Normal Behavioral Relations of Female and Young

As kittens grow, the suckling pattern that developed neonatally undergoes further modifications reflecting developmental progress in perceptual abilities, motor processes and motivational organization. Thus, from birth there is set in motion a course of interrelated changes in the suckling behavior of the young and in the nursing and other maternal behavior of the female. These changes are the products of reciprocal stimulative interactions that lead, on the one hand, to weaning and independent functioning of the young and, on the other, to the gradual decline of the female's maternal behavior associated with this litter.

[1] The experiments on which this article is based were supported by grants from the National Science Foundation and from the Rockefeller Foundation. The results are to be reported in papers now in MS. or in preparation, cited in the Bibliography.

We have traced development in the suckling and nursing patterns by means of detailed observations in several litters from birth to the end of the eighth week. The general results are represented in Figure 7.

In general, three major stages may be identified in the development of suckling, with each of these involving secondary changes in the suckling pattern. These stages are: (1) a period extending from birth to the end of the third week; (2) a period lasting from the third week to about the sixth week; and (3) a period extending from about the fifth week to the eighth week and including weaning. This entire succession of events is represented graphically in Figure 7.

In the first stage, feedings are initiated mainly by the female. She approaches the kittens huddled in the home region of the cage (usually the main zone of parturition), lies down, arches her body around them, and 'presents' her mammary region. In response to tactual and other stimuli from the female, as from her licking, the kittens first become active, then begin variable movements that in the course of time lead into nipple localization and eventually result in nipple attachment and suckling. The beginning of a participation by kittens in the initiation of suckling in this period is shown by the rapid progress they make in nipple localization, to the extent that by the fourth day most of the kittens in the litter have adopted individually specific nipple regions for suckling.

In the second stage, the kittens initiate their approaches to the female when she pauses for a time, as for example when she is at rest outside the home area or when she is crouched over the food dish. The feeding adjustment of this period involves reciprocal stimulative-response relationships of female and kittens. To the approaches of the kittens, increasingly vigorous and versatile, the female is appropriately responsive. She may join actively in the initiation processes, or, if she is already lying down, may stretch out or at least remain immobile, thereby facilitating the nipple localization process of the kittens. For the kittens, perceptual developments underlying improved efficiency in feeding are indicated by the results of tests demonstrating an increased facility and scope of orientation in the cage, and by other results disclosing an improved resourcefulness in transferring reactivity from cage localities to the female as the focus of adjustment.

We interpret these changes as the products of a steady improvement in the perceptual-motor abilities of the kittens, a developmental process for which an increasingly comprehensive motivational basis for response to other individuals is indicated in many ways. Thus, a

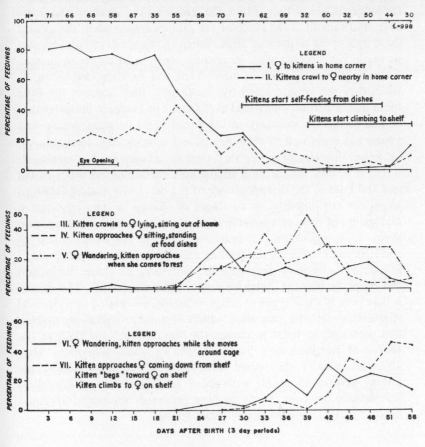

FIG. 7

Stages in the initiation of maternal-young feeding relationships in the domestic cat (data from three litters). Graphs show percentage of responses of each type recorded in the daily observations in each three-day period

rapid development is observed in the frequency and versatility of casual joint activities ('play') among the kittens, and of a variety of non-suckling responses to the female. It is not surprising that feeding

53

proves the basis for socialization of the kittens, as feeding itself, considered at any stage, is a reciprocal activity and is therefore social.

In the third stage, the initiation of suckling depends increasingly, and finally entirely, upon the kittens. With increasing frequency and for longer intervals they follow the female as she wanders about the cage, and remain at the place of her disappearance when she evades them by leaping to the wall shelf. When she happens to be accessible to them, they persist with increasing vigor in attempts to nuzzle. These actions may result in attachment and suckling, but often, as when they are counteracted by the female, they account for little more than a perfunctory social exchange. The evidence indicates that in this period the intimacy of the social bond between female and young has decreased as their behavioral relationships have altered, or, as another way of saying this, their social distance has increased.

These results, indicating a predictable chronological order in the rise and later in the disappearance of the described feeding relationships, are attributed by us to stages of change in the organization and nature of these relationships and in social processes arising from them. Our conclusion, as indicated, is that the development of socialization centers on the feeding relationship. In the processes of individual behavioral development, therefore, no sharp distinction can be made between nutritive and social adjustments. The reason is that both of these types of adaptive action are related to reciprocal stimulative-response processes which become progressively diversified with age. In these processes the female functions both as the source of nutrition and as the center of social activities. Also, although initially the varied stimulative interactions among the kittens have to do mainly with group feeding, it is clear that these interactions are basic to developing processes whereby littermates become increasingly potent as social factors.

Theoretical Considerations bearing on Socialization

Social experience is thus a broad term, the meaning of which we find highly variable according to the age and previous developmental situation of the kitten. Study of the normal processes of socialization in mammals has been an increasingly active subject of research. One attempt to express the mammalian socialization processes didactically is that of Scott (1958), who borrowed the term 'critical period' from

Jay S. Rosenblatt, Gerald Turkewitz and T. C. Schneirla

embryology to express his idea that there is a crucial interval in the behavioral development of puppies at about 18 days, or roughly at the beginning of the interval we have described as beginning the second period in the development of suckling behavior in kittens. Reports of 'imprinting', or the chronologically distinct, limited onto-genetic intervals in which social responsiveness may be optimally fixed, seemed to encourage Scott's conception of the critical period as one in which significant social adjustments can occur maximally. Fuller's (1950) findings, confirmed by James and Cannon (1952), that a conditioned leg-withdrawal to a buzzer cannot be formed in puppies until after their 18th day, was taken by Scott as an inde-pendent confirmation of his conclusion that this time marks for the puppy '. . . the beginning of the period of socialization, in which its primary social relationships are formed' (1958, p. 43). This corre-spondence of events seems impressive, yet we may seriously question whether this type of consideration alone can provide us with an adequate perspective for investigation and theory concerning mammalian social development.

From the theoretical viewpoint of Schneirla (1946, 1951, 1956), the socialization process begins at parturition or even before. The principal factors in social ontogeny are those involving the per-ceptual development of the female, processes of individual ontogeny of the young, and reciprocal stimulative relationships between female and young as well as among the young. In the analysis of socialization, as in the case of behavioral development in general, concepts of intervening variables of 'maturation' and 'experience' provide a theoretical framework to guide both analysis of specific developmental situations and the evaluation of their long-term effects on individual development.

Studies in our laboratory have tested hypotheses derived from this theory. With regard to the first stage of socialization, the results indicate that the behavioral bond between the female and her off-spring begins in parturition, through a progressive integration of stimuli centering first on adjustments to organic events such as uterine contractions, next on stimuli (e.g. from fluids) pertaining to the genital zone, and soon on the neonate itself (Tobach *et al.*, in MS.). In other words, the event of parturition, in which the neonate participates rather passively and incidentally at first, provides a comprehensive basis for the social bond involving stimulus-response

55

processes which soon become increasingly bilateral and reciprocal. The adequacy with which this behavioral basis is admitted by circumstances, and the condition of both female and young in the course of the litter period, govern the general trend of maternal-young relations and of socialization.

In its application to the second stage of socialization in the domestic cat, our research program has involved detailed investigations of the processes of group behavior in the litter situation and tests of related functions such as individual orientation, from the time of parturition to weaning (Rosenblatt, Turkewitz and Schneirla, in MS.). To summarize one part of these studies, evidence on the course of early feeding shows that the neonates, although at first inept and variable in their activities, within the first hours accomplish increasingly specific adjustments to the female's mammary surface, so that in the first two days after parturition most of them come to adopt individually specific nipple positions (Rosenblatt, Wodinsky, Turkewitz and Schneirla, in preparation). That is, in the course of time, some of them rather consistently feed on specific posterior nipples, others feed anteriorly, and others feed at intervening nipples or are variable. Our tests of cage orientation indicate that these processes, also, begin shortly after birth, and the results point clearly to discriminative spatial adjustments and to corresponding processes in autonomic control, progressing steadily in efficiency and in scope during the first three weeks. These results are to be reported in separate papers now in preparation.

Theoretically, our findings lead us to postulate developmental accomplishments dependent upon an intimate fusion of rudimentary learning processes with processes of maturation. The learning postulated is viewed as a maturation-fused elementary pattern of conditioning involving proximal stimuli such as those through tactual, olfactory and thermal experience with female and with the nest situation, and with approach and suckling as nuclear responses.

Isolation Experiments

The experiments with which this report is mainly concerned represent a third phase of the investigation in which the suckling behavior and maternal adjustments of litter-reared kittens were compared with the behavior of kittens returned to female and litter after experimental isolation periods introduced during their first two months of life. The object was to determine the effects of social deprivation inserted at different times on the feeding behavior and other social adjustments of kittens.

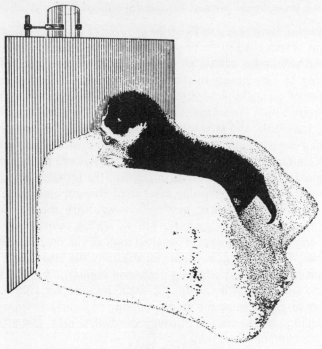

FIG. 8

Seven-day old kitten suckling at nipple of the 'artificial mother', a brooder enclosed in the incubator in which subjects lived during their isolation periods (see text). Rear-guard panel and milk supply are indicated

A. *The Incubator* – The experimental kittens were isolated in a special incubator or brooder, a cubical enclosure in which a feeder (or 'artificial mother') was placed on the floor near one wall, as a U-shaped vessel with its open side outward (Figure 8). The feeder was designed to present not only a nipple from which the isolated kitten could draw, through its own efforts in suckling, a synthetic formula (Esbilac) available at a controlled temperature but also to offer a model which would be attractive by virtue of its thermal, tactual and spatial properties, as a crude partial substitute for the female.[1] The incubator served these purposes, as well as obviating any important need for substantial amounts of forced feeding by hand and other special attentions which might have been equivalent in some sense to the normal behavioral role of the female.[2]

B. *General Treatment and Behavior of Isolated Kittens* – To start the process of independent feeding equivalently in different subjects and without any undue delays, all of the isolated kittens were helped in effecting an attachment to the brooder nipple. In the course of a number of manually guided feedings, all of the neonates were able to acquire within three days the ability to crawl up into the brooder, locate the nipple, and attach independently. Thereafter, self-initiated suckling occurred at regular intervals in these isolated subjects, and in the course of time a gradual change was observed in their manner of approaching the nipple from in front of the brooder. The earliest trend was to follow a more or less canalized path along one or the other arm of the brooder, in close contact with the soft surface. Next, after the first few days, the kittens tended to make a variable approach through the open U-shaped area of the brooder, between the arms. Improvement in nipple localization was also shown as the amount of preliminary nuzzling decreased regularly. Finally, kittens held in isolation until the fourth week became versatile in their manner of approaching the nipple, passing to it directly from different angles, over the arms or through the central area, and attaching with a minimum of nuzzling.

After their isolation periods in the incubator, kittens detained there for scheduled intervals were returned to their female and litter for observations of individual reactions, with emphasis on their suckling responses to the female, but also with attention to general cage orientation and social reactions to female and littermates.

[1] A prototype of the 'artificial mother', in the functional U-form and covered with a soft towelling, was developed in 1949 in connection with experiments on parturition in the cat (Tobach, Failla, Cohn and Schneirla, in MS.), was modified for further use by Dr Alan Frank, Fellow of the National Institutes of Mental Health in our laboratory during 1950-1951, and was further improved for the present experiments (Rosenblatt, Turkewitz and Schneirla, in preparation).

[2] One other special procedure carried out in this situation as a substitute for normal activities of the female involved a brief manipulation of the isolate kitten daily in the first two neonatal weeks with routine stimulative operations appropriate to the facilitation of defecation and urination.

C. *Results* – The Appearance of Suckling after Isolation – Adaptive suckling was shown on the test returns to female and litter situation of *all* of the kittens isolated from birth to the 7th day, from the 6th to the 23rd day, and from the 18th to the 33rd day. In contrast, suckling was not accomplished in corresponding tests by any except one of the kittens isolated from the 23rd to the 44th day, or by any of the kittens isolated from the second to the 44th day. These kittens, moreover, although left continuously with their females from the time of the tests, never suckled. The results for the cage-return tests of these kittens are reported in Table X–A.

TABLE X

Suckling Response in Kittens of Different Isolate Groups after Return to the Female and Litter. (A) Kittens Suckled from Brooder during Period of Isolation: (B) Kittens did not Suckle from Brooder during the Isolation, but were provided with Dishes of Food

Period of Social Isolation	Number of Kittens	Average Number of Days Isolated	Percentage of Group that Suckled upon return to Female
(A) Kittens suckled from brooder during period of isolation			
days			
0–7	3	7	100
6–23	5	17	100
18–33	2	16	100
23–44	4	22	25
2–44	4	41	0
(B) Kittens did not suckle from brooder during period of isolation			
34–49	4	16	100
46–54	3	7	100

The failure of these kittens to suckle in the cage-return tests was not due to insufficient hunger. Strong hunger was indicated by the activities of the returned isolates in the cage situation, and independent tests show that these kittens would have fed readily had they been returned to the brooder. In a special test, two of these brooder-kittens that had failed to suckle were placed with their female and left for a period of two days without food. During this time the female was fed on schedule outside the cage, then was returned to the litter situation where suckling by two mother-reared kittens occurred promptly. The isolates, although they had been without food for more than 48 hours, failed to join the feeding situation in which the resting female nursed the other kittens, and displayed no other signs of suckling.

Further tests were carried out with two groups of isolates (Table X–B). All of these kittens suckled after their return to the litter situation at the 49th or the 54th day, after isolation periods in the brooder, in which they had been fed from dishes without any opportunity to suckle. These results indicate that the failure of suckling in the groups represented in Table X–A cannot be attributed to any 'natural decline' in suckling – as might be suggested by the fact that suckling normally declines by the 44th day in litter-reared kittens.

The difficulty did not lie in an inability to suckle, as efficient brooder-suckling behavior was observed in all the test isolates not long before their removal for the cage tests. Also, as a control, several of the kittens that failed to suckle during three days in the litter-situation tests were then returned to the brooder, and all of them then promptly suckled from the brooder nipple. Clearly, the interference with the suckling adjustment was specific to the female, to the litter situation, or to both of these.

A kitten's inability to accomplish a feeding adjustment to the female has no necessary relationship to the adequacy of the suckling reaction developed prior to isolation, or indeed whether any such reaction had developed. All three of the kittens isolated at birth developed a suckling response after their introduction to female and litter on the seventh day. In contrast, two other kittens isolated from birth but not returned to the female until the 44th day failed to suckle during lengthy test periods. The duration of the isolation from birth is therefore critical. The duration of pre-isolation suckling experience is not necessarily a factor, however, as all of the kittens in three groups that had suckled for periods of 6 days, 18 days and 34 days, respectively, reinstated this reaction on their return to the female after various periods of isolation. When the isolation begins seems much more critical, from the fact that only one of a group of kittens that had accomplished suckling in an early period of 23 days with the female could develop this reaction in a post-isolation test with the female. Isolations of four or five weeks that began early (e.g. at the third day) were followed by even less effective suckling adjustments than were those of comparable duration beginning later. The deficiencies or the failure of a suckling adjustment in tests following isolation thus seem related not only to the timing of the isolation period in its beginning and duration but also to the age of the subject at the time it is re-tested with the female.

Suckling Latency – The appraisal of our results for cage-return tests with regard to the relative delay of suckling, when suckling appeared, provided one valuable lead as to the effects of isolation. In Figure 9 are shown the latencies for suckling in each of the five isolate groups in which this reaction appeared. Latencies were short in both the birth-to-seven-day isolates and in the 47-to-54-day isolates. The values for latency were greater in the 6-to-23-day and the 18-to-33-day isolates, for which the average latency was 15-20 hours and the greatest delays as high as 38 hours. The maximal latencies were obtained in the fifth group, isolated from the 34th to the 49th day, in which the average was 48 hours and the longest delay 93 hours.

Analysis of the behavioral facts shows that the delay in suckling on return to the litter situation depends upon two different adjustments to the female by the isolate. One of these is an initial general adjustment, scored by us as ending at the appearance of the kitten's first sustained contact with the female (and called 'contact latency'), the second was the subsequent more specific adjustment in the course of which suckling appeared, called by us the 'suckling delay'. In Figure 10 these two measures are differentiated for each of the groups of isolates.

An examination of the results for suckling in the five isolate groups in which suckling appeared (Figure 10) indicates that in most cases the principal difficulty lay in the initiation or in the performance of the suckling act, or in both of these, and not in achieving a preliminary adjustment to the female. The figure shows that in most cases the first sustained contact with the female was accomplished in a relatively short time (e.g. as in the 6-to-23-day and the 34-to-49-day isolates), after which the accomplishment of suckling required a variable and generally protracted interval. In the two isolate groups that did not suckle (days 2-44; days 23-44), the behavior protocols pointed to the existence of an additional and exceptional difficulty in effecting any sustained contact with the female, marked by an evident tension and by a heightened excitement in her proximity, of so intense and lasting a nature that the attainment of any suckling adjustment seemed out of the question.

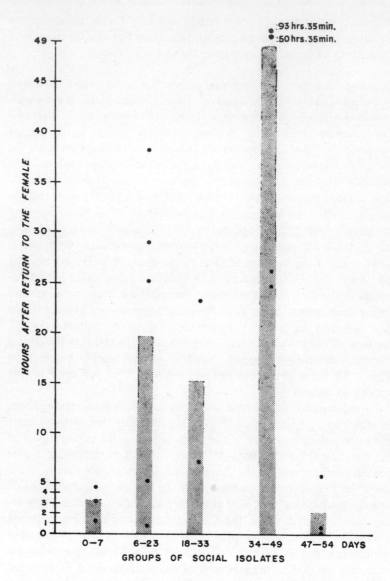

FIG. 9

Latencies for suckling in kittens of five isolate groups upon return to female and litter after isolation in the incubator. (Bars indicate group averages; points, individual scores)

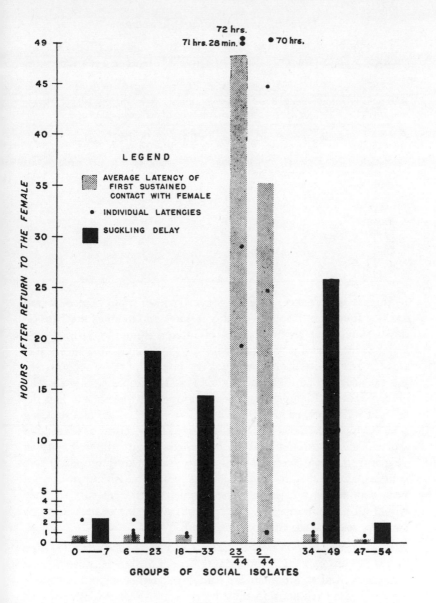

FIG. 10

*Latencies of suckling in kittens of five isolate groups: general adjust-
ment to female (sustained contact) differentiated from additional time
needed (suckling delay) for a suckling adjustment*

The reliable signs of high disturbance that characterized the non-suckling isolates are represented in Table XI. Hissing and other signs

TABLE XI

Reactions of Kittens returned to the Female in the Litter Situation after Different Periods of Experimental Isolation in the Incubator

Period of Isolation	No. of Kittens	Measures of disturbance and withdrawal (percentages)		
		Hissing	Disturbance Signs[1]	Overt Withdrawal
days				
0–7	3	0	0	0
6–23	5	0	0	0
18–33	2	0	0	0
34–49	5	40	40	60
23–44	4	75	75	100
2–44	4	100	100	100
47–54	3	0	0	0

of intense disturbance, including overt withdrawal, were observed in three-fourths of the 23-to-44-day isolates and in all of the 2-to-44-day isolates. Furthermore, it is of interest that the 34-to-49-day isolates, the one other isolate group to show the disturbance signs, was the group with the longest suckling latency of those accomplishing the suckling adjustment (Figure 10). The impression is thereby enforced that although disturbed reactions to the female had decreased sufficiently in intensity within two hours to admit a suckling relationship, these reactions, characterized by withdrawal tendencies and sufficiently pronounced to be called 'fright', differed only in degree from those observed in the two non-suckling groups. There is little question that, had the kittens of these three isolate groups not been confined in a cage with the female, but free to run off, they would all have disappeared, thereby obviating the chance that any suckling relationship could come about.

Maternal Responses of Isolate and of Litter-raised Kittens – Suckling marks the attainment of an adaptive relationship between female and young, and we are therefore studying social behavior in terms of how a feeding relationship may be accomplished. We have shown that the attainment of a sustained contact with the female is only a

[1] Signs of disturbance in kittens are: ears drawn back, piloerection of fur of tail and body, arched back posture, widely dilated pupils, and a general aspect of fright.

Jay S. Rosenblatt, Gerald Turkewitz and T. C. Schneirla

preliminary or partial adjustment, and that delay in suckling may be attributed to behavioral interferences beyond those inhibiting this limited relationship of female and young. We note that in certain of the isolate groups both the initial phases of the suckling act and its further progress towards completion were affected. To understand the difficulty in these cases, we must consider the facts pertaining to the isolate's adjustment both to the litter situation and to the female.

Cage-orientation tests were carried out regularly with the isolates after their return, and the birth-to-seven day isolates, for example, were found seriously deficient (as compared with litter-raised kittens) in their ability to orient spatially and return to the home corner of the cage even from close by. Because of this deficiency in their cage adjustments, these kittens were unable to regain the home corner readily when they strayed from it, and all of them spent considerable intervals of time alone at a distance from this locality. In their cases, therefore, the initial contact with the female usually had to occur largely by chance. When an isolate happened to brush the female, this initial contact was usually followed by a turning towards her, and next by a pushing against her body with a nuzzling into her fur. The readier responses of these isolates to the female as compared with those of neonate kittens may have resulted from an appreciable stimulative equivalence between the tactual and thermal properties of the incubator and those of the female. These experimental kittens, however, in their cruder orientative movements, and particularly in the lower efficiency of their nipple-localizing actions as compared with normal subjects, revealed the handicap of their initial week of isolation.

Let us compare the week-old isolates with litter-raised kittens of the same age with respect to the single but important action of nuzzling. Female-reared kittens at this age locate an area of the female's abdominal surface soon after having reached her, and thereafter nuzzle about very little before attachment to a nipple occurs, with this nuzzling usually confined to the immediate nipple area. When littermates happen to be touched in the preliminary orientation process, they are never nuzzled. The seven-day isolates, in contrast, after being set down in the test, reached the female only through much wandering which brought them to the home corner accidentally, or through being retrieved by the female. Often in the tests these events were combined by the female's retrieving an isolate

E   65

that chanced near her. If the isolate chanced close to the female while she was lying down, nursing the litter, she would respond by licking it. A common effect of this action was to exert an orienting effect upon this kitten, causing it to turn toward the female and push, as described, against whatever part of her body was touched. In this situation the isolate would nuzzle over the female's entire furry surface including even paws, neck and back, although somewhat more frequently around her genital region. The isolate's proximal orientation to the female thus was at first quite generalized and not significantly more efficient than that of neonate kittens. Female and incubator evidently were equivalent to the extent that each furnished attractive low-intensity tactual stimulation and optimal thermal stimulation, but localizing a nipple clearly was a rather different problem in the two cases.

These isolate kittens are not on the same behavioral basis, however, as are the neonate kittens. At first sight the fact is surprising that the birth-to-seven-day isolates required more time to accomplish their first suckling adjustments in the litter situation than did neonates. Analysis of the protocols shows, however, that the difference is particularly attributable to the female. Her nursing behavior, as described, has changed progressively in the first week, in relation to the changing suckling pattern and litter situation of the kittens that have been with her since parturition. Because these kittens are, *as a group*, still attractive to the female, and begin their suckling almost at once when she arches her body around them in the home corner, they often hold her to this spot for some time. This state of affairs reduces the chances that the female will respond readily to the isolate, as by retrieving it from where it wanders elsewhere in the cage. The first-week isolates, therefore, through their superior motility and their situation as solitary individuals, were at a disadvantage as compared with neonates with respect to factors in female behavior promoting the first suckling.

Kittens isolated from the 6th to the 23rd day also were clearly inferior to normally raised littermates in the initiation and the early performance of suckling. Notwithstanding the fact that these kittens achieved their first contacts with the female early in their test periods, as for example through being attracted visually to her from a distance, the latency of their first suckling reactions was much longer than that for the first-week isolates. While the littermate controls were suckling once or twice each hour, the 6-to-23-day isolates each continued for nearly 20 hours in a persistent orientation to the female's face and anterior body but not to her mammary region. These kittens also, as with the first-week isolates, were generalized in their nuzzling, all of them spending long intervals nuzzling over the bodies of other kittens and the furry non-mammary surfaces of the female, before localization of a nipple and attachment occurred. These isolate kittens did not appear to be benefited particularly by their being attracted visually to the female, nor did their early suckling experience in the litter situation prior to isolation seem to have helped them in the process of first localizing a nipple. There are reasons to believe that the latency of suckling in their case had to do with the intervening period in the brooder, but indirectly rather than directly, in that it deprived them of specific litter experiences.

The situation was somewhat different in the testing of kittens isolated from the 18th to the 33rd day. Although these subjects, like the preceding group, were slow in localizing the female's mammary region, they had less difficulty in localizing nipples. Their difficulties centered more on adjusting to the female as an obejct from which to suckle. Kittens isolated later in the litter period, from the 34th to the 49th day, needed an even longer time to accomplish their first suckling adjustments in the tests. In all of these isolation groups, however, the deprivation period seemed to handicap the kittens chiefly with respect to effecting an appropriate suckling orientation to the female, rather than to the specific operations of localizing a nipple and suckling.

In the results for suckling latency, there is a sharp difference between the groups already described, isolated for periods starting at different times between the sixth and the 34th day, and the group isolated from the 47th to the 54th day. These last kittens were introduced to the brooder for one week, starting at the normal time of weaning in the litter situation, yet they all accomplished suckling in the return tests. Moreover, their delays were the shortest of those in all isolation groups, despite the fact that they accomplished their nipple localizations while the female was moving around the cage. One of these kittens was suckling within a minute after the test began, and a second required less than one hour, in contrast to the intervals of many hours needed by other kittens isolated after the first week.

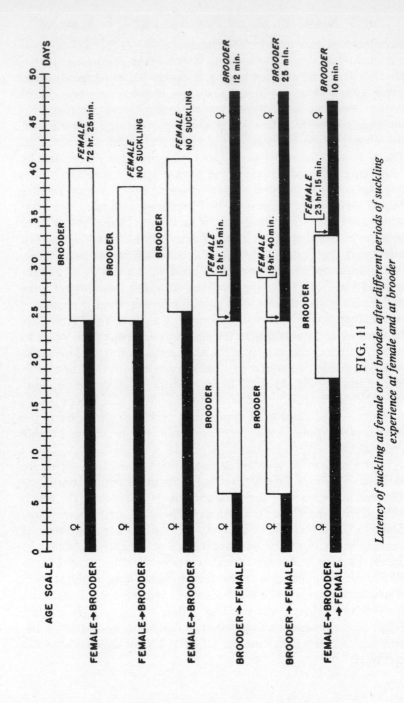

FIG. 11

Latency of suckling at female or at brooder after different periods of suckling experience at female and at brooder

Jay S. Rosenblatt, Gerald Turkewitz and T. C. Schneirla

Reinstatement of Suckling at the Female and at the Brooder – In what way is recall of the act of suckling at either the brooder or the female affected by a subsequent period of suckling under the other condition? To compare the recall of these two acts and also to establish the possibility of interference by either with the other, readjustment to the brooder was tested in kittens that had suckled at the female for several weeks, and readjustment to the female was tested in kittens that had suckled at the brooder during lengthy periods of isolation.

As Figure 11 shows, after an initial period with the female in which all of the subjects suckled from her, three of the kittens were placed in the incubator on either the 24th or the 25th day for isolations lasting to times between the 39th and 42nd days, when they were tested in the litter situation. Readjustment to the female was exceedingly difficult for all three of these kittens – one of them had a suckling latency of more than 72 hours and the other two did not suckle at all. By way of contrast, the two kittens that spent an early period (day 6 to 24) in the incubator, equivalent to that spent with the female by the others, but then were returned to the female on the 24th day and remained with her in a suckling relationship while the others were in the incubator, both reinstated suckling from the brooder almost at once in their terminal tests on the 49th day. The sixth kitten – which had an early period of suckling from the female, then a period in the incubator from the 18th to the 32nd day and finally a period with the female from the 33rd to the 47th day – in a test on the 47th day needed only ten minutes to reinstate suckling at the brooder. In contrast, these last three kittens, taken from the brooder at times before the 25th and 35th day for tests with the female, needed periods of from 12 to 23 hours to reinstate suckling from the female, much longer suckling latencies than those obtained either in female-return tests at later ages or in brooder-return tests at any age.

The effects of differences in the duration of the intervening period, in relation to the nature of the suckling adjustment in that period, are reported in Table XII. In tests with the female after intervals in the brooder ranging from 8 to 17 days, 11 kittens averaged 31 hours in their suckling latency. In tests with the brooder, however, after intervals with the female ranging from 10 to 36 days, nine kittens scored a minimum suckling latency of only 12 minutes. The shortest latency in female tests after brooder isolation was 33 minutes, and

TABLE XII

Recall of Suckling Reactions to the Female or to the Brooder after Different Intervals and Conditions of Preparation with Female and with Brooder

Female, then Brooder, then Test with Female

Intervening Period with Brooder	Latency of Suckling Reaction to Female	
days	hr.	min.
17	26	5
16	72	25
16	23	15
15	93	25
15	50	35
15	24	40
14	7	5
14	no suckling	
13	5	35
8	5	56
8	0	33

Mean interval = 13·7 days   Mean suckling latency = 31 hours

Brooder, then Female, then Test with Brooder

Intervening Period with Female	Latency of Suckling Reaction to Brooder
days	min.
36	immediately
24	25
24	12
17	3
15	8
14	10
12	21
10	16

Mean interval = 19 days   Mean suckling latency = 12 minutes

followed an isolation period of eight days, the longest was more than 93 hours, with one kitten not suckling at all after 16 days in the brooder. The shortest latency in brooder tests after intervening periods with the female was three minutes, after 17 days with the female; the longest was 25 minutes after 24 days with the female; but one kitten suckled at once after having been away from the brooder for 36 days (living part of the time with its mother, and the remainder alone, feeding from a dish).

As these results indicate clearly, the brooder-suckling pattern was far more readily reinstated than was that of female-suckling in kittens that had fed from one or the other of these sources during equivalent periods in early development. We may conclude therefore that the capacity to recall an earlier mode of suckling depends upon the conditions under which this pattern has developed in relation to conditions prevalent at the test. The results suggest that the difficulties or the failure of subjects to reinstate the female-suckling pattern under certain conditions must have been due to specific circumstances prevalent in the litter-situation at the time of the test, concerning in particular the nature of the feeding reaction required at that time. The brooder situation, in contrast, which had not changed in the meantime independently of the kitten, presented no such difficulties in the tests.

Interpretation

These suckling tests with altricial mammalian young bear some similarity to 'imprinting' or ('approach-fixation' – Schneirla, 1959) tests in which avian young are exposed to a test object after a specified post-hatching period in the dark, with later testing for their reactions to the first object or to others considered similar. In our studies with kittens, the initial exposure to the feeding object and its situation occurred within three weeks after birth, and the subsequent tests with this object and situation came at about the seventh week, after an intervening exposure to a *different* feeding object and situation. Viewed from the standpoint of a competing perceptual exposure following an initial fixation, the results may be taken to indicate the striking fact that an early approach-fixation to the brooder was definitely more effective for later reinstatement than was an early exposure to the female and litter situation.

Our experiment stands in contrast to the conventional case of 'imprinting', however, in that exposure to the experimentally critical object and its situation was not followed by the subject's being returned to a presumably neutral situation until the subsequent test. Instead, our subjects were exposed to a different object and situation, also admitting the critical reactions of approaching and suckling. We draw from our results, reported here in a summary form, the conclusion that an intervening period of female-approach and female-suckling in the litter situation impaired only minimally a reinstatement of the kitten's previous adjustment to the brooder; also, conversely, that the specific approach adjustment to the brooder and the specific act of brooder-suckling impaired only minimally a reinstatement of the kitten's previous adjustment to the female and the litter situation. Nevertheless, our results show clearly that although isolation from the brooder did not greatly retard subsequent performance at suckling in the brooder, isolation from the female and litter situation very substantially interfered with later suckling performances under those conditions.

For an understanding of these differences, the results of our analytical studies of normal events in the litter situation are enlightening, if reviewed in terms of a contrast of the pattern of relationships between female and young (1) prevalent at the time the isolate kittens were removed from the litter and (2) the pattern prevalent at the return. As we stated at the outset, in summarizing our results for maternal-young relations in the litter period, this pattern is a complex and changing one in which the roles of the participants are modified progressively in terms of three very different periods of perceptual-motor relationship. As a consequence, the litter situation confronting isolates returned from the brooder at different times differed radically from that prevalent at the earlier time of removal, especially as concerned the general behavior of the female and her responses to the kittens. To meet the different conditions of a new stage, without having participated in their general genesis, constituted an increasingly difficult task for kittens returned at later stages, as it required a progressively complex and specialized social and nutritive adjustment, diverging more and more from that formed earlier by the kitten in the litter situation. Adjustment to the brooder, on the other hand, involved meeting a relatively unchanged situation, because this situation could be modified in its functional relevance *only* in dependence on the kitten itself. A relatively simple and stereotyped approach-conditioning pattern arose thereby, which was not greatly disrupted by intervening adjustments to the litter situation and which could be reinstated without much difficulty on the kitten's return to the brooder.

For the most part, therefore, the disturbed behavior and the deficiencies of adaptive adjustment in kittens isolated late in the litter period may be attributed to their deficiencies in dealing with differences which had arisen in the litter situation during their absence. Both the evidence summarized here and results to be reported in further detail emphasize the necessity of a continued behavioral and functional interchange with female and littermates if the kitten is to develop an adequate suckling adjustment typical of its age-group. As we have mentioned, the feeding adjustment may be considered a central process in behavioral development; this, however, is not just any mode of feeding by suckling, as in the brooder, but one appropriately adapted to the current behavior pattern of the female and to the prevalent social situation.

Our findings lead us to favor a rather different view of the concept of 'critical periods' than the one now adopted by many investigators. For social ontogeny in the domestic cat, our findings instead support the interpretation that striking behavioral changes are attributable not only to growth-conditioned processes (i.e. to maturation) but also to factors of experience characteristic of the existing developmental situation. From this standpoint, we are led to emphasize not just one or a few striking time-conditioned changes in the pattern but to recognize that in general every age-period is *critical* for the development of certain aspects of the *normal, progressive suckling pattern*. Because factors of experience dependent upon the developmental situation are always significant for this pattern, in close relation to growth-dependent factors, we find that isolation from the normal developmental situation so deprives a kitten of developmental advantages available to normal littermates that it cannot adjust adequately when returned later.

The extent of recovery following a period away from female and litter is so dependent upon the age, the duration of the isolation, and the conditions of the isolation, however, that much further research is essential to clarify what factors of maturation or of experience at any one stage may become critical for specific as against inclusive and highly organized adjustments of the same or of later stages. The entire problem is complicated by questions concerning the equivalence of different kinds of maturational processes and of experience for the specific or for the general attainments of any stage in ontogeny.

It seems clear from our results that understanding the effects of any

73

condition of isolation or deprivation, in relation to those of the standard ontogenetic situation, requires an investigation of developmental processes in both of these situations with respect to their equivalences and their differences at successive stages.

REFERENCES

FULLER. J. L., EASLER, C. A., & BANKS, E. M. (1950) 'Formation of conditioned avoidance responses in young puppies' *Amer. J. Physiol.* **160**, 462-466

JAMES, W. T., & CANNON, D. J. (1952) 'Conditioned avoiding responses in puppies' *Amer. J. Physiol.* **168**, 251-253

ROSENBLATT, J. S., WODINSKY, J., TURKEWITZ, G., & SCHNEIRLA, T. C. 'Analytical studies on maternal behavior in relation to litter adjustment and socialization in the domestic cat. II. Maternal-young relations from birth to weaning. III. Development of orientation' (In MS.)

SCHNEIRLA, T. C. (1946) 'Problems in the biopsychology of social organization' *J. abnorm. soc. Psychol.* **41**, 385-402

SCHNEIRLA, T. C. (1951) 'A consideration of some problems in the ontogeny of family life and social adjustments in various infra-human animals' *Trans. 4th Conference, Problems of Infancy and Childhood* Josiah Macy Jr. Foundation, 81-124

SCHNEIRLA, T. C. (1956) 'Interrelationships of the "innate" and the "acquired" in instinctive behavior' In *L'instinct dans le Comportement des Animaux et de l'Homme.* Paris, Masson et Cie., 387-452

SCHNEIRLA, T. C. (1959) 'An evolutionary and developmental theory of biphasic processes underlying approach and withdrawal' In *Nebraska Symposium on Motivation* Univ. of Nebraska Press, 1-42

SCOTT, J. P. (1958) 'Critical periods in the development of social behavior in puppies '*Psychosom. Med.* **20**, 42-54

TOBACH, E., FAILLA, M. L., COHN, R., & SCHNEIRLA, T. C. 'Analytical studies on maternal behavior in relation to litter adjustment and socialization in the domestic cat. I. Parturition'

The Development of Affectional Patterns in Infant Monkeys

HARRY F. HARLOW

There exist in the newborn rhesus monkey powerful reflex mechanisms which will play an important part in the developing tie between the infant and the mother. The first of these is a contact-clasp reflex, which may be demonstrated as follows. If the newborn monkey is placed on its back, the righting reflex is immediately released, and the animal assumes normal stance within the limits of its motor capabilities. However, if the newborn is placed on its back and a cloth-covered object is placed against its chest and belly, the baby clutches the object and makes no effort to attain normal posture. This is apparently the basic response out of which the subsequent contact-comfort pattern develops.

Most newborn rhesus monkeys are apparently capable of very limited progressive whole-body movements. However, if a cloth is applied to the face, the monkey buries its face in it, and if the cloth is withdrawn gradually, the baby may follow with surprising agility and speed and even be drawn off a table top. This reflex, a reflex essential to nursing, may be thought of as a variant of the contact-clasp reflex, and both these reflexes may be specialized, primate postural responses.

A third primate reflex is that of sucking, which is probably inter-dependent with the first two. If a baby monkey is on the 'demand' schedule supplied by the ever-present normal monkey mother, almost all suckling, nutritional and non-nutritional, is supplied by the mother. If the baby is isolated and bottle-fed or cup-fed, on a fixed schedule, a large amount of non-nutritional sucking to any and all appendages appears. The act of sucking appears to be self-reinforcing. Bottle-fed babies show more sucking, nutritional and non-nutritional, than do baby monkeys that are cup-fed from birth onwards.

75

If these three systems constituted the entire behavior repertoire of the infant baby monkey, the infant should cling to the mother and show progressively stronger attachments. If this were true, there would be fewer baby monkeys, and other primate forms, than there are in the world today. It becomes important, therefore, to search for other basic, primate response systems – releasing systems that overcome the immediate infant-mother affectional systems and prepare the infant for a wide, new world.

The primary system of release from these mechanisms is probably that of curiosity and exploration. One component of this release system, strong visual curiosity, appears in the baby monkey under five days of age and can be measured by a modification of the Butler Box shown in Plate 6. We have had three-day-old monkeys which pressed the release lever several hundred times and peered out of the exploration window dozens of times during the 30-minute period of the initial test-day. Actually, limited visual and contactual exploration have been observed from day 1 onward. Although this system is existent during the first five days, the infant-mother ties are such that the mother does not actually release her infant for intimate, worldly exploration for a very considerable time thereafter.

Intense manipulatory exploration appears at about 20 days of age and becomes progressively stronger, increasing in strength during the next two to three months. This augmentation is a function of maturation in considerable part, even though there is every reason to believe that manipulation, like contact-clasping and sucking, is self-reinforcing. Again, the exploratory mechanism exists long before it operates as an infant-releasing mechanism.

Initially, visual and contactual exploration are positive to all objects that are not actually painful; in other words, all, or almost all, stimuli elicit approach responses, and the larger, stronger, brighter and more mobile the stimuli, the stronger the approach responses. Such a system would undoubtedly be lethal if it were not held in early abeyance by the mother monkey in the wild and by the experimenter in the laboratory. However, at about the age of 20 to 40 days there is gradually developing a check-and-balance system, the fear-response system. Stimuli, particularly large, mobile, strange stimuli, cease to call forth approach responses and come to elicit avoidance responses, and the same holds true for new, strange environments even though devoid of any specific fear-arousing stimulus

PLATE 6. Monkey responding in visual exploration apparatus

PLATE 8. Contact vs. feeding conflict

PLATE 7. Infant monkey in dual surrogate situation

PLATE 9. Typical fear-stimulus

PLATE 11. Response in the open-field test with cloth surrogate absent

PLATE 10. Young infant's response to cloth surrogate in the open-field test

objects. Out of these five systems there develop efficient check-and-balance mechanisms determining in large part mother-infant interactions.

During the last three years we have been working, and are continuing to work, on the relatively limited problem of the role of the multiple variables determining the infant's tie to the mother. We initially attacked the problem of the relative importance of contact motives contrasted with nutritional motives. In our original experiment, eight newborn rhesus monkeys were separated from their mothers and placed in individual cages with access to two inanimate mother surrogates. Both surrogates were made of welded wire, but one was covered with a terry-cloth sheath, as shown in Plate 7. Half the monkeys received milk from a small nursing bottle in the wire mother's body, and half the monkeys received milk from the cloth-covered mother. As can be seen in Figure 12, all the babies, regard-

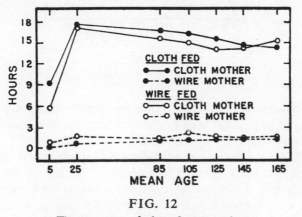

FIG. 12

Time spent on cloth and wire mothers

less of nursing condition, came rapidly to spend most of their time on the cloth mother. Not only did it seem that contact comfort was a system completely superordinate over activities associated with nursing, but there was no evidence that nursing, through the mechanism of secondary reinforcement, became an affectional variable of any real importance. The strength of the contact response is dramatically shown in Plate 8. This proves that you can eat your cake and have it too.

We also tested out baby monkeys in their home cages when a fear stimulus, such as the mobile toy dog presented in Plate 9, was shown to them. Regardless of nursing condition, the majority of the responses were to the cloth mother as shown in Figure 13, and from 100 days onward almost all the responses were to the cloth mother.

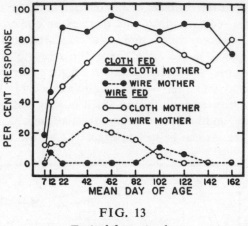

FIG. 13

Typical fear-stimulus

During the first 20 days the infants frequently failed to respond, either through physical inability or the fact that this kind of fear responsiveness had not yet matured.

An efficient test for measuring infant-mother affection is the open-field situation, which consists of a room six feet by six feet by six feet containing a number of unfamiliar objects such as a small artificial tree, a crumpled piece of paper, a folded gauze diaper, a wooden block and a doorknob. When the cloth mother was present, the infant would rush wildly to her, climb upon her, rub against her, and cling to her tightly, as shown in Plate 10. However, when the cloth mother was absent, the infants would rush across the test room and throw themselves face downward, clutching their heads and bodies and screaming their distress (see Plate 11). Objective emotionality scores were almost tripled in the absence, as contrasted with the presence, of the cloth mother surrogate.

The presence of the wire mother provided no more reassurance in this open-field test than no mother at all. Control tests on monkeys

PLATE 12. Unresponsiveness to wire surrogate in the open-field test

PLATE 13. Exploration-manipulation in the open-field test by 150-day old infant

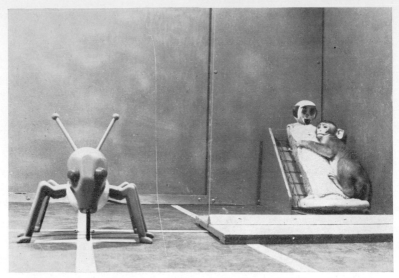

PLATE 14. Response to surrogate in the open-field-fear situation

PLATE 15. Exploration-manipulation of the previously feared stimulus

that from birth had known only a nursing wire mother revealed that even these infants showed no affection for her and obtained no comfort from her presence, as shown in Plate 12.

The early responses of the baby monkeys in any fear situation are largely limited to achieving and maintaining mother contact. However, as the babies mature, a new type of responsiveness develops; it is as if the cloth mother provides the infant with a sense of security, releasing positive responses of exploration and play, as indicated in Plate 13.

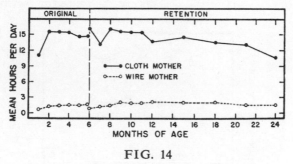

FIG. 14

Retention of affectional responses after prolonged separation

Even more striking data were obtained in a variant of the open-field test in which direct access to the surrogate was blocked by a large Plexiglas screen which was adjacent to a fear stimulus. In the early trials the infants would rush around the fear stimulus and clutch and cling to the mother (see Plate 14). After a number of trials the infants would go first to the cloth mother and then, and only then, would go out to explore, manipulate and even attack and destroy the fear stimulus (Plate 15).

In most of our experiments the infants lived with their mother surrogates during the first 180 days of life and then were separated from them. Retention of the affectional responses was tested during the first nine days of separation, then at three successive 30-day intervals, and then at four intervals of 90 days each. As can be seen in Figure 14, monkeys raised under any condition affording contact with a cloth mother showed amazingly efficient retention of the affectional bonds. Obviously, the affection of the infants for the cloth mother surrogate is extremely persisting.

79

In recent years there has been established a body of research on the importance of critical periods for the formation of both intellectual and social bonds. We placed one group of monkeys in the dual-mother situation after they were 250 days old. Figure 15 shows that these animals did come to spend considerable time on the cloth mother, but less time than infants placed with the two mother surrogates at birth. However, these infants failed to develop any sense of security in the open-field test in the presence of the cloth mother, and their lack of responsiveness in all the retention tests made it obvious that 250 days was past the time for the formation

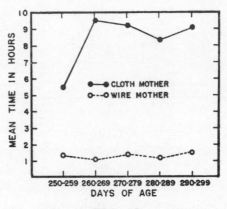

FIG. 15

*Response to cloth mothers by the 250-day
delayed monkeys*

of strong infant-mother affection. Recently we first placed a group of baby monkeys in the dual-mother situation at 60 days of age, and our data to date, though admittedly incomplete, suggest that even this relatively brief period of motherlessness inhibits the formation of a fully developed infant-mother attachment.

There is every reason to believe that the importance of different variables underlying infant-mother affection changes as a function of age. In one experiment we tested differential responsiveness to the mother surrogates and to other infant monkeys. Under these circumstances there was little indication of developing responsiveness to other infants, a discovery which in retrospect has certain frightening implications. It suggests that delay in, or limited opportunity for, infant-infant interaction leaves the monkey infant hopelessly tied to the mother and incapable of proper infant-infant affection.

On the positive side one notes increasing responsiveness to the mother's face and head, beginning at about 45 days of age. This finding is supported by observation and motion-picture records, and is in keeping with the responsiveness that human babies show to the mother's face, beginning at two to three months of age. We have attempted to obtain visual-auditory imprinting in one baby monkey

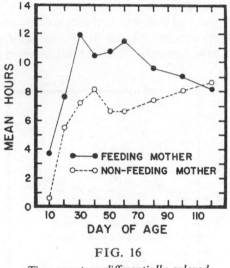

FIG. 16

Time spent on differentially colored surrogates

and have not been successful. However, we know that infants at later ages obtain considerable emotional support in the open-field test from the presence of a cloth mother surrogate enclosed in a Plexiglas box. Thus, there is every reason to believe that vision, at a particular maturational stage, becomes an important variable underlying the development of the affectional responses to the mother.

In an effort to demonstrate that activities associated with nursing are variables of measurable importance for infant-maternal affection, we tested the responsiveness of four monkeys, each having two cloth mothers available, one green and one tan. The mothers had differential faces, and only one of them nursed, the tan one for half the babies, the green one for the other half. The data from Figure 16 show that initially the babies did form a preference for the nursing mother, but this initial preference disappeared at about 100 days of age. The monkeys were also tested in the open field with both mothers present. In early tests they went to the nursing mother predominantly, but even before the cage preference disappeared, the open-field preference for the nursing mother dropped out. The advent and waning of different variables certainly cause no surprise in spite of the obvious implication that these data have for the role of derived drives or motives.

Earlier researches had indicated that rocking motion was a variable of measurable importance for the development of infant-mother attachments, but the data from Figure 17 indicate that this is another

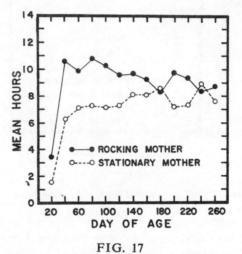

FIG. 17

Time spent on rocking vs. stationary
surrogates

variable of importance early in life and of little or no importance subsequently. Converse data are obtained in relation to body form and posture, as shown in Figure 18, which indicates time spent on cloth mother vs. cloth-covered plane. A relatively flat plane or 'cradle' provides the primary contact need for the young infant, but the need to cling becomes evident as the monkey matures. Actually, we suspect that these data are an artifact dependent upon the inability of the armless surrogates to provide their babies with proper support early in life.

One of our goals has been the production of neurotic monkeys raised on inconsistent and rejecting mothers. To achieve this, we have produced a mother whose ventral surface is lined with tubes through which jets of compressed air may be forced, for air blast is a strong aversive stimulus for monkeys. A buzzer serves as a conditioned stimulus warning the infant of approaching air blast. Our single subject to date has learned this conditioned response, and when the buzzer is presented, it clasps the mother's body with increased vigor,

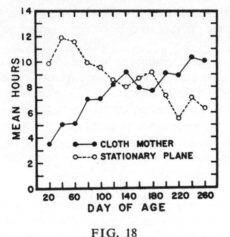

FIG. 18

Time spent on cloth surrogate vs. cloth plane

insuring that maximal blast intensity will strike its face and body. (Apparently this infant monkey either has not read or does not believe Miller's brilliant theoretical chapter in Volume 2, *Psychology: A study of a science*,[1] which demonstrates so convincingly that, 'The strength of avoidance increases more rapidly with nearness than does that of approach.')

Perhaps we do not need to worry about devising techniques for producing experimental neuroses in monkeys. For all our early

[1] Ed. S. Koch.

groups we have already succeeded – apparently in 100 per cent of the cases. Our interests in analyzing the maturation of learning, infant-maternal affection, and retention of infant-mother affection led us to keep our infants in separate cages for periods of from two to five years. When these infants were subsequently paired, they showed little or no interaction except in the case of certain animals which engaged in violent and vicious assault upon the partner. Those monkeys which we have successfully paired sit in their cages, suck their thumbs and stare into space, maintaining a state of happy coexistence and proving that propinquity can be consonant with perfect propriety as long as no one cares. Like Immanuel Kant they live their lives in a state of genteel solipsism, undisturbed by recreational or procreational thoughts or activities. We already have on hand an adequate number of subjects for a large psychotherapeutic program.

Although love may be enough, love of mother alone is not. The feral rhesus mother guides the infant through two kinds of affectional stages. It provides its baby from birth throughout early infancy with the nutritional and comfort needs upon which are formed affection and security, and it safeguards its infant until effective danger signals are recognized. Furthermore, it is entirely possible, indeed probable, that the infant learns to become socially responsive and socially imitative during this period.

The second guided affectional pattern consists of the gradual relaxation of these affectional bonds between mother and child. The first bond to be overridden is that of clasping and clinging. Van Wagenen has warned that newborn rhesus monkeys should not be placed together, since the clinging response may be so strong as to be lethal. We are now tracing the development of our first pair of infants placed together at 30 days of age (see Plate 16). We do not yet know whether or not their almost constant mutual clinging will inhibit the more mature forms of infant-infant interaction.

The second affectional stage develops gradually and is characterized by the infant's increasing exploration of the physical environment; it is entirely possible that this is an essential stage for the subsequent development of normal infant-infant affection. We hazard the guess that environmental exploration is followed by infant-infant exploration and that out of this arise patterns of play. The comparatively immobile stimuli of the physical environment

PLATE 16. Together-together infants

PLATE 17. Social-surrogate situation

must be relatively unstimulating compared with other real, living infants having almost unlimited capability of providing variable and novel stimulation. The patterns of play are gradually overridden by the aggressive patterns and the sexual patterns, but play is an essential precursor if either of these subsequent patterns is to follow a normal course. The development of infant-infant affection through play holds in check the murderously aggressive patterns of the adult monkeys, and the patterns of play are essential training for normal adolescent and adult sexual behavior.

We have approached the problem of tracing the development of normal affectional interaction between infants by testing them in what we call the social-mother situation. Each of a pair of monkeys is raised on its own cloth mother surrogate, but from birth onward they are free to make contact with their baby monkey partner through the grill seen in Plate 17. Three groups of four baby monkeys have been tested in this situation, Group A after spending 180 days in individual wire cages with no mother surrogates, Group B after spending 180 days in individual wire cages with a cloth mother surrogate, and Group C raised from the first day of life onward with freedom to contact a partner and its own cloth mother surrogate. We are primarily interested in the amount of time spent in the partner booth, since this is a measure of interaction between the infants.

All the members of these three groups were denied contact with their partners for a six-hour period by replacing the grill in the rear of the booth with an opaque door. At the end of the deprivation period observational records of behavior were made for a three-minute period. Figure 19 shows that after a four-hour period of partner deprivation the Group B monkeys, the animals raised for 180 days on a mother without another infant's being present, show practically no interaction with the partner, data favorable to our theory that prolonged fixation to the mother surrogate adversely affects the subsequent capability of forming adequate infant-infant social contacts. The Group C babies, which had a partner available from birth onward, show a high incidence of partner contacts and play responses oriented toward the partner. The Group A infants, which had neither mother nor infant contacts until 180 days of age, also show a large amount of infant-infant interaction but very limited play-oriented responsiveness.

All three groups were also tested after a six-hour period of mother-

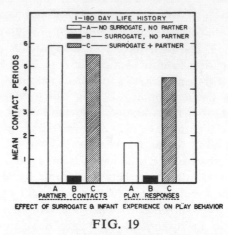

FIG. 19

*Partner contact and play responses after
partner deprivation*

surrogate deprivation, with results indicated in Figure 20 for one
form of responsiveness to the mother, play on and about her. The
results are very similar to those presented for play with the partner,

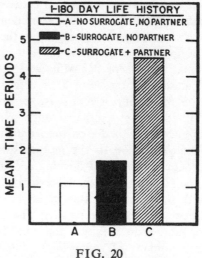

FIG. 20

*Play on mother after mother
deprivation*

again suggesting that too prolonged and intimate contact with the mother inhibits all types of play responses, even play responses to the mother. A stuffed mother, of course, lacks a certain amount of spontaneity and playfulness.

We have limited data on the social development of four infant monkeys being tested in all paired combinations. The test situation is an observation cage 6 feet by 3 feet by 2·5 feet with a Plexiglas front. The behavior of each animal is observed by a single experimenter, and observers shift animals on alternate days to permit reliability measures. Two of these infants have been social-surrogate babies from birth on, and two are not. As can be seen in Figure 21,

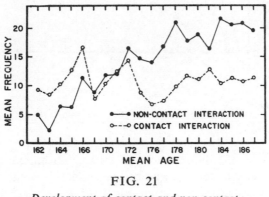

FIG. 21

*Development of contact and non-contact
interaction*

there has been a progressive tendency within the social-surrogate pair to decrease immediate bodily contact and to increase non-contact interaction. 'Non-contact interaction' involves such behavior patterns as alternately running back and forth toward the partner and such responses as mutual, oriented jumping up and down, mutual somersaulting, mutual approach and lip-smacking responses. Thus, these limited data suggest that non-contact interaction – particularly non-contact play – is developing rapidly from 160 to 200 days of age. In Figure 22 are presented the developmental data comparing non-contact interaction with sexual play, which includes such responses as mounting, thrusting and presenting. In no case did the true pattern of normal adult sex behavior appear. In this particular

87

situation sexual play appeared at the beginning of testing and tended to wane as non-contact interaction increased. All these behaviors appeared in spite of the fact that the test situation was originally a strange situation which presumably inhibited interaction between the infants.

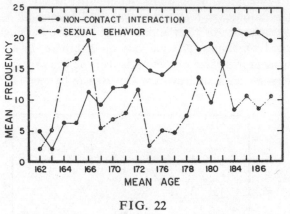

FIG. 22

*Development of sexual play and non-contact
interaction*

The data on the development of interaction among infants are admittedly limited, for the number of animals and the number of observations are as yet too small. Furthermore, we had far less idea of the relative importance of behavior to be observed when these studies were designed than we do now, after the first of our preliminary data have been tabulated. For example, in our social-surrogate test we limited the amount of possible infant-infant interaction by the bar-grill, and we suspect this was an error.

If one has limited data and the opportunity to make a speech, one has very little option but to present a theory, and this we have done. I only wish I could present facts, not guesses, about the normal development of infant-infant interaction. We are certain that as more and more data are collected, our present theory will have to be modified or possibly discarded, for it is very hard to spin an adequate theory out of whole cloth, even if it is terry cloth.

Discussion following
Professor Harlow's Paper[1]

BOWLBY *As you remarked, most of these infants brought up on surrogate mothers suck their thumb or toe. Is it true that monkeys brought up with their own mothers do not?*

HARLOW *That is correct – or if it does occur it is very rare. All babies not brought up on a real mother have strong tendencies to non-nutritional sucking, which is sometimes quite violent.*

THOMAS *It looks as if, in these experiments, you have separated the clinging behaviour and the sucking, and now the infants are trying to put them together again.*

BOWLBY *But isn't it the case that, where the infant is reared on a surrogate which feeds it, the infant still sucks its thumb?*

HARLOW *That's so. I'm not sure of the explanation, but it may be concerned with the feeding schedules. The experimental babies were fed on schedule, whereas those reared with their own mothers are fed on demand.*

ROWELL *Doesn't Levy's work with puppies suggest that the amount of non-nutritional sucking which goes on depends on the kind of thing which is being sucked? The less satisfactory the feed, the more sucking.*

HARLOW *I'm sceptical of that interpretation. We have experiments in which bottle and cup feeding of monkeys were compared.[2] Those reared on the bottle did more non-nutritional sucking, although they had fed much more satisfactorily. My impression, is that the act of sucking is self-reinforcing, and so gets perpetuated.*

*   *   *

APPELL *We have been very struck by the behaviour of these young monkeys under stress, because it is so very like the behaviour of deprived children – the folding up, the freezing, the rocking, and the going to walls and corners.*

[1] And a showing of his film 'Contact Comfort'.
[2] Benjamin, Lorna S. (1961) 'The effect of bottle and cup feeding on the nonnutritive sucking of the infant rhesus monkey' *J. comp. physiol. Psychol.*

RHEINGOLD *You are talking of disturbed children. If we were to take normal children and put them in a strange situation, I don't think these reactions would occur.*

DAVID *If he was not separated from his mother, I would say he would cling to his mother and turn away his head from the source of threat. And only then turn and look interested: very much as the baby rhesus does if the surrogate is there. But if he had been separated long months, in a threat situation he would prefer a wall to a so-called mother figure.*

ROBERTSON *But, with the exception perhaps of creeping along a wall, one can see all this behaviour in short-term separated children. Children under the age of two who go into hospital show much of it – hiding, 'playing possum' as they call it – trying not to exist in the face of the stranger. Almost all one sees in these monkeys in distress can be seen in short-stay hospital children.*

* * *

ROSENBLATT *Have you ever compared the type of behaviour these experimentally reared monkeys show towards the models with their behaviour towards a real monkey? We have, in our work with kittens, found that brooder-reared young that had been taken from the mother at birth and reared in isolation until just prior to weaning at 45 days were terrified by the sight of their mother and they remained frightened for several days. In these kittens, suckling from the mother was never established upon their return to her.*

HARLOW *No we have not. Baby monkeys in the wild show their mothers a lot of affection for at least two years – but my guess is that the tie is not as strong as it would be with a model surrogate mother. The real mother may actually have techniques to break the connection – to force the infant to leave her, and explore, and develop attachments to other infants. This development of infant-infant interaction is just what we want to study. It will have to be done in the animals' home cages, because putting them in a strange cage leads to fear which inhibits the very patterns we want to look at.*

RHEINGOLD *From my observations on monkeys in the Santiago colony and in zoos, I would say that the infants in zoos are much more protected by their mothers.*

HARLOW *In the zoo there is constant fear. As soon as these animals are taken out of their natural situation, the development of mother-*

Discussion

infant and infant-infant ties alters. As soon as our infants are the least bit frightened they run to the surrogate mother and cling.

RHEINGOLD *To a non-responding partner. Whereas the real mother would interfere with these clinging activities?*

HARLOW *That's right. The result is, I think, we have babies that have a complete fixation on the cloth surrogate mother. I used to think that once an infant had developed affection for its mother it would generalize this affection to other infants. Now I am extremely sceptical. I have a feeling the infant does not perceive another infant as a member of the species to which its mother belongs.*

ROSENBLATT *With respect to this general question, that is, of mother-young interaction and the process of weaning, it is our impression that the waning of maternal behaviour in cats is related to the growth of play in the kittens. It appears from our studies as though the play of kittens among themselves and with the mother throws the mother out of her maternal mood, or contributes to this process.*

HARLOW *With a baby monkey that has been raised entirely on a cloth mother, you can see a play pattern developing. It is centred entirely around the surrogate, but, of course, the surrogate cannot force the infant to transfer play to other infants.*

ROSENBLATT *Have we any information in monkeys as to the age at which maternal behaviour receded in the free-ranging situation?*

RHEINGOLD *My impression is that the young are forcibly weaned by the mother at about nine months.*

HARLOW *The mother apparently has a much better sense of the timing of these things. A surrogate mother seems to be quite unimaginative.*

*   *   *

ROSENBLATT *I would like to open a discussion of what is probably the central issue which has been raised in these studies. In this respect I am not quite sure that the experiments have demonstrated that nursing or rather suckling does not form a strong part of the bond with the mother in conjunction with clasping.*

HARLOW *I'm sure it is a variable of importance, if for nothing else but what it does for the mother; but I do not think it is a variable that gives persistent affection in the infant.*

FOSS *Were the infants fed 'on demand' by the wire mothers? If not, could you so to speak force the animal to go to the wire mother more by making it hungry, or by giving it a variable schedule?*

HARLOW *They were on a fixed schedule, starting at once every two hours, later dropping out the 2 o'clock and 12 o'clock feeds. We have never tried hunger to force an attachment.*

GEWIRTZ *You might have gotten a stronger attachment if you had done so.*

FOSS *Could it be that you have been very successful in providing a situation for eliciting clinging, but that the nursing situation is far from optimal?*

HARLOW *Actually the teat used is not unlike the mother's nipple, and there is every reason to believe that they feed effectively because they gain weight more rapidly than do animals with their real mothers.*

BOWLBY *You could argue that, for clinging, the model is even more schematic. After all this towelling is rather unlike the mother – it's not hairy, it's not warm, it's the wrong shape. . . .*

ROSENBLATT *As I see it there seem to be two questions involved here. The first is whether clinging itself, apart from suckling, forms a basis for the attachment of the young to the mother. Certainly Dr Harlow has suggested this and his experiments seem to demonstrate this fact. A second question is whether, when an animal is suckling, it is the clinging rather than the suckling itself which is the stronger of the two actions as a basis for attachment to the mother. In the normal sequence of an infant's behaviour, clinging and suckling occur together. Evidently, however, they can be placed in opposition to one another as you have done in the test situations with the monkeys. Yet I wonder whether this sheds light on what is happening when both clinging and suckling are going on together?*

BOWLBY *Isn't it true that in some of the experiments they do go together?*

HARLOW *Yes – let's take the model where nursing and clinging were not confounded – for instance where there was a choice between the brown and green cloth mothers.*

ROSENBLATT *But didn't that experiment show that suckling was a factor in the development of attachment to the mother-object?*

HARLOW *Yes, but only right at the beginning: and it doesn't seem to affect the imprinting, if we can call it that, in the long run.*

GEWIRTZ *What seems to me to be all important is the fact that infants of the macaque species characteristically cling so intensely to certain rough surfaces, fur, terry-cloth or other towelling and the like, from the very beginning of life. Clinging and its consequences appear thus to constitute the focal behaviour pattern for these newborns. On this basis, made up as she is of smooth wires of small diameter which may be difficult to hold comfortably, with neither hair nor a pliable skin, of an awkward shape possibly, apparently inadequate for maintaining a cozy warmth during clinging, the wire mother surrogate may have provided a surface so inadequate for the monkey infant's clinging behaviour as to disrupt that entire behaviour pattern. So much so that food, which is potentially a most potent reinforcing stimulus for the hungry animal, seems not to have operated as such, in so far as it did not serve to establish various characteristics of the wire mother as conditioned reinforcing stimuli.*

RHEINGOLD *To what extent is the wire mother an aversive stimulus? In my limited observation this young animal is manipulating surfaces all the time, and wire might be painful or obnoxious to their hands.*

HARLOW *A baby monkey raised with a cloth mother will spend a lot of its time climbing all over the wire cage, and this is real climbing, grasping the wire with no sign of an aversive response.*

GEWIRTZ *From a learning standpoint, there would be several other possible reasons why feeding seems to be unimportant in producing attachments. At this point I would like to mention just two. The first is concerned with the visual and other characteristics of the surrogates. It is possible that these characteristics are not sufficiently discriminable by the young rhesus for food reinforcement to result in the characteristics becoming conditional reinforcers. The second point is perhaps more important, and it seems never to be taken into account in explaining the development of attachments. I'm referring to the fact that different aspects of the environment are reinforcing to the infant at different stages of its development – and here I'm talking about unconditioned stimuli. For instance, it's likely that food is prepotent as a reinforcer at first, but it may lose some of these reinforcing properties at later stages of development, when sheer novelty – environmental change – becomes of greater importance as an unconditioned reinforcer. Some of these might be environmental changes brought about by the infant's own movements, so that the infant's most recently acquired, and most complex movements might acquire reinforcing properties. To return* to Harlow's experiments, it seems likely that, for the macaque infant, but almost certainly not for the human infant, there is a stage at which contact-clinging constitutes the focal behaviour pattern or central arena for interaction with the environment.

ROSENBLATT *It seems to me that the scheme Dr Harlow has presented for development of an attachment between mother and infant does propose successive periods in which different factors are important. As an example, he has suggested that clasping and clinging provide an effective basis for attachment to the mother at an early period followed by attachment mediated through visual responsiveness when this sensory system is incorporated into behavioural systems. Yet we have no idea of the way in which earlier episodes influence later ones, and the links that are formed between them. There seem to be simply a series of critical periods that follow in succession but except for the fact that in each episode attachment to the mother is maintained and becomes more complex, as Dr Harlow has shown, the relation between one period and the next is not clear. These are difficult problems with which all of us doing research that is developmentally oriented are faced.*

HARLOW *When I first heard of critical periods I was very much opposed to them, but now I think we know a great deal about critical periods in the development of a rhesus monkey's learning ability, for instance. The ability to learn discriminations between black and white comes in at eight days of age, and the animal then learns this as rapidly as he learns anything at that age. But in learning to discriminate between objects – which is more complicated – there seem to be two critical periods. This is a period when it can learn, given unlimited opportunity, which starts at about twenty days of age; but the period for learning with maximum efficiency doesn't start until about 120 days. And the ability to transfer from one such discrimination to another – in other words, the ability to acquire learning sets – doesn't show until 180 days, and reaches its maximum at two years. So the thing about a critical period is that it's not here today and gone tomorrow; once an ability shows itself it is here to stay, and will influence everything that happens afterwards. Now my guess would be that the various stages of affection and other emotional development also have their critical periods. For instance, fear responses to exteroceptive stimuli won't start coming in until, say, between 20 and 60 days of age – the exact time depending on the stimulus strength, suddenness and so on. Or again, when does an infant rhesus start reacting to another infant other than by contact clinging? My guess is that limited play behaviour can first be elicited at about 120 days of age, but there are several play patterns, each probably having its own critical period, and the complete form isn't seen until about 180 to 200 days. Now I think the situation is the same as in learning abilities: once an ability comes in, it comes in for ever so to speak. It doesn't wane, you see.*

BOWLBY *It has always seemed to me that the term 'critical period or phase' has been applied to something which clocks in at a certain point in time, as you suggest, but also clocks out again.*

HARLOW *Nothing ever clocks out. It is only overridden by another pattern.*

RHEINGOLD *I agree with John Bowlby. My impression is that the term is used in a situation where an ability emerges, but if there are no stimuli to support the emergence of the behaviour, it will never emerge.*

BOWLBY *Yes, now this seems quite crucial. I wonder if it is wise to use the term in this other way. What would the ethologists say about it?*

HINDE *I think it is a question of the stage of analysis you have reached. People use the term 'critical period' in learning to indicate that learning of a certain kind first appears between two points in time. The next stage of the analysis is to determine whether or not the end limit is set by something else overriding or competing with the particular kind of learning.*

BOWLBY *It seems to me that there are many clear cases of critical periods. For instance in Sears' work on sucking one can see that if there is no early experience of sucking, then it is elicited hardly at all in later life. I think this is true of pecking too isn't it?*

HINDE *Yes, but that might be because some other response is over-riding it, as Harry Harlow says. But I think he's overgeneralizing to say that this sort of thing is always the reason for the ending of a critical period. I think there may be other reason. A good case is of song learning in birds. Some birds can learn several songs at a certain critical period of their lives, but once the period is over they can't learn any new ones.*

HARLOW *Well, thank you for reminding me of that. Life's very difficult. I gave up not using the term 'reinforcement' and I gave up not using the term 'critical period' because no matter how tactfully you* don't *use these terms, you get extinguished.*

HINDE *If I get you rightly, that means that you are still willing to talk about reinforcement. I was surprised and I think delighted to hear you talking about the self-reinforcing nature of what you call innate responses. Would you tell us exactly what you meant?*

HARLOW *I think I could illustrate it, not in terms of the mother-surrogate, but in terms of monkeys' responses to simple wire puzzles.[1] Usually a 90-day-old monkey will show more responsiveness to these puzzles than will a 30-day-old. But if the younger one has had more experience of them than the older, then it will be the one that shows more responsiveness. It's as if apart from the maturational factor the very act of manipulating these things is reinforcing. And I think this happens to a lot of systems. The very act of clinging augments the tendency to cling.*

HINDE *And would you place the emphasis on the act of clinging or on the consequences of clinging?*

HARLOW *I think perhaps on the consequence, though I'm not sure.*

HINDE *Then perhaps it's not necessary to draw a sharp distinction between classical reinforcement and these 'self-rewarding' activities. When you talked about feeding, you called it 'good old primary reinforcement', implying that self-reinforcing activities were something different. But, if in both cases the emphasis is on the importance of the consequences, the distinction need not be so sharp.*

RHEINGOLD *Except that they would be different systems.*

AMBROSE *But sometimes learning seems to occur when the consequences of the activity are totally non-adaptive. For instance, when animals become imprinted on inappropriate objects.*

GEWIRTZ *I assume you mean that many of these objects are 'inappropriate' in the sense that they are not the ones on which the young of the species become imprinted typically.*

AMBROSE *Not just that. They are inappropriate because they are not reinforcing in a way beneficial to the animal. For instance, a young sheep may get imprinted on a rock.*

GEWIRTZ *I didn't think the case was so clear for imprinting on inanimate objects. Still, if we approach the following behaviour*

[1] Mason, W. A., Harlow & Rueping (1959) 'The development of manipulatory responsiveness in the infant rhesus monkey' *J. comp. physiol. Psychol.* **52**, 555.

Discussion

pattern of imprinting as a possible case of rapid instrumental learning in earliest life, as many of us are inclined to do, we must identify the reinforcing events involved and specify how they enter into learning contingencies with the imprinting behaviours. So far (as I did in my earlier remark) we have advanced but loose speculations about the identities of the reinforcing events and the nature of the learning contingencies involved. Even so, from what we know of the operation of reinforcing stimuli in other learning contexts and from such studies as that of H. James' of a flickering light as an unconditioned stimulus for imprinting[1], it seems unlikely that even highly discriminal inanimate (non-moving) objects would be imprinted upon unless they were associated effectively with reinforcing stimuli. Further, I would guess (as I suggested earlier) that, for the imprinting-as-learning behaviour pattern to develop, this association between the 'to be imprinted' object and reinforcing stimuli would have to occur in the earliest phases of life, when there is a complete absence of competing response systems.

[1] James H. (1959) 'Flicker: an unconditioned stimulus for imprinting' *Canadian J. Psychol.* 13, 59.

PART III

Social Behaviour

Case Notes on Monique[1]

Contribution by GENEVIÈVE APPELL
and MYRIAM DAVID

In this report we present the case of a young girl, 2 years 2 months old, Monique B., who, when she arrived at the institution, showed very serious mental retardation that could easily have been judged to be organic in origin. But on the one hand her history of being moved from place to place, and on the other hand certain fleeting reactions, suggested the hypothesis of a psychogenic retardation.

Social History

Monique was born on the 24th August 1947. Her father is of modest means and seems to be in good health. Her mother is Russian; she became a displaced person at the age of about 16 and seems to have undergone hard experiences. Mr B. met her in Germany. He brought her back and married her because she was pregnant with his first son. This son is entirely normal. Very soon after the birth of the first child, Mrs B. became pregnant again with Monique; during the first three months of this pregnancy she was treated for appendicitis and underwent an operation. Mrs B. complained also of occipital headaches with transitory lapse of vision. Her husband and family thought that her extreme fatigue, her changing moods and her refusal to eat were due to her depatriation. After the delivery which was normal but took place at 7 months (1 kilo 100 grammes), Mrs B. insisted that she breast-feed Monique, 'although she herself ate

[1] The work reported here formed part of a research programme directed by Dr Jenny Aubry. A version of these notes was previously published in French (*Revue de Psychiatrie Infantile de Zürich*, 1951). They are published here by kind permission. The Study Group was shown the film 'Maternal Deprivation in Young Children' which centres on Monique. The film was produced by Mlle Appell.

nothing and spent hours and hours sitting around in an unhealthy dwelling doing nothing'.

In October 1947, when Monique was 2 months old, Mrs B. left home suddenly during her husband's absence, taking a slice of meat with her. She was found in the street and then taken to hospital. Monique was given back to her, and breast-fed for two days. But the doctors noticing that the mother squeezed the child too hard and that her behaviour was not normal and could become dangerous for the child, took it away from her. Since that time Mrs B. has remained in the hospital where a diagnosis of 'Hebe-phrenic-catatonia' has been made.

Monique remained for some time in the hospital and was then sent to a nursery somewhere between 3 and 9 months of age. She had a very severe attack of bronchial pneumonia from which she recovered quite well from a physical viewpoint, but even at that time she took fright at the slightest noise.

At about 9 to 17 months of age she was placed in a foster home with three other children. During a visit her aunt found her in a very bad state, thin, agitated and trembling all over when taken in the arms. The family then gave her into the care of her brother's foster mother, in whom they had confidence (January 1949). She, noticing Monique's quite abnormal behaviour (banging her head on the wall, and inability to walk or talk at 17 months), suggested that she be examined by a doctor. Monique then became ill with chicken-pox and was hospitalized at a children's hospital. (Whooping cough was an unconfirmed diagnosis.) She was then sent to a nursery in the mountains, till August 1949 (2 years). At that time she was taken back to her brother's foster mother, who could not keep her, however, since her behaviour was so abnormal. (The child did not sleep, cried a great deal, etc.) Monique was sent again to hospital, and arrived in our institution on the 21st October 1949, when 2 years 2 months old.

Description of the Child at Admission

Amid the comings and goings of the other children, Monique sits alone in the centre of the room, all hunched up and rocking. She has thick black hair, dry and stiff, partially covering her small, pale, moon-shaped face. Her skin is smooth and livid. The immobility of her expression gives her a dull and 'closed-off' look. With her head bent forward, her neck sunken between the shoulders and her legs apart, she rocks back and forth with a monotonous, quick, slight movement. Her trunk is the only part that moves, in a stiff and jerky manner, her arms and legs seeming to be joined to her trunk without articulation. This movement does not give the slightest impression of ease or joy.

This behaviour is nearly continuous; she never stops of her own accord. Toys do not interest her in the least, and she is never seen on her feet running about the room. All kind of motor activity is lacking. Anything that disrupts this immobility seems to plunge her into a state of anxiety which manifests itself in fits of inconsolable distress during which she rolls over and over on the floor, bangs her head on the floor, pulls her hair, slaps herself, and repulses any attempt to approach her or to help her. She always calms down very slowly of her own accord but is ready to begin again at any time, and sometimes she ends by sinking into sleep. Her tantrums very often burst out without any visible cause. If she is watched while she is rocking, the rhythm of this movement increases and her expression becomes more fixed. In spite of that, Monique looks about her, towards the ceiling or sideways in an active and apparently perceptive manner. Occasionally we noticed an almost imperceptible smile with a lively and mischievous look. This contrasted so strangely with her usual refusal of any contact that doubt was thrown for the first time on the very gloomy prognosis suggested by her appearance.

Tested on the Gesell scale on the 5th November 1949, Monique had a D.Q. of 35 with general retardation. A slight superiority in adaptivity over the other sub-tests was nevertheless noted. This D.Q. 35 is based on the facts that she was unable to talk, that she understood only one or two words, that she was not clean, that she could not feed herself and that she was scarcely at the level of an infant of 40 weeks. During the test she retained her hunched-up posture. She refused to look at the examiner and would respond to the demands of the test only when the examiner seemed not to be paying attention to her. The test lasted a very long time. Only certain brief and rare flashes of vivacity and certain nimble and dexterous hand movements brightened up this very dark picture.

The medical examination showed no sign of organic defect.

Considerations relevant to Diagnosis and Treatment

Monique's unusual and alarming appearance and her very abnormal behaviour had led all those who had examined her to consider her as an incurably defective child, more especially since the mother's psychosis and the premature birth could be held responsible for the child's condition. Several doctors who were consulted did not give any precise diagnosis, the foster mothers refused to keep the child, and the family, being possessed by the fear that she might be insane like her mother, never visited her and seemed to abandon her.

However, the medical examination brought to light no precise physical signs pointing to organic cause for retardation. The factors of maternal psychosis and prematurity did not seem to be more likely as causes of retardation than the many changes of home and the long periods of institutionalization. The psychological observations as well as the test, while showing her loneliness and withdrawal, suggested that she was not totally cut off from the world but maintained some contact with the external world. It was chiefly the fleeting vivacious expression, above described, which confirmed the hypothesis of psychogenic retardation and led to the decision to put the child under psychotherapy.

Development during Treatment

FIRST PERIOD (December 1949 – January, February 1950)

13th December 1949 – at the time of the first treatment session Monique was terrified when I first took her away, completely withdrawn into herself. She seemed to be trying to make herself grow smaller. Her breathing was imperceptible; she did not move at all; she frequently lowered her eyes and would only lift them in fear. For ten minutes I kept her on my knee, perfectly still, not touching her but only speaking very gently, as to a little baby; I began to sing and very slowly I put my arms round her and rocked her. At the end of half an hour, she seemed to brighten up a bit; a little smile appeared; she played with my hands which she had previously refused to touch. She took the rattle, played with it, smiled, laughed: her face was truly transformed. There was life in her look, some expression. She seemed to be at ease, almost happy. When the time came to leave she reacted violently: she threw herself on her back, hid her face in her hands, cried inconsolably and clung to the rattle.

The same happened during the two following sessions; she seemed to enjoy the situation and to be like a baby of nine months; she watched me intently, pointing her finger at my face, playing with my hands, pressing her face against my shoulder, laughing; all this with much affection. She continued to dislike the termination of the session, although less violently. Her first act was to throw herself on her back, with a desolate expression, but later she pressed herself against my shoulder.

Then two things happened which caused Monique to react very violently: the visit of an aunt and her grandmother, which led to an outburst of uncontrollable anger; and the Christmas tree, to which she reacted with panic.

During the sessions which followed, on every occasion at sounds and movements which were slightly loud and often for no apparent cause, she left my knee, and let herself fall on the ground, absolutely still, and stretched herself out on her stomach, her face still and impassive. At first she got up by herself, turned towards me, smiling, but later she no longer got up, but remained still, her face on the ground, until I picked her up and carried her; or if she got up by herself, she no longer turned towards me but went and pressed her nose against the wall, and thus walked round the room. She seemed to be afraid and unable to let herself go as she had done previously.

27th December (6th session) – She became tremendously angry when the time came to leave. She could no longer endure my presence; she only became calm when she fell asleep, when I was in her room, but far from her bed.

The next day she whimpered when I picked her up. There were no real tears but hardly perceptible inner sobs which ended in a sigh. It is difficult to know what this represents, fear, anguish or un-expressed anger. One can only note the essentially different character of these suppressed sobs to the explosive outbursts of anger where she seemed to give free vent to her impulses. As I approached she fell to the ground and started to cry. Later, she turned her back on me. At last, after about half an hour, she seemed more responsive. I sang gently; she crept into my arms and became more active, and collected little bits of rubbish which she made me eat, as well as her rattle. She ended by resting in my arms. She laughed loudly and chattered.

Until March, during more than 20 sessions, Monique alternated thus between the desire to withdraw and have no contact and a state of abandon in which she seemed to find pleasure. The frequency, rapidity and intensity with which she passed from one to the other was remarkable. During this long period when Monique seemed to come out of her state of withdrawal, she manifested the same behaviour in the institution as she did in the sessions, with great emotional fragility and instability. Although she could be at times active and cheerful she very easily fell back into her previous attitude: an unexpected sound, a sharp movement, a disagreement, an interval longer than usual between two sessions, any of these were enough to upset her. At this time, paroxysms of laughter appearing without apparent reason occurred in addition to her fits of anger. She passed from one to the other quite instantaneously.

Also, at this time, certain dodges enabled her to cut short her seemingly irremediable despair: a strip of paper or a piece of cotton round her neck threw her into ecstasies. She put her head down on her shoulder for a long time rolling the cotton and giving little piercing cries. She often rocked herself in a new way, standing upright, going sideways, putting one foot on the other. This form of rocking had exactly the same rigid and impassive quality as the other had. However, little by little, by almost imperceptible stages, she cheered up. Her modes of expression became richer, her face more mobile and changing. In the kindergarten she was still mostly alone, but once she started in an activity she became absorbed in it and avoided the interminable rocking.

In the sessions, through all the often discouraging alternations of rejection and acceptance, little by little acceptance began to win. She appeared happy at the first contact and, e.g., on 2nd February 1950 she remained on my knee throughout the whole session. She looked at me intently then suddenly burst out laughing and threw herself against my shoulder. I sang, she appeared pleased; I talked, she repeated the words; I moved my head, she did the same. She always sought my help, never trying anything by herself. Several days later she said 'Yes' for the first time.

It seemed that she was becoming very dependent. It was therefore decided to put some food and a bottle in the therapy room. She put everything to her mouth, sucking them and making me suck them, exploring my face with her hands. She often left my knee to look for an object, but watched all the time to see if I was looking at her, showing me the objects, bringing them to me, coaxing me – she needed my encouragement and help in all difficulties. Once or twice she wetted her diapers, and left the room on all fours.

SECOND PERIOD (March to July 1950 – 2 yrs. 7 mths. to 2 yrs. 11 mths.)

The presence of the bottle in the room seemed to start a new phase. In fact, on the 25th March 1950 the session started as all the others of this period had done. Monique was gay and active, but suddenly she stopped (without any sign which could make me think she had seen the bottle) and went down on all fours, face against the ground, rocking her posterior. When I approached her, she whispered 'No'. I remained very quietly by her side; but she did not relax at all, only stopped her rocking. Thinking that my presence upset her, I moved away, and she glanced around her, watching me, but every time I moved she started crouching and rocking once more.

After ten minutes I took the bottle in my hands; at that moment Monique jumped to her feet. She flung herself on the bottle, her whole countenance lighting up. Settled in my arms, she drank, her eyes closed, totally abandoned, in a state of complete happiness. She seemed to be enjoying the situation intensely. After several minutes she chewed rather than sucked. Once the bottle was finished, she got up and went to eat the cakes and sweets, rocking herself and becoming very active.

For several sessions these initial reactions of inhibition at the sight of the bottle persisted, always followed by the same intense joy. Finally, on the 1st May 1950, in spite of an interval of one month, she was able to take the bottle herself without any hesitation and abandon herself completely to the pleasure of taking it, leaving it and then returning to it.

On the 8th May 1950 she made a new step forward and seemed to have command of the situation. In fact, on the one hand she seemed no longer to be overwhelmed by the pleasurable reactions; she drank actively, her eyes open, watching me and laughing. She put the nipple in and out of her mouth, not drinking it all in one go. On the other hand, she put the bottle down, left it, then took it again. She left my knee, then returned and settled herself comfortably there. She ended by putting the nipple in my mouth. She chattered all the time, sometimes repeating my words and sometimes talking spontaneously. When the time came to leave she seemed happy and walked in a 'silly' manner. She herself decided the moment of departure and that seemed to mark the beginning of a new pleasure: to be independent and to control the situation. At the same time she manifested a new aspect of unruliness. She liked to come and go, leave me and come back to me to run through the house and move about freely and aimlessly.

In the midst of this fluttering behaviour appeared new sources of interest: the plasticine that she liked to cut in tiny pieces and fed to me; the cakes and chocolate that she crushed between her fingers and smeared all over; hiding all the toys in the doll's cot; showing great interest in containers. All this gradually began to reduce her interest in the bottle; at the same time a slight hesitation about coming to the sessions appeared, then for fifteen days there was refusal to come at all. When she returned during the days before the holidays, she no longer showed the same warmth, and her behaviour was empty and stereotyped. However, at this time she showed considerable progress in the kindergarten; she could start a game, join in another child's game, assert herself and react to a difficult situation. But she was at the same time very sensitive, and was upset by the slightest innovation.

A test at that time yielded a D.Q. of 83, with a marked improvement in motor ability (63 to 106). Monique appeared playful, stimulated by the presence of a little girl at her side; she sought the sympathy of the tester, watched her and smiled at her. She even showed interest in the test, after having played with the blocks for several minutes. This equilibrium was maintained in spite of the interruption in the treatment, and in September 1950 we found a more settled girl, who during the summer had been able to establish a real tie with the cook and with a little boy, also under treatment. However, her D.Q. had descended to 77.

THIRD PERIOD (September – October 1950 – 3 yrs. 1 mth. to 3 yrs. 3 mths.)

On my return Monique seemed rather unsure of herself. At a test given on the 24th October, 1950 she had a D.Q. of 77 and her behaviour was different from that at the preceding test. First of all she refused to go with the tester. She only made up her mind 45 minutes later, after another attempt. She performed the test without making use of the tester – but, on the other hand, she showed a spontaneous interest in the different parts of the test. The test lasted 20 minutes. The fact that the D.Q. is as low as that of the preceding test does not mean that Monique has regressed, but only that she has developed more slowly and has made no progress in certain fields. Nevertheless, during sessions from the month of October, she recovered the sort of behaviour which she had had during her best period, namely the month of June. Her games were varied and, while a new and timid interest in water play appeared, the basic themes were sleeping, eating and drinking. At the same time she began to nurse the doll, towards which she showed inhibition and contradictory attitudes. Little by little she seemed to abandon herself to the pleasure of pouring out the water and splashing; but she had only just started coming to the sessions with anticipation and happiness when I saw that once more she was withdrawing into herself. She became very strained; she crouched, her head hanging down: she stood with her body bent. Only her hands moved in a rapid jerky fashion. She seemed spellbound by her actions, incapable of stopping them; not only did she show no pleasure, but her whole body was tense with misery. She got out of it only at my intervention.

During the following session the same thing happened once again, then during the following days Monique showed her distress only by her accelerated breathing which indicated that she was not fully relaxed. In turn she wet the doll, soaked herself, me, and the floor. She wet her diapers. At the kindergarten she was difficult, tearful and troublesome. She was aggressive towards the other children. She began to soil again and would only eat with her fingers.

FOURTH PERIOD (November – December 1950)

For two months immediately after this, Monique was constantly bright and happy during the sessions. She talked a great deal for her and demanded replies in her conversation with me. Her games were organized and realistic. For example, on the 29th November 1950 she carefully made the doll's bed, put it in a corner of the room and then put the doll on the pot, saying 'Caca le pot', then took the bottle, first made me drink, then, gently lifting the doll's head, made it drink, saying 'bois bon'; she tried at the same time to make it stand. At another time she pointed to the different parts of the doll's body. She did the same thing with me, showing me the different

109

parts of my body after she had shown the different parts of hers and then put me in her place reversing the roles. She made me sit on the little chair, gave me orders. I had the impression that she was trying all the time to communicate and share her feelings with me. She was gay, happy and gave spontaneous demonstrations of affection.

FIFTH PERIOD (From January to May 1951 – 3 yrs. 5 mths. to 3 yrs. 9 mths.)

Soon afterwards she changed her attitude to me. Her affectionate gestures towards me became hesitant; for example at the time of leaving she offered me her hand but then withdrew it. I no longer found her so gay. The roughness of her voice and gestures gradually increased and for the first time she expressed aggressiveness in all her games, however happy and easy.

She submitted both the doll and myself to the most violent treatment, in the beginning camouflaged but soon clearly expressed. For example, on the 7th March 1951 when she was playing at eating, making me eat, she put the food in my mouth more and more roughly; one moment she said 'eat' then 'swallow', tapping her hand against my mouth with an angry and irritated expression.

On the 9th March 1951 while playing at washing and bathing the doll she suddenly flung it roughly into the water, splashing everywhere and watching me. Several minutes later she lifted her foot above the doll's head as if she was going to crush it, but she missed her aim and only tipped the bath. Afterwards she crushed the face and stomach of the doll with her hands.

At other sessions she scolded me, said I was dirty, and pretended to give me a shower bath, something which she herself hated.

In all this, especially at the beginning, Monique seemed to express in the form of her game, some of the things which happened to her. Not content with expressing them in her games with the doll and verbally, she showed she wanted me to share in her misfortunes. She began to cling to me and seemed unhappy when I was not able to give her immediate satisfaction.

For example, at one time she had been able to renounce a coveted object at my request, but now that became impossible for her and on three different occasions she could not endure the frustration I caused her to suffer – finding herself without an object which I was unable to let her keep, she became very irritable and unhappy. She did not say a word or make any sound. As I tried to coax her and console her she flung herself on her back and slid from my arms, lying on her back silently but with a curious expression, as if she wanted to cry very badly but did not dare to do so. After a few minutes she got up again, pushed me, saying 'No', and picked up a toy which she carried away as compensation.

She became more and more greedy, trying to carry off everything she could, taking quantities of cakes, wanting to keep me to herself and being unable to endure the sight of me with anyone else. Once she pushed Nicole who was sitting on my knee. On the 12th March 1951, when she was in the playroom with Jacques, she had a sulky appearance, her lip pouting; she pulled her hair and wrung her hands. She threw everything on to the floor, and did not seem satisfied with anything. She argued with Jacques about the cakes, and made herself cry and scream. She was lying on her back and when I tried to comfort her she seemed to hesitate between tears and laughter, then became again exacting and insatiable. At that moment Jacques went away. As if by magic her expression changed; she kept her stubborn air but was more 'guarded'. She watched me covertly and managed a little smile. She came towards me saying 'No', hit me and flung herself into my arms. After a few minutes she cheered up and became relaxed.

One was able to detect more and more the dissatisfaction tied to her insatiability. Little by little she could express it verbally as well as through her unreasonable demands and very real aggressiveness, which was no longer a game and began to be directed against me. On the 21st March 1951 she shut me in the playroom, barricaded the door with chairs, saying 'She is a nasty Geneviève' then 'Monique is angry'; she let me out after some time, but kept away from me, laughing. Then, taking again her usual toys, the session ended quietly.

With this possessiveness and insatiability grew a stronger and stronger attachment to me; she called me by my name and talked about me to others, going to see if I was there. She was always very happy and excited when she saw me. When she was with me she always had a very confident expression, and if we met a third person she would turn towards me and make me share her welcome.

In the institution, Monique most of the time behaved like a normal child; in fact she was probably less impoverished than the other children of the same age that we had in our institution. She was perfectly adapted to the institution, knew the routine there and seemed perfectly at home; she had friendships with some of the nurses and children whom she knew well. At the kindergarten she played in a constructive fashion, showing initiative and diverse interests; she was able to play with another child. Eventually she became capable of defending herself and attacking. Her D.Q. was now 97. Only her speech remained inferior. She approached the tester voluntarily, holding out her hand. She once again sought her sympathy, watched her, laughed and chattered. She seemed to enjoy herself. She interested herself in everything, seeking contact with the adult, and did not appear upset by the presence of a third person. She left without any fuss and went to play with the group. The test lasted 30 minutes.

Nevertheless, Monique showed in her irregular moods and unreasonable demands that her adjustment to the institution was precarious and, above all, one felt that little happenings menaced her and made her seem guarded. Without the permanent support of treatment and the understanding which she found morning and afternoon in the kindergarten and the affection of her nurse, one felt that she would soon be reacting once more by withdrawal. Monique's treatment had to be continued.

Conclusions

Reading over the development of therapy we see that Monique has gone, in the relationship with her therapist, through different stages of early development. However, each new step was very slow and produced anxiety spells during which she reverted to withdrawal and self-destructive attitudes.

We can schematize as follows the main phases through which Monique has passed.

(1) Expression of strong ambivalence towards contact with therapist.

(2) The therapist meeting this ambivalence by supporting carefully her efforts to reach out, and giving understanding for her fears, allows Monique to come very slowly closer to her.

(3) This ends in strong passive dependent relationship in which she gives in completely to the pleasure of abandoning herself to oral

pleasures of bottle feeding on the therapist's lap. Simultaneously she acted as an eight-month-old baby exploring the therapist's face with deep enjoyment.

(4) By controlling the eating situation and turning to solid foods, she slowly moves towards smearing and anal interests while at the same time turning towards symbolic games and verbalizing much more.

(5) Finally, she relives in her play the traumatic experiences through which she had passed and all the hostility they had aroused. Progressively this hostility is transferred to the person of the psychotherapist, changing the quality of their relationship from that of the preceding period; she can no longer bear to share her with the other children. She was insatiable both during the sessions and in the institution and she was able to express her dissatisfaction through aggressive behaviour towards the psychotherapist, which did not prevent but rather facilitated a closer tie between them and a greater enjoyment of the relationship.

Going along with this progression in therapy she showed increasing psychomotor ability as shown by D.Q. improvement, in general adjustment and ability for a variety of meaningful relationships with adults and children.

Though not described here, treatment was continued for another year when Monique proved able to join her family and enter school, where she adjusted well for a child of her age.

Discussion Following 'Monique' Film

BOWLBY *I wonder if you could tell me anything about the continuous rocking movements which Monique carried out so frequently, and which seem typical of many children in a state of grief? Did you see the onset of these movements?*

APPELL *In the setting where the film was taken we have not been able to see the actual onset since the children are already in this state when they get there. But I might mention one infant in the present nursery of around five months who was very much cared for by one nurse. The nurse left for five days, and during this time the rocking movements started and developed, but stopped when the nurse returned.*

RHEINGOLD *I have seen something like this movement at three months of age, when the infant rocks on its back, moving the head from side to side. And at five months when it is able to turn on its front it rocks on its belly. This can often be eliminated temporarily by giving the child its freedom, taking it out of its crib, which makes me think that the need for exercise in a confined child is at least an associated cause.*

DAVID *We see it quite often in infants who are not confined at all but lying on the floor surrounded by toys. They ignore the toys, and just rock.*

GENESE (of CIBA) *Primitive people in Bengal will, when in a condition of considerable grief, sit quite silently and rock backwards and forwards just like these children for hours and hours, quite indifferent to their surroundings and refusing to eat or sleep.*

GUNTHER *I have seen this happen amongst women in labour in this country, as though there were some comfort in it.*

BOWLBY *In Harry Harlow's film we saw young monkeys in the 'open-field test' doing just the same, because there wasn't a mother figure present.*

HARLOW *These are of course penned animals. In lots of animals that have been housed alone for some time you see them rubbing themselves repeatedly against the cages, and these develop into stereotyped movements. Or sometimes they sit absolutely passively, showing no signs whatever that they've got an environment.*

HINDE *When you get stereotyped movements in caged animals it is often associated with the performance of the initial stages of a chain of behaviour when the later stages are impossible. When this happens the initial stages seem to get stereotyped, and sometimes elaborated. For instance some chaffinches which had been deprived of nest-building material looked for material and showed the movements of picking it up in the manner characteristic of the species. This became abbreviated finally to a sort of lunge, which appeared again in the following breeding season. One wants to know what the reinforcement is that results in the persistence of these movements. Is it that they provide continually changing stimulation?*

HARLOW *I would think they might be self-reinforcing movements. In the same way that the rocking model was more reinforcing to some*

Discussion

infant monkeys than the stationary one. If the movements are self-reinforcing, they might well become stereotyped. Perhaps the more puzzling thing about children and monkeys is the way they frequently bang their heads, as well as rock. It looks like an aggressive pattern – attack, against themselves.

THOMAS *When you apply behavioural explanations to these activities, which I should call auto-erotic, there seems to me something very queer. There is no sequence which could be initiated by head-banging, nor is there anything which it could have developed from. Especially in institution babies you may find them actually looking for something suitable against which to bang their heads.*

HINDE *It seems to me that the conventional model of motivation – that the behaviour is an outlet for something – won't do for this behaviour. Perhaps it would be more useful to put the emphasis on the seeking of a particular kind of stimulation.*

RHEINGOLD *And then the paradox is that apparently painful stimulation is sought, because sometimes children bang their foreheads hard enough to raise welts.*

ROSENBLATT *One could argue that the aim is to gain stimulation very rapidly, and that the injury is incidental.*

RHEINGOLD *But the behaviour may persist for a long time, and involve spending a lot of energy.*

HARLOW *I would like to know if there are other differences between children that bang their heads and those that do not. Are they more aggressive?*

THOMAS *They are usually withdrawn. But you will find stereotyped rocking in what you would think of as a normal, happy child if he is left alone for comparatively long periods. I am thinking of one particular child who would rock backwards and forwards in its perambulator just as much as its shoulder straps would allow. On one occasion it spent the whole of an afternoon on a settee, rocking in just the same way, and with what seemed exactly the same extent of movement, though without shoulder straps.*

PRECHTL *Dr Hinde mentioned earlier that stereotyped movements might be a means of seeking stimulation. I have seen two cases of children who rocked sideways for long periods and the movement seemed highly stereotyped. I would have thought that the stimulation obtained from proprioception would not be very important since sensory adaptation would be rapid in this condition.*

115

HINDE *I don't know what happens in children, but in animals rocking is not all that stereotyped. There are often slight changes in the motor pattern which would prevent adaptation occurring.*

FOSS *These patterns are seen in monkey and human infants when deprived of a mother figure, and the simplest description is that the child is trying to comfort itself; or, in sophisticated language, the nervous system is recapitulating a state of affairs which was pleasurable in the past. As some depth psychologists have pointed out, the position of the child and the movements are reminiscent of the foetal stage where the movement is imposed by the mother walking. Or perhaps the movements are even more like when the baby was rocked to sleep – possibly after crying.*

PRECHTL *It's important to remember that all these movements are seen in the normal child, but they don't last so long. Some other activity interrupts them.*

* * *

SUTHERLAND *May I ask what role the adult plays in this situation? All this stereotyped behaviour seems to go with the absence of an adult, but as soon as the child starts to make some kind of relationship with an adult, this behaviour goes. To use psychoanalytic jargon, it is as though the child has to internalize somebody before she can make any progress.*

DAVID *With most of the children there was a long period during which the child did not accept the therapist. The sight of the therapist in several instances increased the stereotyped behaviour, as if it was a means of keeping her out.*

GEWIRTZ *How did you get accepted? By just sitting there?*

APPELL *Not only. With most of the children the first stage of therapy was just offering the child a somewhat passive, non-threatening presence to which he could get acquainted and finally accept. Only then would he develop some kind of activity and the actual therapeutic work would start. During this period one would try to notice any cues that the child would give about either his wishes for isolation, that we would respect, or his first awakening of interest for us. To these we would try cautiously to respond.*

HUNTER *Was not the first important step that you went with the child somewhere where there were no other children?*

APPELL *Not always. To take some children alone in a new room would arouse a state of high anxiety. In such cases the first contacts were made in the child's own room among other children. However, as soon as possible the child would be introduced to the therapy room.*

BOWLBY *What I find very interesting in the film is that Geneviève (Appell) seems almost impassive in relation to Monique. You make only slight gestures, and Monique may not react; when she does you try to carry on the chain of interaction. But I think if the film were analysed in detail one would see quite a lot of interaction on the basis of micro-movements. It reminds me of Helen Blauvelt's film of interaction between mother and baby. It seems to me the secret of your entry was to go very slowly.*

APPELL *Yes, this is what I mean by answering the cues the child gives. One starts by trying to answer small cues given by the child and offering her just a little more in reply. If she can take it, good, but in many instances one's answer is a threat to the child and one has to follow the child in her withdrawals as well as her advances.*

BOWLBY *I think this interaction would be an interesting topic for research. Are the cues gestures, or voice, or movements? Perhaps all of these. I think Helen Blauvelt is studying the beginnings of these interactions as they normally occur. The difficulty with the deprived child is to start these interactions again. Most children, if they have a human being to interact with, will prefer interacting to rocking privately. But the deprived children prefer rocking to interacting. These rocking habits seem to get so much of a chance to establish themselves in the lonely infant that they are difficult to break later. It would be interesting to know to what extent Monique in later life might find herself adopting these response patterns in conditions of stress. One might expect that she would.*

APPELL *The last time I saw her she was seven and at school. Apparently when she was upset she would take a piece of wool and unravel it as she used to do with pieces of paper in the nursery.*

THOMAS *To take up Dr Bowlby's point, it seems to me that the problem is not just to restart a chain of interaction with these children. If it were simply a case of breaking habits which the child has developed in isolation, why should there be such a tremendously aversive reaction when one does try to make contact?*

HARLOW *This could be partly a fear of the strange. In monkeys any new person coming in, or a new room, will give aversive responses. But if you just sit around and become familiar long enough, it is when you leave the room that the monkeys find it strange, and are fearful.*

BOWLBY *I think there is something more than this. We all know that if an adult builds up a relationship, and the other half of the partnership is lost, there may be tremendous grief and a difficulty later in making new relationships. It is the same with young children: when the relationship is broken they are often unable to start a new relationship with anyone else.*

HUNTER *One must also take account of the fact that with many deprived children, if they do try to start a new relationship with an adult, such losses are liable to be repeated, and the inability to restart becomes intensified. It's as though the child learned that relationships are unrewarding.*

ROBERTSON *That is what we see in long-stay hospitals. You get an intense and painful reaction on the first separation from the mother. When the child does try to re-establish a relationship with someone, say a nurse, this is often broken by the nurse going elsewhere, and such experiences accumulate so that the child's attempts to establish relationships get slower and shallower. In the end you get a child resembling Monique, except that superficially he may seem happy. These children associate very freely with strangers. Official visitors get a charming, immediate response and are quite disarmed. But all the child's relationships are completely superficial – undiscriminating, promiscuously friendly, attached to no one.*

GEWIRTZ *I wonder if these children you have just described would be behaving with the extreme withdrawal and fear shown by Monique?*

ROBERTSON *I imagine their experiences of deprivation have not been as extreme as those of Monique and other children appearing in the film, in the sense perhaps that, although cared for by frequently changing nurses with whom they had no opportunity to establish stable relationships, the general atmosphere and the individual contacts were friendly and stimulating.*

DAVID *I have seen such extreme cases as Monique in cases of a six months' stay in hospital.*

GEWIRTZ *Was Monique deprived?*

DAVID *What do you mean by that?*

GEWIRTZ *Is it typical for a deprived child to show as much fear as Monique? She was separated from her mother at two months, and we don't know what happened to her before that which might have*

118

made her so fearful. Perhaps her behaviour is not so much due to deprivation as it is of some other etiology?

APPELL *Monique was not specially selected. Her behaviour is fairly typical of many other children, and the one thing they seem to have in common is deprivation. In the film you could see three other children and they all went through this stage of fear of people. However, it is true that in studying their past histories many intangled factors are found: the loss of mother, life in large institutions where maternal care was poor, scattered and discontinued, and very frequent changing from one institution or ward to another. Would children show less fear if one of these aspects was absent? Is there an individual sensitivity which makes some children more fearful than others under similar circumstances? What would play a role in this sensitivity: innate character, age at separation, the quality of previous mother-child relationship? All these seem to be unanswered questions.*

* * *

GEWIRTZ *Dr Bowlby, you talked about the inability of an infant to make a new relationship once the first one was broken off; but probably there are all sorts of ways to facilitate the new relationship. The discriminating power of the child was probably very poor when it formed its first relationship, and its behaviour may have been governed by very few stimuli provided by the caretaker – in just the way that pigeons can be 'dominated' by a single cue. Now in the case where a new caretaker shares these characteristics with the first, the child should transfer its relationship without difficulty.*

ROBERTSON *But many of the hospitalized children I have described don't re-form their original relationships when they return to their own families, even when the original caretaker is there. I am shaken if you think that the relationship of a small child to his mother can be so unparticular and un-intense that you can change caretaker without the child noticing.*

ROWELL *When a human recognizes another human, he is recognizing a Gestalt, not discriminating separate stimuli or responding to single cues.*

GEWIRTZ *But Gestalten can resemble each other.*

BOWLBY *These are not just visual Gestalten. We recognize people through several modalities, and particularly by their behaviour.*

Two people would have to be very similar indeed – identical twins reared together perhaps – for a quite young child not to be able to tell them apart.

*　　*　　*

HARLOW *When these children who are emotionally damaged come into an institution, do they ever form an association with another child, who then unwittingly acts as therapist?*

THOMAS *You see one child seeking out another in this way, but the recipient usually refuses very quickly to be used as such an object.*

DAVID *In this institution contacts between children were very rare. When they did occur they always took the form of violent attacks.*

ROSENBLATT *On this point, our results on rearing two kittens together under conditions of isolation from their litter may be of interest. The behaviour of these kittens contrasted markedly with that of kittens isolated individually. When they were returned to their litter, the 'double isolates' were quite well adjusted to the other kittens and showed no disturbance toward the female, however neither did they nurse from her, although they were still capable of nursing. The single isolates of the same age (45 days) were greatly disturbed by their littermates and particularly disturbed by the female and they too did not nurse from her. We concluded that a second kitten may provide stimulation that is somewhat equivalent to that provided by the female but that those patterns of behaviour which must be adapted to specific features of the female, as for instance with regard to suckling adjustments, cannot be developed toward a stimulus which is only partially equivalent to her.*

A Study of Nursing Care[1] and Nurse-Infant Interaction

MYRIAM DAVID and GENEVIÈVE APPELL

A Report on the First Half of an Investigation

Introduction

Work with severely deprived children of pre-school age indicates that many variables shape the effects of maternal deprivation. Two of them are the age of the child when deprivation occurs, and the length and nature of the deprivation. It seemed interesting, therefore, to study a situation where these variables were controlled. The Pouponniere Amyot offered this opportunity. It is a residential nursery of twenty beds, admitting exclusively healthy infants under one year old, for the purpose of giving them B.C.G. vaccination. Separation is necessary because these infants come from families where there has been tuberculosis infection.[2] The total process of isolation-vaccination, and thus the length of separation, is on the average two and a half to three months, the infants going home thereafter. Such privileged conditions made it possible to study the effects of institutional care on the infant's behaviour and development during his stay in the nursery through the first three months and after his reunion with his mother during the following years.

It was first necessary to clarify what kind of care was being provided by the Institute. What were its main components and what was their impact on the child? Does it result in deprivation and in what ways?

Also, attention was to be given to what were the relevant kinds of

[1] We wish to acknowledge that this investigation has been aided first by a contract with the World Health Organization and is now continued with a grant from the Foundations' Fund for Research in Psychiatry.

[2] They should not therefore be in contact with any source of infection before vaccination and until allergy to tuberculine is established.

121

behaviour to observe in the children in assessing the effects of institutional care. Indeed, apart from rather gross criteria of development, knowledge about 'normal' or 'deviant' behaviour in infants is rather limited; relatively little is known about how individual differences in the personal equipment of children may govern the effects of deprivation on development.

Keeping this in mind, a pilot study was started, the aim being to:

(*a*) study the development and behaviour of the infants in this setting;

(*b*) describe as completely as possible the milieu and care to which the infants were exposed;

(*c*) observe the intimate interaction between the infant and his surroundings in an attempt to understand what part this plays in development.

In order to do this, during a pilot study infants were observed for long periods during which the child's behaviour and surroundings were recorded in as much detail as possible. Both direct observation of the child in its natural environment, and in reaction to standardized sets of stimuli in a test situation were used. Observation in the natural environment was carried on for periods of two to four hours several times a week; testing was done every two or three weeks. This programme was carried out on eight infants for a year.

It became possible to organize observation of the infants around a rather wide range of behavioural or developmental items which emerged progressively from the observations, and to describe the care and environment.

The present paper is concerned only with this last point.

A number of striking features in routine care during this pilot study was noticed:

(*a*) multiplicity of persons taking care of one infant during its stay in the nursery;

(*b*) small amount of social contact offered to the infants together with long periods of isolation during waking time;

(*c*) poverty of interchange between nurse and infant during social contact.

This led to the idea of organizing a comparative study between two groups of infants receiving in one case Routine Care, in the

122

other case a different type of care, which will be referred to as Intensive Individualized Nursing Care (I.N.C.), and in which these three variables were to be modified.[1]

I.N.C. consists, as its name suggests, in the fact that one nurse takes over most of the day care of one or two infants at a time. devoting to them all her working time, giving the morning bath and four feeds out of six. On days of leave, one nurse, always the same one, takes over with the same schedule. The early morning feed and the last evening one (6 a.m.–9 p.m.) are still given by a variety of night nurses. Both these feeds remain the same in I.N.C. and Routine Care (R.C.).

Thus two categories of infants are now under study: those who are receiving Routine Care and those receiving Intensive Individualized Nursing Care. Up to now, besides the eight infants of the pilot study, five infants in R.C. group and six in I.N.C. group have been observed, the ultimate plan being to observe at least ten infants in each group.

The present report will be concerned exclusively with the care received by infants, the study of which should help in a better grasp of the concept of maternal deprivation. In passing, some consideration will be given to the impact differences in caretaking might have on the children.

R.C. and I.N.C. can be described and compared under three main heads:

    I. Multiplicity of Caretakers.

    II. Amount of Social Contact and of Isolation.

    III. Interactions between Nurse and Infant.

Multiplicity of Caretakers

One of the first striking findings during the pilot study was the *high number of nurses* who took care of an infant during its stay in the nursery.[2] On an average, 25 persons shared the care of one child, the

[1] The idea of comparing nursery children with family children was abandoned for a variety of reasons, the main one being the near impossibility of getting a group homogeneous in respect of maternal care and practice. It seemed preferable to introduce in the care of the infant in the nursery some experimental changes which could be standardized, measured, and compared to Routine Care.

[2] This was easy to check since each child has a book in which the nurse writes down and signs the care she gives to him.

range being 16 to 33. In I.N.C. the day care was organized in such a way that it should be shared mainly by two nurses. In this respect R.C. group and I.N.C. were to be very different. However, the head nurse became aware of this multiplicity of caretakers and tried to reduce it. The number of nurses who have handled the five infants in the R.C. group has been somewhat smaller than in the pilot group. The average is 16, the range 12 to 20. On the other hand, it has not always been possible to introduce I.N.C. as soon as an infant has come into the nursery. As a result the average number of nurses sharing the total care of an I.N.C. child is still 11 (Range 10 to 13).

However, it is important to consider *the distribution of care* between nurses: in this respect differences between R.C. and I.N.C. are greater. In I.N.C., although there are still 11 people caring for the infant during three months, they are mostly night nurses and give only occasional and small amounts of day care (an average of 12 per cent); whereas on an average 88 per cent of the day care is given by two nurses – the main nurse and her assistant (who are called first dominant and second dominant nurses).

In R.C., 36 per cent of day care is given by a great variety of nurses, whereas the first and second dominant nurses, though existing, give only 64 per cent of day care (see Table XIII).

TABLE XIII

Average Number of Nurses attending Children, and the Percentage of Time given by Dominant Nurses and Others

	Pilot Study	Routine Care	Intensive Individualized Nursing Care
Number of nurses for total care .	25	16	11
Percentage of day care given by first dominant nurse . .	40	40	65
Percentage of day care given by two dominant nurses . .	55	64	88
Percentage of day care given by a variety of nurses . . .	45	36	12

Another variable which might be of importance *is the variation of percentage of care given by each nurse from week to week.*

In the experimental group, because it may take a few days before I.N.C. is established, it is during the first week that there are multiple caretakers and then the percentage of care given by the dominant nurse is lower. After this I.N.C. is well established and until the departure of the child the number of caretakers becomes quite small, while the percentage of day care given by the two dominant nurses rises almost to 100 per cent. Figure 23 is typical of I.N.C. cases.

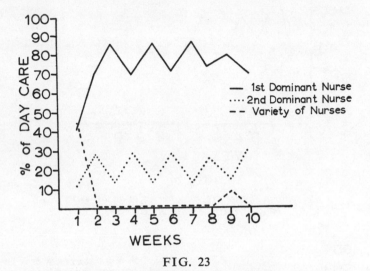

FIG. 23

Percentage of care given by nurses in an INC case with a
total of 12 nurses

In R.C., the picture is different: the percentage of care given by the dominant nurses varies irregularly from week to week. In four out of the five cases, during the first part of their stay in the nursery the infants have a fair amount of good day care from their dominant nurses; but during the last weeks, when the child is around two months old, she is replaced by a variety of nurses (Figure 24) or by a new first dominant nurse (Figure 25).

Figure 25 shows, yet another pattern of R.C. Considering the total amount of care given by each nurse during the child's stay, Nurse A appears as a rather weak first dominant, giving on an average 30 per cent of care, Nurse B, the second dominant, giving 13·5 per cent, the remainder of 56·5 per cent being shared by a variety of 17 nurses. However, it can be seen that Nurse B is as dominant as Nurse A. They do not work together but follow each other, Nurse A giving 43 per cent of the day care during the first six weeks,

125

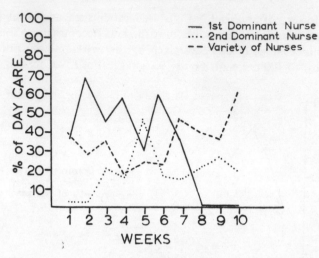

FIG. 24

*Percentage of care given by nurses in an RC case
(Pascale) with a total of 20 nurses*

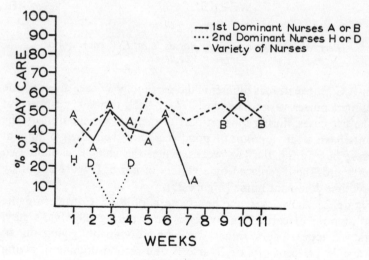

FIG. 25

*Percentage of care given by nurses in an RC case (François)
with a total of 13 nurses*

Nurse B 50 per cent during the last three weeks. A gap exists on the seventh week when Nurse E appears to be a first dominant, with 33 per cent. Two second dominant nurses appear intermittently: Nurse H in the first week, Nurse D in the second and fourth weeks. During remaining weeks the lack of a second dominant explains that the percentage of day care given by a variety of nurses remains high (around and above 50 per cent).

While in the I.N.C. group each infant has a pattern rather similar to that shown in Figure 23, in the R.C. group the children have widely differing patterns of care.

One wonders what are the effects on infant and nurse of this multiplicity of caretakers. A nurse who attends a child only occasionally does not know him. She acts towards him more automatically and not so much in response to the child's idiosyncratic demands. She does not know his habits, she may not be aware of his crying, nor does she know his rhythms, and cannot adjust her care to his needs. (It seems, for instance, and this will require more systematic checking, that in I.N.C. the increase of food intake and changes in rhythm of feeding are done more readily than in R.C.) There is a minimum quantity and amount of continuity of care the nurse has to give to an infant in order to become interested in him, to enjoy him and to have some sort of interaction.

It is more difficult to find out the impact of this multiplicity of nurses on the infant. Is this multiplicity of any importance in R.C. since care remains so stereotyped and impersonal that the differences between one nurse and another are small? A few observations in I.N.C. suggest strongly that some infants have been able to discriminate the dominant nurse. They express greater enjoyment and smile more at her than at occasional nurses. These cases will be studied closely in order to find out if this is related to the quantity and quality of care she gives. Another question to investigate is whether or not these children who have been able to discriminate and enjoy their dominant nurse react to the loss of her in a way different from the others.

Amount of Social Contact and of Isolation

Another striking feature of R.C. which was noticed during the pilot study was the *shortness of contact* between nurse and baby during caring acts and the nearly total lack of social contact in between these acts. For feeding, the infant was held on the lap but the bottle was emptied often in less than five minutes; as soon as the infant had burped, his diapers were changed in a few more minutes, and he was put back to bed. The total process of feeding and diapering lasted eight to twelve minutes.

In introducing I.N.C. it was suggested to the nurse that feeding could take more time, that she could keep the infant on her lap for longer and play with him until she felt he needed to sleep. It was also suggested that she took some care of her child in between feeds, when awake.

The amount of social contact experienced by each child during his stay in the nursery was recorded and compared to the amount of waking time. This varies from one group to another, and from one child to another inside one group; it differs also according to the age of the child. To date, these percentages have been established for three infants in each group during their last week at the nursery (Tables XIV, XV, XVI and XVII).

Table XIV shows that on the whole I.N.C. infants are less isolated and get more attention than R.C. infants, though there are large differences between infants of the same group.

In both groups most of the attention given to the child occurs during nursing care. The child has little social contact in between feeding times, except for one child in I.N.C.[1]

TABLE XIV

Percentage of Waking Time in Isolation and in Social Contact. The Numbers of Minutes Awake are indicated in brackets

	Routine Care		Intensive Individualized Nursing Care	
Percentage of isolation during waking	Claire (751)	80·9	Alain (759)	52·4
	Pascale (900)	70·0	Pierre (983)	37·0
	François (1036)	67·7	Dominique (276)	29·8
Percentage of social contact during waking	Claire	19·1	Alain	47·6
	Pascale	30·0	Pierre	63·0
	François	32·3	Dominique	70·2

[1] See page 29.

TABLE XV

Social Contact during Care, and at Other Times

	Routine Care		Intensive Individualized Nursing Care	
Percentage of nursing care proper during waking	Claire	17·9	Alain	47·0
	Pascale	27·1	Pierre	40·5
	François	29·2	Dominique	64·4
Percentage of social contact other than nursing care proper during waking	Claire	1·2	Alain	0·6
	Pascale	2·9	Pierre	22·5
	François	3·1	Dominique	5·8

The increase of time given to nursing care proper in I.N.C. is due to the fact that the I.N.C. nurse permits a longer time for sucking, being careful that the teat is not too fast, and permitting rest periods during which the infant is allowed to play with the teat. In R.C. it is customary to see the nurse stimulate sucking each time it stops. Also, the I.N.C. nurse keeps the child longer on her lap after the feed (Table XVI).

TABLE XVI

Average Time in Minutes spent Feeding and Diapering

Routine Care		Intensive Individualized Nursing Care	
Claire	23½	Alain	36
Pascale	19	Pierre	26
François	26	Dominique	41

The number of times the nurse goes to a quiet baby awake in his crib between feeds is very small. It is usually crying that elicits contact (Table XVII).

This, as well as the time spent for comforting the baby is higher in I.N.C. than in R.C.

One I.N.C. child only seems to get a larger amount of social contact in between feeds (Pierre, Table XV). During waking the nurse, instead of leaving him alone in his crib, as is usually done, sat him in a high chair in a wide corridor where she and other nurses

TABLE XVII

Time spent with Children (other than during Routine Work)

	Routine Care			Intensive Individualized Nursing Care		
	Claire	Pascale	François	Alain	Pierre	Dominique
Total waking time (mins.) . .	751	900	1036	759	983	276
Total crying time (mins.) . . .	251	41	193	61	44	39
Percentage time spent crying . . .	33	5	19	8	4	14
Percentage crying time when nurse is with baby . . .	2·3	7·5	2·5	13·1	13·3	15·4
Percentage non-crying time when nurse is with baby . .	0·2	0·5	0·0	1·2	0·0	1·7

fed other children. During 22·5 per cent of his waking time this child was not isolated. There were a lot of people moving about around him, and frequent occasional short contacts with the nurses: however, he was the one infant to whom the I.N.C. nurse gave less personal attention during nursing (40·5 per cent). Two distinct factors are at work: one is the amount of attention received, the other is isolation. Pierre was the least isolated child of all, but he was not the one who got the greatest attention. Personal attention given to the child will be discussed later under nurse-infant interaction.

The impact on the child of long periods of isolation seems to have three aspects.

1. There is a small amount and a reduced variety of stimulation coming from the outside world. The environment, though pleasant on the whole, is quite poor in this respect. Even though the infant is in an open crib, which allows him to see what goes on around him when he is old enough to do so, nothing much happens as a rule. The only objects in sight are few and always the same. There are a variety of sounds: crying of infants in the same room, outside noises, the going in and out of nurses, the opening and shutting of doors. We are investigating whether or not the infants are sensitive to these stimuli and what are their responses.

Another important fact seems to be that these stimuli happen at random, whatever the state of the child, and not as a response to something coming from the child. This is different from stimuli coming from nurses, which may be initiated by the nurse, but which may also be in response to the child.

2. The second important consequence of long periods of isolation is that the child gets little or no response to what he does, whether it be crying, smiling or achieving new progress. The impact of isolation, together with the multiplicity of caretakers, results in a situation where it is very difficult for a nurse to judge if the infant's needs are satisfied.

If crying, smiling, doing things, or showing interest are considered important signals for attention, they receive a response only occasionally and irregularily. The infant in Routine Care, in between caring periods, has to be self-sufficient for soothing as well as for finding pleasure and interest. There is no support or reinforcement from an external human figure.

3. The shortness of contact during caring acts, and even more so between them, does not permit interaction to establish itself. Indeed, the infant needs time at an early age to respond by smiling, or in other ways. He needs time also to recover after feeding and become aware of his surroundings. This usually occurs in R.C. after he is back in bed. The nurse has little chance of getting interesting behaviour during care, since she has to go fast in order to move on to other babies, and is anticipating this rather than concentrating on her baby.

Interactions between Nurse and Infant

The concept of interaction between two human beings is a complex one. When an infant is bathed by a nurse, he is exposed to social contact and there is inevitably a certain amount of interaction, each one reacting to the other in his or her own way. However, ongoing mutual responses one to another may be either lacking or existing in different degrees.

In order to assess the amount and quality of interaction between a nurse and an infant, one may ask at each moment of social contact (initial contact, feeding proper, after feeding on lap, toileting, parting from one another, occasional contacts in between feeds, etc.) the following four questions:

1. Is the nurse sensitive and responsive to signals coming from the child or to the child's state? On the other hand, does the infant take any notice of the nurse? Does he react to her and how?

2. Does the nurse try to promote something in the baby, such as getting his attention, and his smile, soothing him when he cries, etc., and what are the infant's reactions?

3. Are there chains of emotional reactions from one to the other? Such as looking, smiling at each other, showing mutual interest, sharing pleasure, interest and pain. (For instance, the nurse looks at the baby because he has just made a sound; baby smiles, nurse smiles, nods and speaks; baby tries to make a sound, stretches a stiffened arm towards the nurse; the nurse holds and shakes gently the tight fist, the baby watching intently.) How frequently does this happen, how long does it last, with what intensity and in what circumstances does it occur?

4. More generally, what are the emotional responses of the nurse and baby to one another – indifference, irritation, sympathy, interest?

In Routine Care, from first observations, it seems that the child is not looked at much, or smiled at or spoken to; neither is he tickled much, fondled nor moved around – actions which are usually carried out for sheer pleasure or for the pleasurable purpose of obtaining progress and lively expressions of wakefulness and liveliness. Nurse is certainly pleased when she notices the child is smiling at her or looking at her, but quite often she does not notice it, and anyhow will not spend much time, if any at all, in order to obtain this from the child. When it happens it is mostly after feeding, before the burp; it does not last long and is followed by a long period of isolation. As has been mentioned, during these periods the nurse seldom goes to a quiet child, and when she does there is no real interaction. She may wipe his mouth if he has been dribbling, change his position on the pillow, arrange the rattle so that he can see it better. She will more rarely speak to him, ask for a smile or stroke his hand. This list is exhaustive and shows both poverty and stereotypy of interaction. Also the short time of contact between nurse and infant in these instances does not allow the establishment of a chain of responses.

Moreover, in Routine Care, little notice is given to the spontaneous manifestations of the child, and they are seldom a starting-point for further interaction. They remain unanswered. For instance, left on his own, the two-month-old infant smiles a lot, makes noises and new playful actions, but these have no witness and get no response. This happens also during nursing care.

The concern of the nurse is over food intake, digestive process, production of stools, burps and cleanliness. When speaking occurs, it is often when something goes wrong with one of these things. The good child is the one who drinks fast, burps promptly, has a stool before a clean diaper is put on. But even if he is 'good', the child does not get much reward out of it. It does not bring much more stimulation nor attention from the nurse. In general, nurses have a low tolerance for crying or suffering. These are met by indifference and not infrequently with impatience and resentment; the child is blamed for being naughty, and there is often an attempt to pass on the child to another nurse. Thus difficult infants will tend to get multiple caretakers.

All this shows that communication between nurse and infant is rare. On the whole, one gets the impression that the feelings of the nurse towards the infant are shallow, so that she is not motivated to have any exchange of feelings with the child. Sometimes there is mutual interest in some stages, but it is usually transient and fades out instead of developing. In some cases the interest develops at the end of the infant's stay when he becomes able to do a lot on his own; but only if he is more attractive to a nurse than the average baby.

The introduction through I.N.C. of stability of care and of increased time devoted to the child was made in an attempt to create conditions where it might become possible for nurse and infant to be exposed to a greater amount of contact and to increase the amount and intensity of interaction. In many cases this seems to have been successful.

However, the nurses have found difficulty in turning from an efficient, quick, stereotyped type of care to a slower and more personal one. There are many reasons for this; the monotony of the job; the inevitable and repeated loss of a baby at an age when he begins to be rewarding and to show signs of affection; having constantly to return to caring for newborn babies with no chance of seeing their further development. Often there is either sympathy or antipathy for some features of the child: for instance, his physical appearance, facial expression, intonation of crying. . . . All these influence greatly the feelings of the nurse towards the child, and in turn her care. It is also true that the infants have their preferences in nurses.

For all these reasons it will be necessary to assess carefully each individual case before comparing cases with one another; and to use quantitative measures of the frequency and duration of interaction in its various forms. However it may be even more important to observe the differences in quality of interaction, and the particular occasions when it occurs. Does it mostly or exclusively happen after feeding? Does it occur in relation to crying, smiling or play? What are the modes of responses both of the child and nurse? Is there a rich variety of responses, or are they stereotyped? What is the intensity of the feeling.[1]

Conclusions

Although we have analysed care into three main factors, it is obvious that each of these is a compound of many others. This diversity is somewhat difficult to deal with, since every child receives a pattern of care which is highly individual. However, it seems that these factors, in many instances, reinforce each other: a comparison of extreme R.C. and I.N.C. case (Table XVIII) shows this strongly.

It is true also that the differences between the groups are gradually lessening, since the nurses now believe that I.N.C. is better than R.C. It is likely that the pattern of care in both groups will change, and that extremes such as those shown in Table XVIII will cease to exist.

It is likely, therefore, that sub-categories of care will appear which will have to be studied and compared between themselves and with extreme cases.

To summarize the initial impression of the impact of institutional care on the infants, two factors appear dominant: (*a*) isolation,

[1] These categories are being quantified by rating methods demonstrated to us in Denver by John Benjamin.

leading to poverty of external stimuli, lack of response to spontaneous behaviour such as crying, smiling and new achievements; (*b*) lack of communication and interaction, leading to a decrease or lack of pleasure or pain provided by or related to human beings; a decrease of stimulation coming from human beings; and poverty and inconsistency of responses to signals coming from the baby.

TABLE XVIII

Comparison of Two Extreme Cases
(D1 and D2 are first and second dominant nurses)

	Routine Care François	I.N.C. Dominique
Number of care-takers	19	11
Percentage of care given by D1	32	74
Percentage of care given by D1+D2	45·5	93
Percentage of care given by variety of nurses	56·5	7
Percentage of isolation during waking[1]	67	29·8
Percentage of social contact during waking[1]	32·3	70·2
Percentage of nursing care during waking[1]	29·2	64·4
Percentage of contact apart from nursing care[1]	3·1	5·8
Average length of nursing care[1]	26 mins.	41 mins.
Percentage crying during waking[1]	19	14·1
Percentage number of times nurse goes to crying baby during crying time[1]	8·2	84·6
Percentage of time spent with crying baby during crying time[1]	2·5	15·4
Percentage number of times nurse goes to the quiet baby during quiet waking[1]	0·09	1·43

Both variables seem closely related to one another and add up in their effects. They seem to be reinforced by a routine in which there is a multiplicity of nurses, and a small amount of time devoted to social contact with the child. The nurse is in a position where she cannot know the infant and his needs nor establish a relationship with him; as to the baby, he is in the peculiar position where human beings are at the same time all alike and yet not the same, and are neither strongly nor consistently associated with pleasure and pain. However, one notices that when these two factors, multiple care-takers and short amount of time for social contact, are changed as in I.N.C., interaction may increase, but not outstandingly nor consistently.

[1] All these numbers concern exclusively one week at the age of two months, eight days.

All these impressions indicate the need for further study of inter-relationships of factors and of their impact on the child, so that the complex nature of maternal deprivation may be better understood.

* * *

The next stage is the study of the immediate reactions of the infants and the evaluation of the more global effects which have not been considered in this paper. This is being handled in several ways, combining longitudinal and cross-sectional study.

Discussion following Paper by Dr David and Mlle Appell

BLAUVELT *When I visited your nursery, I remember that some of the children were so placed that they could see each other and watch people passing, but that others were isolated in glass-walled rooms. They could be seen, but could not see or hear others. The first group of babies got more social stimulation. Do you find differences in behaviour between the groups or individual differences that might relate to the social environment?*

DAVID *I can't tell you at this point about the effects of this on the infants. The distribution of infants between beds has been quite at random in both groups. However, I think we will be able to answer your question in time, since we are recording what is happening around the child and how the child reacts to it. There seem to be great differences between infants according to age, but also individual differences at a given age. We will relate this to the way the infant reacts to us, as observers.*

BOWLBY *Another practical point – it would be interesting to know in what way the nurses were aware of the aim of the observations.*

DAVID *The nurses know what is the aim of the study and they also are aware of some of the points we are interested in, both concerning behaviour of the child, and the care it gets. This was necessary, in order to be fully accepted and get their co-operation. On the other hand, it has had the obvious and predictable inconvenience of modifying the situation. In our records we keep data which should permit us to assess how and how much the situation has been modified.*

THOMAS *I suppose they have no knowledge of the theories of child development which underly this study; or are you actually educating the nurses?*

DAVID *They have no sophisticated knowledge of the underlying theory. The only point they know about is that babies have a need for affectionate care; they have learnt also about ill effects of maternal deprivation. In this respect we are educating them through group discussions. There is a strong desire among them to be good 'nurses' and good 'mother substitutes'; they are genuinely interested in children. All this has brought about changes in routine care, though, as was mentioned, we have been somewhat disappointed with Intensive Individualized Nursing Care.*

RHEINGOLD *This makes me want to ask – do you think that your intensive individualized nursing care group of babies is really receiving care comparable with what a home reared child might get? I myself often feel that mothers miss the cues their infants give them for more or different care. Perhaps your nurses are more perceptive than a mother with her first child?*

APPELL *I believe that a comparative study would show considerable differences between maternal care and I.N.C. This is quite obvious during the early part of the follow-up at home. As Dr Rheingold suggests, it would be valuable to compare the cues, to which mother and nurses do answer, and how they answer them. Another point to look at is the amount of stimulation coming from the mother or the nurse to the child. I do not believe we are in a position to decide which kind of care is more appropriate for the child, though we may have strong feelings about it. In our experience, one basic difference concerns emotional interchange between child and nurse which, in I.N.C., is almost lacking or at least quite poor.*

HUNTER *Of course, one of the difficulties here is that the nurse who is in sole care of a child in the I.N.C. group is herself in an exposed position. It is natural for her to defend herself against an attachment which will inevitably be broken. I think this accounts for some of your surprising results – that there was not as much change as expected.*

DAVID *It is interesting indeed to question why I.N.C. is emotionally poor and I agree with the points raised by Dr Hunter. I would like to add a complementary tentative explanation: it is mostly at the start that all I.N.C. nurses have felt uncomfortable in their role. We have found that they were upset to discover a lack of feeling for the infant, as if this was morally unacceptable, and showing also an inability on their part to become a mother. These feelings are so upsetting that they can't bear to remain long with the child. One of them has said that if she could not love babies, she had better change profession. We told her that it seems rather normal not to feel love for an unknown baby, that her situation as a nurse was actually very different from that of a mother who has conceived and given birth. It is interesting that she objected passionately that there was no value in 'stimulating' or 'petting' a child if this was not done through 'love'. I think this demonstrates why, in routine care, the nurse has short contact during caring acts. She does not remain with the child because there is no spontaneous interest or personal need to do so, but at the same time she avoids the feeling of being a 'non-loving' nurse. This creates a vicious circle, since, as is obvious in I.N.C., positive feelings develop slowly, only through caring for the child. I feel also with Dr Hunter, that there is self protection against becoming too much involved with the child. All nurses have told us that the child they had loved most was the first one. Some of them, however, seem to have had the ability to repeat the experience, even though they felt acutely the loss of the infant.*

THOMAS *That was the point of my question about education. It seems to me that, if nurses are to participate fully in giving intensified individual care, they must be educated so that they get the required orientation; and that would be asking them to make a very fundamental change.*

* * *

FOSS *In your I.N.C. group, I think you have changed two variables at once. You have reduced the number of nurses having care of the child, but you have also increased the amount of care which the child is receiving, so that it is impossible to decide which of these two factors is causing any difference between the I.N.C. and R.C. groups.*

DAVID *This is one of the problems arising from experimenting in a live set-up. As soon as a nurse is asked to take on the exclusive care of a child, she starts taking more interest in it.*

Discussion

FOSS *Perhaps this could be balanced by increasing the amount of care which the R.C. group receives, so that the groups could be roughly equated for that variable.*

RHEINGOLD *This has plagued me all along. If you reduce the number of caretakers you always seem to get a more sensitive level of care.*

DAVID *I wonder if, at this stage, it is not worth studying the relationship between the three variables: number of caretakers, amount of time spent with the child, and quality of relationship. I would be inclined to study this, before studying the isolated effects of each variable; assuming that to study them isolated is possible, which in fact I doubt.*

BOWLBY *But you, Dr Rheingold, in your earlier study (Rheingold, 1956), got over this difficulty by deciding beforehand what kind and amount of care a child was to receive, and seeing that this was carried out by acting as caretaker yourself.*

RHEINGOLD *Yes, it is rewarding to do it that way, but very time-consuming.*

*   *   *

GEWIRTZ *Mademoiselle Appell mentioned earlier that nurses might be responding well to the cues emitted by the babies, but that their responses were shallow, without feeling. Now I would say that this question of feeling should be quite incidental in the sense that the child does not discriminate feelings; it discriminates stimuli. It disciminates whether it's squeezed hard or gently, put down suddenly or slowly; it discriminates facial grimaces – not feelings.*

DAVID *Except that we do not know how feelings come through. Feelings show in very subtle ways, and we can't tell whether the child reacts to them or not; but I think we should consider the feelings of the nurse or mother as a possibly important variable, and try to assess these feelings, however roughly.*

GEWIRTZ *I think that point is well taken. In the initial phases of the research it may be necessary to use rough classifications, but as the field develops we should focus more precisely on the stimuli which are relevant to the interaction between mother and child.*

RHEINGOLD *I think as students of behaviour it's our job to discover the cues which the infant is relying on. They are subtle, minute, they are difficult to define and measure; but I think this is the pattern for us, Do I put that right?*

139

GEWIRTZ *Yes, very well. I just thought that for some of us, ultimately as behaviourists, what we have is a consistent pattern in the behaviour of the person who is the caretaker. This pattern will include various categories of behaviour. Some will be verbal responses which can be communicated to others, and some will be specific to the caretaking behaviour, and typical of the individual. Some of these responses will be characteristically different for the woman who wanted her child, for the woman who didn't, and for the woman who is ambivalent. And only some of all these behaviours will be discernible by the child.*

THOMAS *This means that we must try to measure all those little signs that indicate that a mother is experiencing a certain feeling – brightness of eye, tightness of mouth, and so on.*

GEWIRTZ *Not necessarily. Those signs may be cues to us as to what the mother may be feeling, but the child may not even be able to discriminate them. We should be interested to observe what the child can observe.*

ROSENBLATT *I wonder if it would be possible to be reasonably objective and yet make some progress by limiting oneself to some small area of behaviour. I have in mind that we cannot control nor observe the entire situation, but perhaps we can concentrate on certain areas of interaction that are inevitably repeated. The opportunity to observe the same situation repeatedly and to watch the changes which occur from day to day would permit us to describe the interaction in great detail and to isolate the important variables. This might be done for example with respect to the feeding situation.*

BOWLBY *I think this is just what Dr Gunther and Dr Blauvelt have been doing. It seems to me that there is a lot to be said for studying interaction. Any interchange between people is a chain response, and presumably the length of each chain of intercourse will vary. Now I would think it possible that, in the case of what we call a warm and spontaneous relationship, the chains might be long, whereas where there is not much feeling they might be short. I wonder if this is a possible way of measuring these not very tangible differences?*

DAVID *I think that this is what we are trying to do in the assessment of 'interaction between nurse and infant', which is the third variable we have studied. As I said, we measure it in four main ways: frequency with which the nurse answers cues coming from the*

Discussion

child; frequency with which the nurse tries to promote something in the child; frequency and length of chains of interaction from one to another; assessment of feelings of the nurse towards the child.

This last point we might drop if we find it too difficult to cope with. But I think that even if we cannot use this as a measurement tool, it will still be interesting to do it in an attempt to find out how we justify our statements and also to see if we find any correlations with the three other criteria.

The Effect of Environmental Stimulation upon Social and Exploratory Behaviour in the Human Infant

HARRIET L. RHEINGOLD[1]

I count myself extremely fortunate to be able to present some of my work and thoughts to so distinguished an audience. I thank Dr Bowlby, the Tavistock Clinic, and the Ciba Foundation for making this possible.

It is my intention to present, first, a brief background of the study, based on my efforts to understand a class of behavior, then to give the main details of the study itself, and finally, to present some speculations and hypotheses arising not only from the study but also from observations made during the course of the study.

The response the infant gives to people has been my subject of inquiry for the past few years. First, I sought to modify the responses of a group of six-month-old infants by increasing the amount of care they received and by reducing the number of persons from whom they received care (Rheingold, 1956). I found that the experimental infants very quickly became more socially responsive, not only to the experimenter who did the mothering but to other persons as well, and that the heightened responsiveness was maintained for several weeks.

The responses had been arranged in order of apparent increasing responsiveness in several categories of behavior, and from them a total score was derived. I became dissatisfied, however, with so global a measure of social responsiveness and turned my attention to only one class of the total sequence of responses, namely, the vocal response. Vocalizations as a response to persons had not been systematically studied, yet it seemed they might provide an even

[1] I am grateful to Mrs Helen W. Ross for her assistance in the planning and execution of the study.

more sensitive indicator of social responsiveness than, for example, the smile. At the same time the infant at three months, instead of at .six months of age, became the subject of investigation, because it was at this age that he first gave the full social response in all its spontaneity, vivacity and delight. We found that the number of vocalizations could be almost doubled in two days, by providing no more than a social response following each vocalization of the infant (Rheingold, Gewirtz, & Ross, 1959).

It seemed pertinent next to find and measure the environmental events which might play a role in the development of social responsiveness. Maternal care was conceived of as providing the infant's environment, both its stimulating (or arousing) and its feedback (or reinforcing) properties. By a time-sampling technique measures were taken of the amount of care and kinds of care (by which I mean the different caretaking operations) the infant received over a period of time in his natural setting (Rheingold, 1958, 1959). Environmental stimulation in home and institution was found to differ widely and on dimensions which could be specified and measured. No differences, however, were found in such infant activities as vocalizing, crying, playing and finger-sucking, activities which were charted simultaneously, but incidentally, to the main purpose of the study.

The Problem

The purpose of the present study was to assess the effects of marked differences in environmental stimulation upon the social and exploratory behavior of three-month-old infants. Two environments, own homes of high socio-economic status and an institution, were the settings in which environmental stimulation was measured. In each environment the responses of the infants were obtained to persons and to objects with which none had any prior experience.

It will be seen that the study bears a close relationship to several areas of research, the theoretical issues of which are pertinent for its outcome.

First, the study is related to investigations on the effects of environmental deprivation and enrichment. The effects of deprivation depend of course upon the species, the organism, its age, the nature of the deprivation, whether of arousing or of feedback stimuli, and the duration of the deprivation. In general, however, long-term environ-

144

mental deprivation may be expected to bring about inappropriate, incomplete, and incompetent responses, while short-term deprivation increases the responsiveness of the organism to the stimuli of which it has been deprived. Conversely, environmental enrichment is believed to increase competence, but much stimulation, especially that of an arousal nature, may bring about satiation or habituation.

Whether the care given by the institution in which I studied infants fulfils the definition of long-term environmental deprivation, or whether the care given in own homes fulfils the definition of environmental enrichment, cannot, I think, yet be said. That the two environments do represent widely separated points on several dimensions of environmental stimulation is clear. Yet, as shall be shown later, the institution environment proved upon examination to be richer in some respects.

Closely related to the deprivation issue is a set of concepts, currently receiving attention and variously named – curiosity, exploratory behavior, and manipulation motive. These behaviors, so characteristic of the living organism, and already vividly clear in the three-month-old human infant, are affected by the presence or absence of environmental stimulation. Therefore, the infant's attentiveness to an object, social or otherwise, may be as susceptible of modification as is his competence. Since attentiveness precedes competence, and in the young organism, yields even more readily to measurement, it becomes a matter of importance.

One final area of investigation and theory needs to be related to the study in hand. When the infant is presented with any object, social or otherwise, his responses may be modified by the extent to which he perceives the object as novel or as familiar. The power of the novel to arouse attention is well known; the equal power of the familiar has so far been ignored, yet it is obviously as characteristic of the young organism as it is of the older one. Still, the *very* familiar tends to arouse only a minimal response, while the *very* novel may produce, at best, a decrement in the characteristic response or, at worst, an avoidance response, the so-called fear of the strange. Integral to these concepts, of course, are the processes of generalization and discrimination.

With these three sets of related theoretical concepts in mind, the questions at issue in the study may now be raised. Will the institution infant show less interest in his environment and less competence in manipulating the objects in his environment? Will his behavior resemble that of the long-term environmentally deprived experimental animal? But, since the institution infant has fewer contacts with human beings, may the latter not, instead, more readily arouse responsiveness in him than they will in the home infant? And, furthermore, since the institution infant, lacking a mother, has not had consistent experience with any one caretaker, may he not also be more *positively* responsive to *any* person?

With respect to non-social objects, will the institution infant show as great an interest in a strange object as will the home infant who has far greater experience with a wide variety of objects? Will his competence in manipulating the novel objects equal the home infant's? But, may not the home infant explore and manipulate the objects less thoroughly because of his greater familiarity with other objects and the consequent possibility of satiation?

Method

SUBJECTS

Thirty infants were the subjects of study. Half of them lived in an institution[1] and half were 'only' infants living in their own homes. The mean age of each group was 3·6 months, with a range in age from 3·1 to 4·0 months for the institution group, and from 3·1 to 4·1 for the home group. Of the institution infants, seven were male and eight female; of the home infants, nine were male and six female.

For the institution group the criteria for selection were age, and residence in the institution since the first week of life. For the home group the infants had to be both first-born and three months of age. Only 16 mothers had to be approached to find 15 who would cooperate. They were located by word of mouth, through physicians, and the good offices of the Parent-Child Society of Washington, D.C.

The socio-economic level of the home infants' parents was homogeneous and high. The fathers had a mean of 19 years of formal education and all practised a profession; for the mothers the mean was 16 years of education. The socio-economic level of the institution infants' parents, on the other hand, was varied and, in general, lower. Data, available on only 11 of the putative fathers, yielded a mean of

[1] I am indebted to Sister Thecla and the staff of St Ann's Infant Asylum, Washington, D.C., for their generous cooperation.

13·5 years of formal education, while for the mothers the mean was 12 years. In addition, they were three years younger, on the average, than the home infants' parents. The mean age of the fathers of the home infants was 29·4 years, of institution infants, 26·0 years; the mothers' mean ages were 27·8 years and 24·7 years respectively.

The birth weight of the home infants was 7 lb. 10 oz., of the institution infants, 7 lb. 6 oz. Their mean heights at birth were 20·5 in. and 20·0 in. respectively. At the time of the tests, that is, at three months of age, the mean weight of the home infants was 14 lb. 5 oz.; the mean for the institution infants was 12 lb. 14 oz. The respective mean heights were 25·4 in. and 24·4 in. None of these differences was statistically significant, and further analysis showed that the apparently large difference in weight at three months of age could be attributed to the larger number of male infants in the home sample, the males in each group weighing more than the girls.

MEASURES OF ENVIRONMENTAL STIMULATION

Measures of the differences between the two environments in the stimulation they offered were obtained by means of a time-sampling technique described in detail elsewhere (Rheingold, 1959).

For each observation the examiner recorded on a checklist what the infant was doing, if someone was caring for him, the nature of the caretaking act, where the baby was, and how many other people were in his environment. Only 17 items were required to cover caretaking operations. Seven items referred to the infant's location, 13 defined his activities, and 8 were used to record the number of adults in his environment.

Observations were made every 15th second for the first ten minutes of every consecutive quarter-hour for a period of four hours. For each subject the hours from 9 a.m. to 1.15 p.m. were systematically sampled in this manner (the additional 15 minutes being used for the examination of the infant, to be described below). The four-hour period yielded a total of 640 observations for each infant.

Scoring – The frequency of occurrence of each item in the checklist over the four-hour period was obtained for each subject. From the frequencies a mean score was derived for each item for each group of subjects.

Observer-Agreement – In the previous report, observer-agreement

147

studies had shown that two examiners making independent simultaneous observations agreed very well indeed. At the beginning of the present study, and at three times during the study, further observer-agreement studies were run to ensure continuing agreement. On 15 ten-minute periods the median percentage of agreement of all 45 items (calculating an agreement as a tally identical both in the identifying and in the timing of the item) was 85 (range 33 to 100). Once again, it appeared that the agreement between independent judges was sufficient to warrant confidence in the method.

TESTS OF INFANT BEHAVIOUR

The responses of the infants were obtained to a Social Test, an Object Test and an Object-in-Hand Test. The tests were administered at that time during the four-hour period of maternal care measurements when the infant seemed to be most comfortable and alert.[1] He was tested in his usual environment and in his own crib. The examiner dictated the infants' responses into a portable dictaphone, directly as they occurred, in a very low tone of voice. To insure constant testing conditions for each subject, the examiner dictated everything the infant was doing, not restricting her speech to the occurrence of the specific responses to be counted.

The Social Test – The social test was adapted from one developed earlier (Rheingold, 1956). In the present study the social object or stimulus person was the examiner, the same person who made the maternal care observations. The examiner was equally strange to all the infants, having had no contact with them before the day of study, and having kept out of the infants' range of vision until the moment of the tests.

The test was composed of four subtests. In the first, the examiner stood three feet from the infant and looked at him with an unsmiling face for one minute. Then the examiner approached the infant, leaned over him, smiled warmly, and in a coaxing tone of voice, said, 'Hi, baby, how are you'? the words being repeated at 15-second intervals in that minute. Third, the examiner picked up the baby, held him in arms so he faced her, and smiled and talked to him as above. At the end of that minute, the infant was returned to his crib, the examiner walked away, but continued to record his behavior

[1] The average time of the tests was 10.16 a.m. for the home infants, 10.31 a.m. for the institution infants.

for the next minute. In all, then, the social test took four consecutive minutes, and the recording was simultaneous and continuous.

It should be noted, first, that the test closely paralleled the normal behavior of a mother and child, and second, that the four subtests differed in the amount and kind of social stimulation given the infant. The second subtest added auditory and additional visual stimuli; the third added tactile stimulation; while in the fourth subtest all social stimulation was withdrawn.

The Object and Object-in-Hand Tests – The objects used in the tests were three rattles, chosen because on pretests, rattles, of all toys, seemed to be most uniformly interesting to, as well as being capable of grasp and manipulation by, three-month-old infants. The rattles were similar in shape, all three having relatively large spherical globes, undecorated, on straight shafts, differing only in color and sound.

The first rattle was presented to the infant directly following the end of the Social Test. The examiner tried to keep the rattle prominent in the infant's line of vision and shook it gently at 15-second intervals.

As before, the examiner dictated a running account of the infant's behavior. At the end of one minute, the examiner put the rattle in the infant's hand, if he had not already secured it, retreated from the side of the crib, and recorded his behavior until he dropped the rattle or until he had held it for 60 seconds. The second and third rattles were presented similarly, and without pause.

The Object Test was composed of the three subtests in which the rattles were presented to the infant's view; the Object-in-Hand Test, of the three subtests in which the rattles were held by the infant. Together, these tests took six consecutive minutes. Unlike the Social Test, the kinds of stimulation offered by the two object tests did not differ appreciably from subtest to subtest.

The Responses – The responses selected for study fell into four main classes: regard, positive facial and vocal responses, negative facial and vocal responses, and changes in physical activity. These four classes of responses appeared to exhaust the components of the total response given to both the social and the non-social objects.

In the class of *regard* fell only two items, whether the regard was immediate or not, and the duration of regard. In the class of *positive facial and vocal responses* fell the latency in seconds of the first smile

149

(in only the Social Test), and the frequencies of smiles and vocalizations. The frequencies of frowns (or sobers), protests, fusses and cries made up the class of *negative facial and vocal responses*. The three responses in this category occurred so infrequently that they were pooled under the heading 'Negative Responses'. The class of *changes in physical activity* had two parts, the cessation of activity (labelled 'Quiet at First'), and an increase in activity. Under the latter the responses were: moves extremities, burst of activity (kicking, arching of back), and reaching of the hand, all of which yielded frequency counts.

In the Object-in-Hand Test the number of times the infant held the rattle in midline, fingered the rattle with the other hand, carried it to his mouth, mouthed it, shook or waved it, and transferred it from one hand to another, was summed under the response 'Manipulates'.

The responses studied differ somewhat from test to test, but those of the Social and Object Tests closely paralleled each other. For some of the responses the only measure was whether or not a subject gave the response, e.g. immediate regard. For other responses duration of time was calculated from the dictated record, e.g. regard, holds rattle, cessation of activity at the presentation of an object. Most often, however, the measure was frequency of the response, e.g. smiles, vocalizations, bursts of activity.

Observer-Agreement – The responses of seven infants to the three tests were recorded simultaneously and independently by two persons, one acting as examiner, dictating the infant's responses in the usual low tone of voice, and the other as observer, standing at a distance and recording responses on a checklist. The examinations of the seven infants, not subjects of the study proper, were spaced throughout the course of the study. The percentage of agreement for the separate responses ranged from 55 to 100, with a median of 76. Some of the disagreements between the two judges in labelling the responses, and the omissions on the part of the observer standing at a distance, can be attributed to the different angles from which the infant was being observed.

Results

MEASURES OF ENVIRONMENTAL STIMULATION

Table XIX presents the means and ranges of the measures of maternal care and infant activities for home and institution infants. The probability values of the differences are also shown; because the variances of the means were much greater for the home data, the Mann-Whitney Test was used.

Caretaking Acts – Caretaking was an all-inclusive item, recorded if at the moment of observation any adult was doing something for the infant while in proximity to him. Not only do the means between the groups differ widely, but the ranges do not overlap. Home infants were cared for on 44 per cent of the observations, the institution infant, on 15 per cent.[1] The home infants, also, received more of every caretaking activity, with the exception of Dresses; for example, they were talked to five times as often, fed on four times as many observations, and played with seven times as often. Thus, they not only received more stimulation in general but they also received much more of certain kinds of stimulation. It is interesting to note, however, that every caretaking activity found in the homes was also

TABLE XIX

Means and Ranges of Maternal Care
N of infants in each group = 15
N of observations for each infant = 640

| HOME | | ITEM | INSTITUITON | |
Mean	Range		Mean	Range
281·8	160–353	**Caretaking	98·6	52–149
1·2	1–2	**N Caretakers	5·1	3–8
6·0	0–19	**Looks*a*	1·0	0–8
66·4	18–146	**Looks at Face	22·5	0–59
16·8	0–39	*Talks	9·8	0–29
113·6	46–217	**Talks to Infant	24·3	5–50
16·8	2–38	**Pats	2·9	0–9
4·0	0–14	**Shows Affection	0·3	0–2
18·1	4–41	**Plays	2·5	0–9
133·3	43–206	**Holds	49·9	26–93
17·4	1–56	*Diapers	8·7	0–19
13·2	0–47	Bathes	6·1	0–14
91·2	36–175	**Feeds	24·4	9–56
16·8	0–55	Dresses	18·7	0–33
4·1	0–11	Adjusts Position	1·9	0–5
17·5	0–153	Rocks	6·8	0–21
12·6	0–51	Other	6·4	1–18

[1] The results for the present sample of 15 home and 15 institution infants very closely parallel those obtained a year earlier with a sample of five home and five institution infants.

TABLE XIX (*continued*)

| HOME | | ITEM | INSTITUTION | |
Mean	Range		Mean	Range
		Location of Infant		
288·8	0–494	**In Crib	499·1	431–607
250·1	21–467	**Prone	70·0	0–295
133·3	43–206	**In Arms	49·9	26–93
63·1	0–222	Seated	62·1	0–177
48·5	0–119	Bathinette	26·0	7–44
112·9	0–425	*Other	24·5	0–177
279·5	0–600	**Out of Own Room	27·6	7–45
		Infant Activities		
445·8	310–539	Awake	400·9	233–534
35·6	12–96	*Vocalizes	14·4	1–37
14·6	0–33	**Vocalizes to Mother	2·1	0–12
12·6	1–37	**Protests	3·7	0–13
22·7	1–47	Fusses	20·3	4–45
12·9	0–65	Cries	17·3	1–48
18·2	0–60	Active	14·4	2–47
42·3	1–203	Finger in Mouth	38·7	0–209
26·7	0–105	**Bottle in Mouth	175·6	30–343
47·2	0–281	**Pacifier in Mouth	0·0	—
53·3	8–141	**Plays Toy	3·9	0–17
24·3	1–99	**Touches	1·7	0–15
29·5	2–124	**Looks	2·2	0–14
0·8	0–4	*Plays Hand	7·1	0–30
6·4	0–29	Plays Other	17·5	0–98
		N Adults in Room		
291·9	158–463	**0	96·3	64–163
317·0	100–470	**1	168·4	105–235
31·1	0–271	**2	99·5	41–190
0·0	—	**3+	275·7	172–341
		N Adults within 6 feet		
325·4	209–463	**0	480·7	403–541
305·7	177–431	**1	105·5	51–137
8·7	0–51	**2	31·7	5–71
0·0	—	**3+	22·1	0–58

ᵃ Caretaking items not mutually exclusive.
* Difference between means significant at the ·05 level (two-tailed test).
** Difference between means significant at the ·01 level (two-tailed test).

seen in the institution, albeit less often. Further, marked similarities appeared in the order of activities performed most frequently. Caretaking of three-month-old infants therefore appears to possess certain uniformities which transcend differences in environment.

Almost all the home infants' care, during the hours of observation, came from one person, the mother, while during the same period of time the institution infant received his care from an average of five different caretakers. Thus, the home infant had many more contacts – but only with his mother; in contrast, the institution infant had far fewer contacts, but those he had were at the hands of several different persons. Different caretakers, with their different appearances, voices, and manners of administering care, must provide a kind of stimulation the home infant would lack in the usual routine of his day.

Location of the Infant – Where in his environment an infant is placed by his caretaker tells something of the changes in posture he experiences, but, even more important, of the number of new things to be seen and heard, or of old things to be seen and heard from new angles.

The results suggest that the home infant was exposed to more changes in this kind of environmental stimulation than the institution infant. He was out of his crib almost twice as often, he was more often held in arms or placed in a playpen or on a sofa. Also, he was out of his own room much more often, although this comparison needs emendation: the infants' room at the institution was very large, it housed 16 infants, and in itself probably offered more visual and auditory stimulation than the usual small room of the home infant.

Number of Adults in the Environment – Table XIX shows that the institution infant more often had more people in his room, but, at the same time, he was more often without any adult in his *immediate* environment.

Infant Activities – To chart the activities of the infant was not, of course, the primary purpose of the time-sampling studies; they were included in the checklist primarily for the information they might contribute to the delineation of maternal care. Still, the data have proved interesting in their own right.

Some of the items included in this category do, in fact, differentiate types of care. For example, the institution infant had a bottle in his mouth much more often. Bottles were propped, and he often fell asleep with the nipple in his mouth. Bottles of milk or tea were used liberally, there was almost always one in his crib, and when he fussed, the first caretaking response was often to put the bottle in his mouth. In contrast, no home infant, of the eight who were bottle-fed, had a bottle always available or fell asleep with a bottle in his mouth. On the other hand, six mothers used pacifiers, upon which the infants had become very dependent, a practice never seen in the institution.

All the play items reveal information about both maternal practices and infant behavior. It will be recalled that the home infant was played with seven times as often as his counterpart in the institution. Then, too, all the home infants were liberally supplied with toys – with rattles, mobiles, stuffed animals, cradle gyms, music boxes, a dozen of them, and often more. The institution infant, if he had a toy, would usually have only a rattle, tied to his crib, but often out of sight and reach at the head or foot of his crib. Six of the 15 infants had no toy in or attached to the crib. Only five had a toy in the crib at the time of observation.

The results obtained by time-sampling (Table XIX) indicate that the home infant more often played with toys, the institution infant more often with his hands or with 'other' objects, which included his dress, the bars of the crib, the bottle holder, etc. If the items 'touches toy', 'plays hand' and 'plays other' are combined, the mean frequencies are 31·7 for the home infant, 26·3 for the institution infant, and the difference becomes smaller. It seems, then, that the infants in both environments played a similar amount, but with different objects.

There remains one last class of behaviors to be compared. The home infant vocalized and protested more often than the institution infant. In the earlier study the five home infants also vocalized and protested more often, but not reliably so.

There were no reliable differences between the groups in frequency of fussing, crying, or, finally, of having a finger in the mouth.

THE INFANTS' RESPONSES TO THE TESTS

Three sets of measures were calculated for each test. First, for each response in which frequency or duration was counted, a mean for each group ($N=15$) was obtained, based on the total score (sum of three subtests). The second measure was the number of subjects of the 15 in each group who gave the response, by subtest and by total. The last measure gave the mean number of responses by subtest *for the subjects who showed the response*.

Differences in the first measure were tested by t tests; the Fisher

Exact Test was used for the second measure; and, for the differences between the groups in performance from subtest to subtest, a test of slope was used.

The Social Test – The institution infants as a group were more socially responsive to the examiner in every response but one, 'moves extremities'. As Table XX shows, they gave the examiner more consistent regard, they smiled faster, they smiled and vocalized more often (Figures 26 and 27), and they gave fewer negative responses

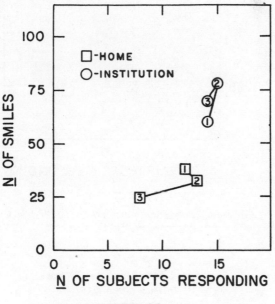

FIG. 26

Number of smiles given in the three subtests of the Social Test

(Figure 28). Physical activity ceased for a shorter period of time in response to the examiner's appearance, they gave more bursts of physical activity and more often reached out a hand to the examiner. The statistically significant differences were 'time to first smile' ($t=2.03$, $p\cong.05$), 'smiles' ($t=4.94$, $p<.001$) and 'vocalizations' ($t=2.99$, $p<.01$).

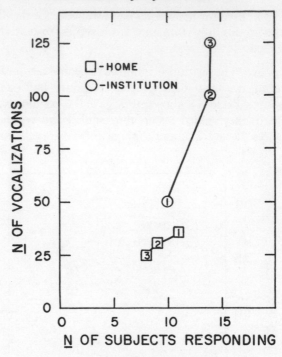

FIG. 27

*Number of vocalizations given in the three
subtests of the Social Test*

TABLE XX

The Social Test: Means and Ranges

N in Each Group = 15

Response	HOME		INSTITUTION	
	Mean	Range	Mean	Range
Duration of Attention	153·0″	100″–180″	163·0″	125″–180″
Time to First Smile	34·7″	3″–138″	13·3″	3″–43″
Smiles	6·3	3–20	13·9	7–20
Vocalizations	6·2	0–15	18·5	2–48
Negative Responses	4·3	0–12	0·7	0–4
Duration of Quiet at First	54·3″	14″–84″	52·0″	24″–84″
Moves Extremities	3·9	0–9	3·7	0–9
Bursts	4·0	0–9	6·6	0–17
Arm Approaches	0·1	0–1	1·4	0–6

156

Table XXI, giving the number of subjects who exhibited the different responses, shows that on one or more subtests all the infants regarded the examiner immediately and smiled. Fewer of the institution infants showed an initial cessation of activity, far fewer sobered,

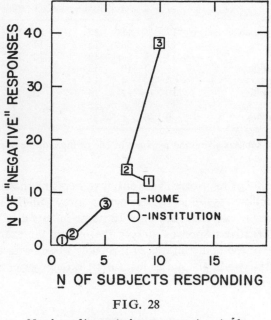

FIG. 28

Number of 'negative' responses given in the
three subtests of the Social Test

protested or fussed, but more of them reached out a hand to the examiner. Two of these differences were reliable, 'negative responses' ($p = \cdot 05$) and 'arms approach' ($p < \cdot 01$).

The results also showed that the number of institution infants who vocalized increased across subtests, while the number of home infants decreased. Also, the institution infants vocalized more in each subtest (Table XXII), in contrast to the home infants, who vocalized less and less ($p < \cdot 01$). On the other hand, the number of

157

negative responses given by the home infants increased from subtest to subtest, but not reliably so.

TABLE XXI

The Social Test: N of Subjects Giving the Response

Response	HOME Subtest				INSTITUTION Subtest			
	1	2	3	Total[a]	1	2	3	Total[a]
Regards Immediately	13	15	11	15	15	15	12	15
Smiles	12	13	8	15	14	15	14	15
Vocalizes	11	9	8	13	10	14	14	15
Negative Response	9	7	10	13	1	2	5	6
Quiets at First	9	10	4	14	8	3	5	10
Moves Extremities	10	10	12	14	9	7	11	13
Bursts	11	9	5	12	8	9	5	10
Arm Approaches	0	0	1	1	5	4	5	10

[a] *N* of subjects giving the response in one or more of the subtests.

On subtest 4 of the Social Test only two items merited study. On the first, 'follows examiner as she walks away', all 15 institution infants gave the response, but only 12 home infants did. The other item was 'negative responses' during the minute the examiner was away. Nine of the home infants protested or fussed with a mean of 5·2 responses, while 10 of the institution infants gave a mean of 3·3 negative responses.

TABLE XXII

The Social Test: Means for Subjects Responding

Response	HOME Subtest			INSTITUTION Subtest		
	1	2	3	1	2	3
Duration of Attention	54·7″	57·3″	41·0″	54·0″	56·3″	52·7″
Smiles	3·1	2·5	3·0	4·3	5·2	5·0
Vocalizations	3·4	3·4	3·1	5·1	7·2	8·9
Negative Responses	1·3	2·0	3·8	1·0	1·0	1·6
Duration of Quiet at First	17·0″	19·0″	18·3″	15·5″	17·7″	19·0″
Moves Extremities	1·9	1·5	2·1	1·8	2·0	2·4
Bursts	2·3	3·1	1·4	4·8	5·8	1·8
Arm Approaches	0·0	0·0	1·0	1·4	1·8	1·4

Harriet L. Rheingold

The Object Test – On this test far fewer differences appeared than in the Social Test (Table XXIII). Both groups of subjects gave similar responses; although the means differ, the differences were small. The institution infants smiled more to the rattle and to the examiner, and also vocalized more to the examiner, but the only reliable difference was their more frequent bursts of activity ($t=4.71$, $p<.002$). The home infants vocalized slightly more often to the rattles, they gave more negative responses, and they showed a slightly longer cessation of activity at the presentation of the objects.

TABLE XXIII

The Object Test: Means and Ranges

N in Each Group = 15

Response	HOME Mean	HOME Range	INSTITUTION Mean	INSTITUTION Range
Duration of Attention	107·3″	70″–145″	104·2″	45″–175″
Smiles to Object	0·1	0–1	1·1	0–11
Smiles to Examiner	1·3	0–8	3·6	0–16
Vocalizations to Object	3·5	0–10	2·6	0–7
Vocalizations to Examiner	1·7	0–11	2·8	0–11
Negative Responses to Toy	2·3	0–17	1·5	0–9
Negative Responses to Examiner	1·0	0–7	0·5	0–4
Duration of Quiet at First	43·0″	9″–74″	35·3″	14″–74″
Moves Extremities	3·7	1–11	2·8	0–11
Bursts	4·3	0–13	13·3	0–54
Arm Approaches	1·1	0–5	1·4	0–3
Hand Contacts	0·5	0–4	0·9	0–3
Secures	0·4	0–2	0·5	0–1

Table XXIV also shows fairly close agreement between the groups in the number of subjects giving the different responses. More of the institution infants reached out for the rattles, made contact with them, and succeeded in securing them. The small number of subjects giving the response, however, made it impossible to test the statistical significance of the differences.

No clear evidence appeared of either increases or decreases in number of responses from subtest to subtest (Table XXV).

The results of the Object Test, then, showed little difference between the groups. For both groups, positive facial and vocal responses were much greater than negative ones. As in the Social Test, the institution infants again gave more positive and fewer

159

negative responses than the home infants. The home infants gave more positive facial and vocal responses to the rattles than to the

TABLE XXIV

The Object Test: N *of Subjects Giving the Response*

Response	HOME Subtest				INSTITUTION Subtest			
	1	2	3	Total[a]	1	2	3	Total[a]
Regards Immediately	11	9	12	14	12	13	9	14
Smiles to Object	1	1	0	2	3	1	2	3
Smiles to Examiner	5	3	3	5	10	5	4	10
Vocalizations to Object	7	7	9	12	7	8	8	12
Vocalizations to Examiner	4	2	3	6	4	5	5	8
Negative Responses to Toy	4	5	6	8	3	3	6	7
Negative Responses to Examiner	2	2	2	5	3	0	0	3
Quiet at First	4	2	2	6	4	3	1	5
Moves Extremities	11	12	10	15	5	8	9	10
Bursts	5	8	6	12	10	9	11	13
Arm Approaches	2	6	5	6	5	8	7	9
Hand Contacts	1	3	2	3	1	6	6	7
Secures	1	2	2	2	1	3	3	4

[a] *N* of subjects giving the response in one or more of the subtests.

TABLE XXV

The Object Test: Means for Subjects Responding

Response	HOME Subtest			INSTITUTION Subtest		
	1	2	3	1	2	3
Duration of Attention	39·0″	35·4″	36·2″	34·3″	37·7″	35·4″
Smiles to Object	1·0	1·0	0·0	2·7	5·0	1·5
Smiles to Examiner	1·8	2·0	1·3	2·7	2·9	3·2
Vocalizations to Object	2·6	2·6	1·9	2·3	1·0	1·9
Vocalizations to Examiner	3·5	1·0	3·3	4·8	1·4	3·2
Negative Responses to Toy	1·8	1·0	3·8	1·3	1·3	2·5
Negative Responses to Examiner	2·0	1·0	4·5	2·3	0·0	0·0
Duration of Quiet at First	17·3″	12·3″	13·3″	16·5″	9·7″	9·0″
Moves Extremities	1·8	1·4	1·9	2·2	2·2	1·4
Bursts	2·6	2·3	3·3	6·0	7·4	6·5
Arm Approaches	1·5	1·2	1·2	1·0	1·0	1·1
Hand Contacts	2·0	1·3	1·0	1·0	1·0	1
Secures	2·0	1·0	1·0	1·0	1·0	

examiner; while the institution infants, in spite of their reaching out to the rattles more often, smiled and vocalized more to the examiner than to the rattles.

One last comparison remains: the number of smiles and vocalizations given to the examiner can be compared with the number given to the objects in this test for the full sample of 30 infants. Fifteen subjects smiled to the examiner, but only five smiled to the rattles. In contrast, while 14 infants vocalized to the examiner, 24 of them vocalized to the rattles. It appears, therefore, that the social object stimulated equal numbers of the subjects to smile and to vocalize but the non-social object stimulated more infants to vocalize than to smile.

The Object-in-Hand Test – The institution infants, as may be seen in Table XXVI, looked at the rattles in hand more often and for a

TABLE XXVI

The-Object-in-Hand Test: Means and Ranges

N in Each Group = 15

Response	HOME		INSTITUTION	
	Mean	Range	Mean	Range
Looks at in Hand	2·7	0–11	4·6	0–12
Duration of Regard	32·7"	0–85"	46·7"	0–130"
Looks to Examiner	1·2	0–4	1·8	0–5
Duration of Grasp	114·3"	17"–180"	125·1"	12"–180"
Manipulates	4·7	0–7	5·9	0–9

longer period of time. They also looked more often to the examiner, held the rattles for a longer period of time, and manipulated them more often.

TABLE XXVII

The Object-in-Hand Test: N of Subjects Giving the Response

Response	HOME Subtest				INSTITUTION Subtest			
	1	2	3	Total[a]	1	2	3	Total[a]
Looks at in Hand	6	8	8	12	11	13	8	14
Looks to Examiner	7	4	5	9	9	5	8	12
Manipulates	10	11	11	13	12	14	11	15

[a] *N* of subjects giving the response in one or more of the subtests.

Table XXVII shows that more institution infants gave the responses. Duration of regard increased across the three subtests for both groups (Table XXVIII). None of these differences, however, was statistically significant.

TABLE XXVIII

The Object-in-Hand Test: Means for Subjects Responding

Response	HOME Subtest			INSTITUTION Subtest		
	1	2	3	1	2	3
Looks at in Hand	1·7	1·9	1·9	1·9	2·0	2·8
Duration of Regard	16·2″	17·0″	21·0″	21·5″	23·5″	25·7″
Looks to Examiner	1·3	1·0	1·0	1·1	1·4	1·2
Duration of Grasp	39·3″	37·5″	37·5″	41·2″	45·8″	38·1″
Manipulates	2·1	2·1	2·4	2·2	2·7	2·2

Correlations between Test Responses – To discover whether a few infants, more active or responsive than the others, may have contributed to the scores out of proportion to their numbers, the degree of association between some representative responses was obtained. Thus, in the Social Test the number of bursts was correlated with the number of smiles, the number of bursts with the number of vocalizations, and the number of smiles with the number of vocalizations; and in the Object-in-Hand Test the number of shakes (or waves) was correlated with the number of bursts. None of the correlations was reliably different from chance, a finding which suggests that the degree of association between different responses within an infant was small, and that the differences between the groups cannot be attributed to the presence of a few infants different from the rest of the sample.

Additional Findings – No reliable differences were found in the number of smiles, vocalizations, or bursts of activity given to the different examiners. For example, the 19 infants examined by the writer gave means of 11·1 smiles, 11·0 vocalizations and 5·3 bursts, in the Social Test. The means for the other examiner were 8·3 smiles, 13·9 vocalizations and 5·3 bursts, for the remaining 11 infants.

There appeared to be no reliable differences, also, between the sex of the infants and performance. The male infants, on the Social Test, for example, gave means of 9·8 smiles, 13·8 vocalizations and

5·1 bursts; the means for the female infants were 10·4, 10·6 and 5·5 respectively.

Discussion

The results of the study suggest that the lesser amount of environmental stimulation provided by the institution did not blunt the interest, that is, the visual exploratory behavior, of the institution infants in either the social or the non-social objects. Further, it did not reduce their *manual* exploration of non-social objects with which they had no prior experience.

It appears, therefore, that the institution environment, sparse as it was in contrast with the environment experienced by the home infants, was nevertheless adequate to develop and to maintain both interest and skills in infants of three months. Wide as were the differences on many environmental measures, they were still not wide enough to produce a difference in many of the behaviors tested. It follows, then, that the institution environment cannot be equated with those set up experimentally to assess the effects of long-term deprivation upon animals; the institution infants, after all, could see people and things, and could use their hands.

The quantity, and even the nature, of experiences provided by the environment, *given a certain minimum*, may be irrelevant for the development of these behaviors in the young infant. Or, the institution infant's greater leisure to explore and to experiment with what his environment did offer may have compensated for what the environment seemed to lack. Or, the stimulation provided by frequent changes in caretakers in the institution may have offset the sheer amount of caretaking in the home. There remains at least one other alternative explanation: while the home infant may get more feedback (or reinforcing) stimulation and more regular reinforcement, a variable schedule of reinforcement, more likely characteristic of the institution's caretaking, is known to be more effective in maintaining behavior.

It should be possible, in the future, to obtain answers to some of these questions. For example, environments could be set up experimentally so that they differ in only one dimension. Specifically, only amounts of care could be varied, or amounts of certain caretaking operations; or, again, with amounts of caretaking held constant, the number of different caretakers could be systematically varied; or,

163

still again, environments could be analyzed for their arousing and their reinforcing properties, and, for the latter, the effect of different reinforcers and different schedules of reinforcement could be assessed.

The second main conclusion arising from the study suggests that not only were the institution infants as interested and as competent, but also they were more positively responsive to the examiner than the home infants. They smiled more quickly and more often; they more often vocalized and reached out a hand. On almost every measure of a positive, self-extending nature they were more reactive and more responsive, although not always to a degree sufficient for statistical significance. They appeared more eager and more delighted.

A finding so at variance with expectation requires consideration. First, the responsiveness of the institution infants appears to resemble the effects of short-term deprivation. It was as though they were happier to see a person, because they saw persons less often; they were more ready to be stimulated; or perhaps they had already learned that a greater response on their part would hold the person at their side where he could continue to provide stimulation. They may have learned that the attention of a person is the necessary prelude to caretaking (Skinner, 1953). In the home infant, on the other hand, who had perhaps already smiled and vocalized many more times that day, responsiveness might have been waning. Or, he may not have had to learn how to hold a person at his side.

An alternative hypothesis, however, may be entertained, one based upon the assumption that the home infant is already capable of discriminating between his mother and another person, between the familiar person and the strange. Accordingly, it would follow that to the institution infant with his greater experience of many caretakers, any person would appear less different. The home infant, to be sure, *did* regard the person, but we may surmise that, with many of the accustomed cues missing, his positive responses were accordingly diminished. The negative responses, although few in number, may have been distress reactions to the sight, sound and touch of a strange person.

Before this hypothesis can be accepted, however, it will be necessary to discover the properties of the object which, on the one hand, are novel, or familiar, enough to arouse attention and delight, and

164

those which, on the other hand, are so novel that they suppress delight and sometimes give rise to distress. Nor is it yet known why a strange person should arouse negative responses, when by the law of generalization any person must resemble the known person in many ways. The hypothesis that the home infant saw the examiner as strange could be tested simply, although not easily or completely, by contrasting his responses to his mother with those to a person unknown to him.

A third explanation remains. There may have been differences between the two groups of infants which stemmed from sources other than the environmental variables measured here. There were, for example, differences between the parents of the infants in each group, differences in age, in years of education, and in occupation. The two groups of infants, therefore, may differ in genetic potentialities, including physical, developmental and temperamental traits. The effects of genetic potentialities upon the behaviors here under study are not known. One might speculate, however, that the home infants were by constitution more attentive and more controlled. But this explanation would not by itself account for the greater number of negative responses given by the home infants. It, too, could be tested – by contrasting the behavior of infants possessing similar genetic potentialities but receiving different amounts of environmental stimulation.

Finally, no one of these hypotheses alone may account for the results, but each in part may contribute to the differences observed.

In addition to the problems raised so far, two others demand consideration. It will be recalled that the rattles were always presented at the hand of the examiner; even though every effort was made to keep the objects central, they were always associated with the social object. It might be profitable in the future, therefore, to obtain the infant's responses to objects alone, unconfounded by the presence of the social object. And, lastly, it would be interesting to vary the order of presentation of the two classes of objects. What, for example, would have been the infant's responses to the non-social objects had they come first in the series of tests?

Summary

The purpose of the study was to measure the effects of two different environments upon the social and exploratory behavior of three-month-old infants. The amounts and kinds of stimulation offered the infants by mothers in own homes and by caretakers in an institution were measured by time-sampling over a four-hour period; the differences on most measures were marked. The infants' responses were then obtained to a person and to toys with which they had no prior experience.

The institution infants were more positively responsive to the person than the home infants; they smiled more quickly and more often; they vocalized more often; more of them reached out a hand to the person, and they gave fewer 'negative' responses.

In contrast, there were no reliable differences in the responses of both groups to the toys, whether they were responses of visual exploration, facial changes and vocalizations, on the one hand, or of kinds and amounts of manipulatory activities, on the other.

The results indicate that the lesser amount of environmental stimulation provided by the institution did not blunt the interest of the institution infants in people and objects, or reduce their competence in responding to them. It did appear, however, to be associated with a quicker, fuller and more positive response to a social object.

THE BEGINNINGS OF SOCIAL RESPONSIVENESS IN THE HUMAN INFANT

In the process of gathering data for the study, a number of ideas came to mind concerning the origins and development of social responsiveness in the human infant.

First, the human infant by three months of age is no passive creature. When awake, he is alert, attentive, active and responsive. He occupies himself continually. Especially is this clear in the institution where there is so little interference and where he is left so much to his own entertaining. Already there are developed both a *responsiveness* to stimuli in the environment and a *searching* of the environment for stimulation.

Most prominent among the infant's waking activities is looking. ✓ His eyes move freely and often, as he fixates on one object after another. Hearing a sound, he moves his head until his eyes locate the source. When his hands close on an object, he looks *to* the object. When he is placed in the prone position, he moves his head freely, and looks. Picked up, his first activity is to look around him. At this age, before he can reach out and grasp an object with any kind of facility, he is already picking up the physical environment, but, as Gesell said, 'with eyes alone' (1949, p. 88).

What are the characteristics of the objects which excite his visual regard? They are those which have long been known as the arousers of attention. He looks at bright and shining objects, and at the lines of demarcation between brightness and darkness. Above all, change or movement in the stimulus arouses visual regard. The novel and the complex – attributes which may be reduced to temporal and spatial *changes* in stimulation (Dember and Earl, 1957) – also attract him. Berlyne's (1958) finding that infants were attracted to patterns with more contour fits the attribute of complexity, a finding similar to Fantz's (1958) that infants beginning at two months of age show a clear preference for patterns of greater complexity.

Intent and fixed visual regard is accompanied by a cessation of physical activity. The infant is showing the orienting reflex of Pavlov, as if asking, 'What is it?' On occasion, however, there follows the responses I have already enumerated, the brightening of the face, the smiles, the marked increase in total bodily activity, and the vocalizations, a sequence which is often repeated again and again.

The simple enumeration of the components of the response, however, omits what is so striking, but so obvious as to be ignored, that the infant is displaying what seem to be the emotions of delight and glee. Parenthetically, as Bowlby (1958) has pointed out, it is just these emotions that his responses evoke in the adult beholder.

This pattern of behavior in the infant is all the more remarkable and worthy of study because of its maturity, relative to his other patterns of behavior. It is already in the form it will keep throughout his life. Fetal as he still is in many ways, especially in comparison with other mammals, in this pattern of behavior he is precocious beyond his age.

What is the nature of the objects which evoke this *full* response? Until the present study I always designated this sequence of responses – with its attendant emotion – a social response, disregarding the many times I had actually seen infants smiling and vocalizing to such non-human things as a ray of sunshine or a wallpaper pattern. It was, however, seeing the full social response given to a rattle that set me speculating, even though, as the results show, the human being did win out over the non-human. My conclusion at this point, in the absence of systematic investigation, is that the more 'interesting' objects bring about responses other than visual regard. Allow me this circularity of thinking, for the present.

Among all the objects in the infant's environment the most interesting, I suggest, is the social object. If one analyzes the social object, the human being, as though it were any other object, one is struck by its extraordinarily high stimulating properties. I can think of no other object with which it can compare. Visually, the human face is bright, parts of it shine, it has contour and complexity. It moves almost constantly, bringing stimulus change with every movement. It produces sound. The human body offers tactile stimulation on occasion. Above all, the social object moves *in response to* the infant's own movements. If he smiles, it smiles. If he vocalizes, it vocalizes in turn.

The significance of these observations for theory can now be considered. In the past, two kinds of theories have been advanced to account for the infant's smile. (I am here taking the smile to be synonymous with the entire pattern of responses, and shall myself think of the theories as accounting for the infant's social responsiveness.) One set of theories ascribes social responsiveness to the infant's associating the human face and form with a history of need reduction. Dennis (1935) and Spitz (1946) espoused such theories. Another set of theories holds that the responses of the infant to human beings are primary developments and are not, or need not be, based on secondary reinforcement. The chief proponents are Charlotte Bühler (1931), Piaget (1952), Bowlby (1958). My hypothesis belongs to the second class of theories, but varies at, what I consider, some important points.

It seems improbable to me that the infant's responsiveness to people springs into life full-born. I think, rather, that in the beginning the human being is not seen as a member of one's own species, that is, as human, or, for that matter, as living. *The human being is but another complex of stimuli, but because he is living, he is more interesting, and because he is human, he is more responsive.*

Harlow's work (1958) on the affectional response in the infant rhesus is apropos, even if he has not had the occasion to advance a theory of smiling. He has said that the course of social attachment in the human must resemble that in the monkey. If this is so, it can be only within the broadest limits, because the timings of different components of behavior are so very different. The earliest and most common response of the infant rhesus to its mother is to cling. Not so the human infant. At three months of age he is already fully responsive to people, yet he will not *cling* to them for months to come. I suggest, therefore, that not physical, but visual, contact is at the basis of human sociability.

With one question Piaget appears to come closest to my own hypothesis. He asks, '. . . is it possible to think that the smile only becomes specialized progressively in its functions as a visual sign and consists during the first months of a single pleasurable reaction to the most varied excitants, even though it begins in the presence of the voice or movements of the human face?' And he continues, ' . . . the smile seems to us a good indication of the existence of recognition in general' (1952, p. 71). The concept of recognition I find troublesome, for the infant will smile at a strange object (although for Piaget 'recognition' may include both the partly strange and the partly familiar); and, as yet, I am not sure that the smile begins in the presence of the voice or movements of the human face.

It is clear, however, that by three months of age the primary stimulus has become the human face. The human voice is still only an adjunct. The infant, hearing the voice, searches the environment until he finds, that is, *sees* the source. But, if he sees the face of a person not speaking, he does not search for the voice, but instead smiles and coos to it at once and without delay.

In summary, the argument may be put very simply. The basic and primary activity is the infant's visual exploration of his environment. Certain objects attract and hold his attention. To some of these, apparently to the most interesting, he gives facial, vocal and bodily responses of delight. Of these objects, the human being appears to be the most provoking of the responses labeled social responsiveness.

This way of accounting for the human infant's response to people appears to fit the observed facts; it requires fewer assumptions than the derived drive theories; it supplies a developmental explanation based on learning for theories which hold that the infant instinctively recognizes another person as human; and, finally, it gives promise of yielding to experimental investigation.

Determinants of Infant Behaviour

The task of the future will be to discover the properties of the objects, including those of both novelty *and* familiarity, which call forth visual exploratory behavior, and those special properties which in addition produce the smiles, vocalizations and other signs of delight. Further, it will be necessary to study the infant's responses to sounds and touch, in an attempt to discover the contributions made by experience in other avenues of sensing than the visual. With answers to these question I think we should be closer to knowing the origins of social behavior in man.

REFERENCES

BERLYNE, D. E. (1958) 'The influence of the albedo and complexity of stimuli on visual fixation in the human infant' *Brit. J. Psychol.* **49**, 315-318

BOWLBY, J. (1958) 'The nature of the child's tie to the mother' *Int. J. Psycho-Anal.* **39**, 1-24

BÜHLER, CHARLOTTE (1931) 'The social behavior of the child' In C. Murchison (Ed.) *A handbook of child psychology* (1945) Worcester: Clark Univer. Pr., Chap. 12

DEMBER, W. N., & EARL, R. W. (1957) 'Analysis of exploratory, manipulatory, and curiosity behaviors' *Psychol. Rev.* **64**, 91-96

DENNIS, W. (1935) 'An experimental test of two theories of social smiling in infants' *J. soc. Psychol.* **6**, 214-223

FANTZ, R. L. (1958) 'Pattern vision in young infants' *Psychol. Rep.* **8**, 43-47

GESELL, A., ILG, FRANCES L., & BULLIS, GLENNA E. (1949) *Vision, its development in infant and child* New York: Hoeber

HARLOW, H. F., & ZIMMERMANN, R. (1958) 'The development of affectional responses in infant monkeys' *Proc. Amer. phil. Soc.* **102**, 501-509

PIAGET, J. (1952) *The origins of intelligence in children* Trans. by Cook, Margaret. New York: Int. Univer. Pr.

RHEINGOLD, HARRIET L. (1956) 'The modification of social responsiveness in institutional babies' *Monogr. Soc. Res. Child Developm.* **21**, No. 63 (No. 2)

RHEINGOLD, HARRIET L. (1958) 'A method for measuring maternal care' *Amer. Psychologist*, **13**, 319 (Abstract)

RHEINGOLD, HARRIET L. (1959) 'A comparison of maternal care in home and institution' Paper read at Amer. Orthopsychiat. Ass., San Francisco, March 1959

RHEINGOLD, HARRIET L., GEWIRTZ, J. L., & ROSS, HELEN W. (1959) 'Social conditioning of vocalizations in the infant' *J. comp. physiol. Psychol.* **52**, 68-73

SKINNER, B. F. (1953) *Science and human behavior* New York: Macmillan

SPITZ, R. A. (1946) 'The smiling response: a contribution to the ontogenesis of social relations' *Genet. Psychol. Monogr.* **34**, 57-125

A Reconstruction of some of the Discussion following Dr Rheingold's Paper

AMBROSE *You said that some of your results on smiling suggest that the institution babies were more advanced than the home babies. This is at variance with some results which Mrs Bernstein and I have obtained. We found that both types of babies go through a period when they smile increasingly at any face, but when the peak is reached, the response to strangers' faces gradually wanes, and only that to the mother figure is maintained. This period following maximal 'smiliness' seems to go with a growing ability to discriminate faces; and it occurs earlier for home babies. The peak of smiling is at about 13 weeks old for home babies, and 20 weeks for institution babies.*

From this you would expect that if babies are tested at about four months old, the institution babies will smile more at a strange experimenter and the home babies less, since they will have passed this peak and be already discriminating.

RHEINGOLD *This early in our investigations of the social response I am reluctant to characterize the greater frequency of any part-response as 'more advanced' behaviour. I found only that the institution infants smiled more often; but I suspect that other variables, in addition to developmental maturity, were playing a role.*

In comparing the number of smiles, or of the other associated responses, given by both groups of infants, the greatest obstacle is

presented by there being for the institution infant no strange person. For him there is not the opportunity to discriminate between the known and the unknown person because there is little continuity, from one day to another or even within a day, in the persons at whose hands he receives care. Especially is this the case in the institutions in which I have worked where at bath and meal times groups of volunteers supplement the corps of regular caretakers.

For any comparison of our results we should keep in mind the differences in stimulating situations. In Test 1, where the stimulus was only the silent and unsmiling examiner (the one test of our three which most closely resembled your stimulating situation), the differences between the two groups in number of smiles (and vocalizations) were small; they only became larger as the examiner offered more stimulation in Tests 2 and 3.

That the home infants would have been more responsive to the examiner had they been tested when younger is, of course, a possibility. An incomplete, but nevertheless pertinent, test of the hypothesis can be made by comparing the responses of younger and older infants in my sample. About half the subjects in each group were 3·0 to 3·5 months of age; the other half were 3·6 to 4·1 months of age. For both the home and the institution groups the frequency of smiles was greater for the older half. It would seem, therefore, that the older home infants smiled more to the observer, just when you might be expecting better discrimination between mother and stranger.

AMBROSE *Even if the home babies had not passed the peak, would you expect them to smile as much to you as they would to their own mothers?*

RHEINGOLD *On three grounds, theoretically, the home infant might be expected to smile as much to the examiner as to his mother. First, by the law of generalization any affect associated with her should transfer, at least in part, to other similar objects; second, if the number of smiles decreases with repeated elicitation by the same stimulus (here the mother), a novel stimulus could be expected to bring the occurrence of their response to some earlier, higher level of frequency; and, third, if one of the original stimuli for smiling is some moderate degree of novelty, as I have suggested, then the infant might be expected to smile to the examiner, regardless of the previous occurrence of smiling. Still, the possibility exists that*

172

infants this early in life are capable not only of discriminating between the familiar and the novel, but also of preferring the familiar. The task still remains, however, of discovering the degree and nature of novelty which suppresses the smiling responses, since on occasion novel stimuli appear not only to be preferred but also sought. We will continue to be handicapped in working out these relationships until the dimensions of novelty are more precisely defined; at present it is confounded with such other dimensions as complexity, surprise, etc.

To measure the difference between the infant's response to his mother and to an examiner presents many difficulties. Both persons should follow the same procedure in approaching the infant, talking to him, etc. I have not yet succeeded in finding a parent who does not do more than he is instructed to, for example, grimacing or exaggeratedly bobbing his head.

These considerations notwithstanding, it is my impression *that the institution infants I saw smiled more quickly, more often, and with greater amplitude to anyone who leaned over their cribs than did the home infants to their mothers.*

QUESTION *The way in which all these babies reacted to you would depend on what had been happening to them immediately before you started to observe them. Is it possible that the home and institution babies may have had systematic differences in these antecedent conditions?*

RHEINGOLD *The measures of maternal care were originally obtained to provide a sample of the nature and amount of stimulation offered by each environment over a period of days, and even weeks, prior to the tests. I now see, however, that the measures also provide, and even more unequivocally, a sample of the nature and amount of stimulation offered by each environment on the day in which the infant's behaviour was tested.*

By the logic of time-sampling one would expect the differences in maternal care in a subsample of the four-hour period to closely resemble those obtained for the total sample of time, although the shorter the subsample the less it might resemble the total sample. Therefore, 'systematic differences' must partake of the nature of the differences already presented. Conceivably there were other differences, but had I been aware of them I would have attempted to measure them.

173

In summary, I attempted to get at differences in the environment by measuring maternal care. These measures did demonstrate significant differences, but testing conditions were controlled by obtaining the infant's responses to the observer and the objects at the time when he appeared alert and comfortable.

QUESTION *Is it possible that mothers might develop a greater repertoire of behaviour towards their babies than do the nurses? Although the institution babies have more caretakers, perhaps they are exposed to less varied, more stereotyped behaviour than are the home babies?*

RHEINGOLD *While this is entirely possible, it is my impression that much of the behaviour of the caretakers in the institution in which the study was conducted was not stereotyped. There was considerable awareness of the temperamental differences between the infants with consequent modification of the care they gave any particular infant. In observing the caretakers I was often impressed by the differences between them in the ways in which they held the infants, or fed them, or talked to them. A mother's responses to some behaviour of the infant would tend to be more similar from occurrence to occurrence, and probably more regularly occurring, than would the responses of different caretakers.*

QUESTION *You suggested in the paper that a baby's social reactions seemed to arise largely from its visual exploring, of which it does a lot. I can see that this might be true for the babies you have studied, but isn't it possible that in some cultures, where babies cling a great deal in the early months, that social reactions might first develop out of such physical contact?*

RHEINGOLD *This is an interesting but difficult and complex question and, in the absence of observation and experimental study of infants in other cultures, I can only offer conjectures.*

The social response in its entirety as I have described it appears to be stimulated primarily by the sight *of another human being. I have not yet tested the response the infant would give at three months of age to the voice or the touch of another human being, in the absence of accompanying visual presentation. If touch (or contact) were a more powerful, or even as powerful, elicitor of smiling, the case for physical contact as the basis of social responsiveness would be clearer.*

As for clinging, observation of Western infants is that they do

174

Discussion

not cling to the mother (in the sense of holding fast by twining round or embracing) in the fourth month of life. They are, instead, carried by the mother. One sometimes sees their hands closing over objects with which they come in contact. Thus, when nursing or held, their hands may close over the mother's clothing. But the grasp is never sufficient to support their own weight, even in part. It is important, therefore, to recognize that social responsiveness of the kind I have been describing appears before the infant can grasp.

Now, even in cultures where the infants are carried by the mother, in her arms or in some device such as a shawl or a sling, I suspect that the infants of three and four months of age also do not cling. I have seen no account of such activity in the literature nor observed an infant this young clinging in any picture showing mother and infant in such cultures. Still, it is just possible that as a result of being much carried the infant of some other culture might be more accelerated in the use of his hands and arms. Geber[1] has suggested that this is true in general for the African infant, although she has not reported on clinging specifically.

Further, the human body offers little purchase for clinging. The human infant, it is clear, has not the grasping proficiency of the rhesus infant, nor the human mother the fur of the rhesus monkey to grasp. Clinging, when it does occur in our infants, in the second half of the first year, takes the form usually of an encircling of the mother's neck or shoulder, with the arms as much as with the hands.

In any comparison between Western and other infants I suspect that being much or continuously carried by the mother constitutes a complex variable offering more than skin contact. The carried infant is exposed to more kinaesthetic, visual and auditory stimulation than the infant who spends a considerable part of each day alone in his crib.

Finally, nothing I have said should be interpreted to mean that I do not think that other senses, besides the visual, play a part in the infant's responsiveness to people. It is only a matter of what seems to play the greater part at this age and to be more important.

[1] Geber, Marcelle (1958) 'The psycho-motor development of African children in the first year, and the influence of maternal behaviour' *J. soc. Psychol.* **47,** 185-195; and
Geber, Marcelle and Dean, R. F. A. (1957) 'Gesell tests on African children' *Pediatr.* **20,** 1055-1065.

Especially as the infant grows older would experiences from other sensory systems be incorporated into his response to people.

QUESTION *One of the difficulties in doing these kinds of experiments is that you must of necessity tamper with the infant's environment. One particular point I want to raise is concerned with the particular temporal pattern of events during the experiments. There was a time interval of 14 seconds between measures.* What was the baby doing during this interval? How might your results have been different with a different interval, or with none at all?

RHEINGOLD *Time-sampling is a respected and defensible method of measuring the recurrence of events of varying durations. Like any other method one might choose, it possesses both advantages and limitations.*

It is clear that the particular form of time-sampling I employed to measure maternal care (and hence environmental stimulation) yields no information about the intervening fourteen seconds; they are silent. Only practical considerations dictated the duration of the interval. To record at shorter intervals would demand a scale with fewer items, for there is a limit to the number of discriminations which can be made and recorded in any interval of time. To record at longer intervals would, as I found by experience, decrease the alertness of the observer by giving him unfilled time.

By the logic underlying time-sampling I think one could fairly safely assert that shorter or longer intervals (if not too far apart) would yield results very similar to those obtained here. Thus I would expect the odd-even reliabilities of the maternal care items used here to be extremely high.

To complete the discussion of this method, let me briefly consider other alternatives. Another variation of the method, and one commonly employed, records all the events which occur during some time interval longer than a second – say, during five or ten minutes. This is probably a coarser technique than the one I employed. Seldom, however, has it been used over periods of time as long as four hours.

More important than the duration of the time intervals, it seems to me, is the nature of the items or the behaviours to be recorded. It would conceivably be possible to record everything that occurs in a mother's care of an infant in some period of time, if only by recourse to photographic recording. To bring order out of such data, however, categories or rating scales or some other form of coding would be required. As a result, information would be discarded at that point, rather than earlier as in the method I employed, and one might not be any closer to a measure of the events one is interested in. Clearly, the decision of what to record constitutes the heart of the problem.

What to record depends, of course, upon one's objectives. The method I used yielded information on what I wished to measure, namely, the amounts of different caretaking operations in home and institution. If it is also important, as some of us believe, to pay attention to the consequences of an infant's behaviour, that is, what the mother does in response to that behaviour (and vice versa, what the infant does in response to the mother's behaviour), these consequences can become the items to be recorded. The task would be difficult, but not impossible. But, even with this method of getting at what may be called 'interaction' we are still only sampling behaviour. It remains only for me to state my conviction that we shall make greater progress if we turn our efforts to specifying in advance exactly which acts of behaviour we wish to record.

The Development of the Smiling
Response in Early Infancy

J. A. AMBROSE

The research I would like to discuss today is not directly about
observations of interaction between infant and mother. It is concerned specifically with the experimental study of one only of the
many behaviour patterns which become available for use by infants
during this interaction in the first eight months or so of life, that is,
the smiling response. The exact study of one single response at a
time, under experimental manipulation, has been criticized, especially
by psychoanalysts, as artificial and as missing out the infant as a
whole human being with his primitive thoughts and feelings. But
this limited microscopic approach is regarded as being an essential
supplement to the more macroscopic type of study in so far as we
are interested in establishing valid relationships between variations
in an infant's behaviour and changes in environmental and internal
factors, and so of unravelling the problem of how these factors
interact under natural conditions both to control an infant's behaviour in relation to his mother-figure and to determine the course
of development in each individual case. The smiling response in
particular was selected for study because it was felt to be one of the
various responses of an infant which clearly must perform a very
significant function in this relationship. Also, as a jumping-off point
in this area, it was felt to be an advantage to start with a response
whose strength is relatively easily measurable and whose occurrence
under natural conditions can be readily subject to some degree of
control.

With regard to control it was apparent from previous studies, viz. ✓
those by Kaila and Spitz[1], that smiling is elicited in the natural
environment only by a very specific type of stimulation, namely the

---

[1] Kaila, E. (1932) *Annales Univ. Aboensin. B. Humaniana*; Spitz, R., & Wolf
(1946) *Genet. Psychol. Monogr.* **34**, 57.

human face, at any rate from about five weeks of age; and that it remains subject to this external control for several months to come. These studies indicate that it is first elicited by the configurational property of any face and then after about the fifth month only by the faces of individuals who are not seen as strangers. More recently Ahrens has shown how the effectiveness of various elements of the face in contributing to the elicitation of smiling grows only gradually over these months, depending on the development of the infant's ability to fixate visually and to discriminate (Figure 29).[1]

These studies, however, were carried out largely on infants living in institutions separated from their mothers and, as the first analyses of the eliciting stimuli for smiling, they were concerned essentially only with whether the response did or did not occur to various different types of stimulation. The conception that responsiveness to external stimulation is much affected by the internal condition of the infant even in normal conditions is very little discussed; though it is acknowledged that the trends in smiling shown by the institution-alized infants studied probably occur somewhat later than with infants reared at home with their mothers. This one-sidedness re-sulted in little or no consideration being given to changes in response-strength: to measuring and explaining variations in this either between different individuals of the same age, or between the smiles of the same infant to a given stimulus on different occasions.

It was out of an interest in issues such as these that the results I wish to talk about now have come. The study of smiling in which I have been engaged, together with Mrs Bernstein, has been essentially of an exploratory kind. Only small numbers of infants have been used, at first infants living in institutions, and later also infants living at home with their mothers. The study was divided into three phases. In the first the aim was to see just how the smiling response varies once it has begun to occur in particular situations; and also how changes in other components of behaviour are related to these variations. This was done with institution infants because these provided greater initial freedom for exploration and experimental control. The second phase was concerned with how the smiling response changes over the weeks once it has become responsive to the face after about six weeks of age. The third phase involved a

[1] Reproduced by permission of the publishers from Ahrens, R. (1954) *Zeitschrift für experimentelle und angewandte Psychologie*, **2** (3), 445

comparison of this long-term trend of smiling of institution infants
with that of home infants.

From the outset it was known that one factor which causes variation in smiling during a social interaction is change in the external

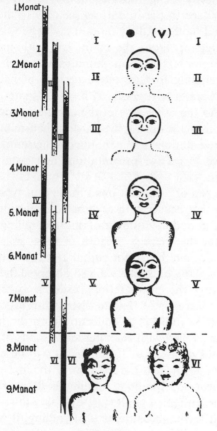

FIG. 29

*Necessary and sufficient conditions for
evoking smiling in infants up to eight
months*

stimulus situation, and especially in the face being smiled at. This
was clear from the work of Ahrens, which shows that the extent of the
face exposed, the expression on it, and whether it is still or moving,
do have an effect; although just how much effect at particular ages

181

he did not study in detail. It was obvious therefore that, if variations in smiling other than those due merely to change in external stimulation were to be shown up, it would be necessary to standardize as far as possible the stimulus situation used for eliciting smiling. This was done, not by using masks, but by myself, as the observer, presenting my face to the infants as they lay in their cots after the lunch-time feed, and standing motionless beside the cot at a given distance of four feet from the infant and without smiling at him. Using this more or less constant stimulus with each infant studied, I observed his smiling for successive periods of half a minute at a time. These were interspersed with half-minute intervals during which I went to the other side of the cubicle or room and recorded the observations made during the previous half-minute. Such a series of stimulus presentations was continued either until smiling died out or until twelve successive presentations had been made, i.e. over twelve minutes.

During this run of presentations I made four types of observation of the smiling that occurred in each half-minute: first the latency of the first smile, second the number of discrete smiling responses which occurred, third, the average breadth of these smiles as rated on a three-point scale, and fourth the cumulative total number of seconds during which smiling took place. I also observed the other behaviour occurring during the presentation, using a system of behaviour categories, but there is not time to discuss this aspect now.

What I propose to do is to concentrate on the results of the last two phases, concerned with the long-term trends of smiling over the first few months of life. But to do that it will be necessary to refer back from time to time to the findings of the first phase concerning the measurement and trends of smiling as it actually occurs at any particular time. In fact, I shall start by doing this.

With regard to the measurement of smiling, it was found in this first phase that the two most fruitful, as well as adequately reliable, measures were the cumulative duration of smiling per half-minute, referred to as smiling time per presentation, and the latency of the first smile in each presentation, referred to as smiling latency. These both have a large range and are highly sensitive to any changes which take place outside or inside the infant. They are related to each other, not directly, but in a special way that I will describe later, since it is of great interest for the interpretation of the long-term trends of smiling. The other two measures, rate of smiling and average breadth of smiling, were directly related to the smiling time measure and to each other, but as their range of variation was very much smaller they were not nearly so revealing. The measure smiling time per presentation was therefore used as the main indicator of the response-strength of smiling over a half-minute period.

The most general finding concerning this, in the standardized stimulus situation, was that over a run of such half-minute stimulus presentations smiling time nearly always commences at a relatively high level and, as the run proceeds, gradually declines until it either dies out or reaches a low level. This was found, for example, with

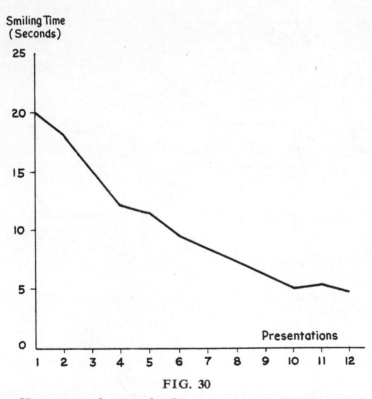

FIG. 30

Vincent curve of waning of smiling time per presentation over a run. Sample of ten institutionalized infants. Three runs carried out on each, on different days

183

a sample of ten institution infants between the ages of 13 and 26 weeks on each of whom three runs were carried out, each on different days. In all 30 runs response-strength waned in this way (Figure 30). This waning may be explained partly in terms of habituation, or a learning not to respond to a stimulus which is not reinforcing, which of course is one of the characteristics of the constant standard stimulus situation. I have evidence, however (Figure 31), that the

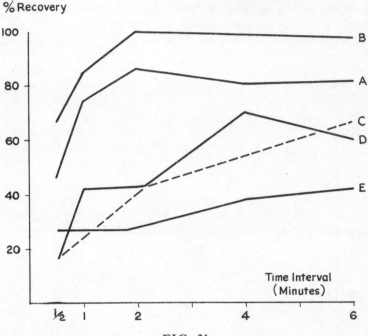

FIG. 31

Individual curves showing extent of recovery of smiling time with time interval for sample of five infants: smiling time per second series of five presentations as a percentage of that of first series, in relation to time interval between the two series. (Five infants: A, B, C, D and E)

waning is the result of at least two decremental processes: one of these is subject to rapid recovery and is probably response-specific, the other is subject to slow recovery and is probably stimulus-specific. Strictly speaking, according to the usage of Thorpe and Hinde, habituation refers only to the second of these.

184

This phenomenon of response-waning over a run provided the basis for measuring variations in the response-strength of smiling over a long-term period of weeks. For at the point of complete waning the infant has ceased to smile not because of any change in the external stimulus situation but because of changes that have gone on inside him. If the smiling time of each presentation in a run is summed, this provides a measure called smiling time per run. This indicates the total amount of smiling which the infant is able to manifest in the particular situation at the particular time. It is the variation in the values of this measure over the weeks between the second and eighth months of life that I now want to consider.

In the second phase of the study a cross-sectional approach was used with institution infants with the object of measuring the response-strength of smiling of infants at varying ages between 8 and 26 weeks. In order to be sure that the level of response-strength would be uninfluenced by an infant having seen me on any previous occasion I measured smiling time on the first occasion on which I saw him. Using a sample of 48 infants I divided these into groups of eight, at three-weekly age periods, 8-11 weeks, 11-14 weeks and so on up to 26 weeks. The smiling time for the first run on each infant was taken and the average value and scatter for each age-group then calculated. These results were (Figure 32) as follows. The youngest group showed no smiling at all. In the 11-14 week group hardly any infants smiled and the average smiling time per run was only 0·1 second. From that age-group upwards all smiled, and the average values were: in the 14-17 week group 9½ seconds; in the 17-20 week group a peak of 32½ seconds; in the 20-23 week group there was a decline to 29½ seconds; and in the 23-26 week group it was down to 10½ seconds. Another group in the 30-33 week age range, studied later, all showed no smiling whatever. There was a significant difference in group values between all groups except between the 17-20 week and 20-23 week groups. For institution infants, therefore, once smiling begins to occur in the experimental situation, it increases in response-strength over the weeks until it reaches a peak somewhere in the period 17 to 23 weeks, and then declines to reach a low level by 30 weeks.

In the third phase Mrs Bernstein set out primarily to compare the long-term trend of smiling of institution infants, in the experimental situation, with that shown by infants living at home with their mothers. For this purpose she used a longitudinal approach. Practical difficulties limited the number observed to four institutionalized infants and four home infants. Using her own face to elicit smiling, she adopted exactly the same method of standardized stimulation as had been used by me. This was carried out at weekly intervals

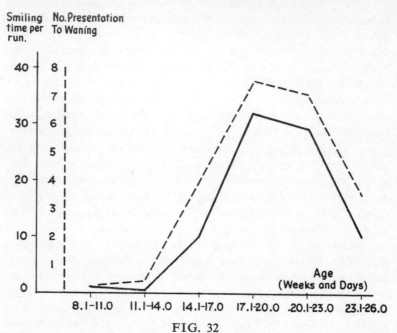

FIG. 32

Curve showing the average smiling time per first run for each sub-sample of eight institutionalized infants in three-week age ranges from eight weeks to twenty-six weeks. The dotted curve shows the average number of presentations to waning involved in the runs of each sub-sample

between the ages of 6 and 36 weeks for all except two institution infants who could not be continued beyond 20 weeks.

Before I describe the results of this comparison I want to refer briefly to two other comparisons that were also made with the data from this phase. One was between the trends of smiling of institution infants obtained in two different ways: the one obtained by Mrs Bernstein using a longitudinal method, the other obtained by me using a cross-sectional method. There is in fact no significant difference between the two: if anything her trend was a trifle earlier than mine. There are two implications of this similarity of trend, and of its timing at least up to about 20 weeks of age. Firstly little or no difference is made to the trend either by the difference in face stimulus used, i.e. the difference between Mrs Bernstein's face and mine. Secondly the trend is not affected by the fact that each infant saw Mrs Bernstein's face regularly every week whereas my face was seen by each infant only once. That is, the smiling time of a run in one week did not seem to be affected by the fact that the infant had both seen the eliciting stimulus the previous week and had, in the experimental situation, learned not to respond to it by smiling.

This is of interest in the light of a second comparison I must next mention. It was desired to get some idea of the age at which it does begin to make a difference to the response-strength whether or not the infant has learned not to respond to the eliciting stimulus the week before. While the sample composed of four home and four institution infants was, with the exceptions mentioned, studied from 6 to 36 weeks, two other samples of eight infants each were also studied in a similar way but commencing at a later age, one sample from 16 to 36 weeks, the other from 26 weeks to 36 weeks. Comparison was made between the trends of these last two samples with that of the 6 to 36 week sample over the equivalent age ranges (Figure 33). This shows that, while the trend of the group starting at 16 weeks is similar to the equivalent part of the trend of the 6 to 36 week group (i.e. from 16 weeks onward) the trend of the group starting at 26 weeks begins at a very much higher level than the equivalent part of the trend of the 6 to 36 week group. In other words, it appears that at 16 weeks it makes little or no difference to the response-strength of smiling if the infant has learned the week before not to respond to the eliciting stimulus. By 26 weeks of age, however, it seems to make a big difference. Whereas if runs have not been carried out in previous weeks response-strength is quite high, if they have been carried out previously, then response-strength is very much lower. The conclusion to be drawn from this is that at some time between the ages of 16 and 26 weeks the institution infant becomes influenced by the effects of smiling at a particular person for a period of as long as one week after the episode.

We will turn now to the main comparison of the long-term trends of smiling response-strength for the institution and the home infants.

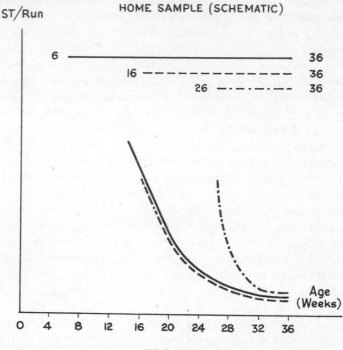

HOME SAMPLE (SCHEMATIC)

FIG. 33

Schematic curves indicating the general type of results being obtained in a study of the long-term weekly trend of smiling response-strength in three samples of 'home' infants smiling at the experimenter's face, commencing at three different ages

It was found that by and large the form of the trends was similar but that the equivalent characteristics of each trend occur significantly earlier in the case of the home sample than with the institution sample (Figures 34 and 35). Thus smiling in the experimental situation starts earlier with the home infants: for them it starts within the 6 to 10 week range compared with the 9 to 14 week range for the institution infants. The increase in response-strength reaches a peak earlier as well: whereas for the institution infants it occurs within the range 16 to 20 weeks, with the home infants it is between 11 and 14 weeks. Once this peak has been reached, in both groups response-strength declines to a low level. Thenceforth in individual

J. A. Ambrose

cases it either remains low or else recovers to some extent, though rarely to the level reached at the earlier peak.

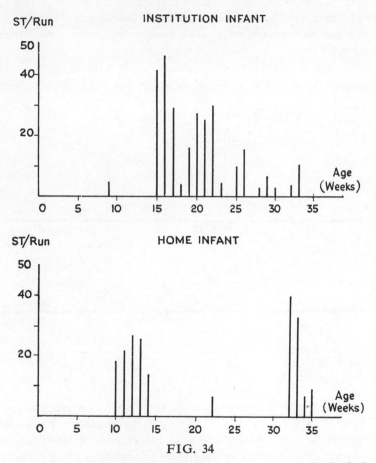

FIG. 34

Examples of long-term trends of smiling response-strength of individual infants responding to the face of the experimenter. Whereas the first peak of response-strength is reached at about sixteen weeks or later in institutionalized infants, it is reached significantly earlier at about thirteen weeks in home infants

Now how should we account for these findings, both the general trends and the differences shown in them between infants living in institutions and those living at home with their mothers? What light

189

do they throw on the processes affecting the smiling of infants in real-life situations over these months? In trying to answer such questions I must reiterate that the project has been a pilot one in which the numbers of infants studied has been small. Therefore at this stage any conclusion I shall discuss can be no more than tentative.

First, let us take the general increase in response-strength of smiling over the weeks, from the time when it first begins to occur

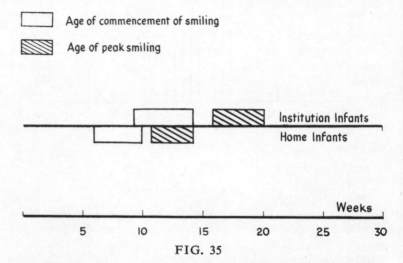

FIG. 35

Age-range of commencement of smiling and of peak response-strength in the experimental situation for samples of institution and home infants

in the experimental situation to the time when it reaches a peak (Figure 32). Light is thrown on this by an experiment by Brackbill.[1] Although her experiment was mainly concerned with the effects on the extinction of smiling on the degree of regularity of its previous reinforcement, it is the manner and the immediate effects of the reinforcement used which are of interest at the moment. Briefly, what she did was this. In the first part of the experiment, every time a particular infant smiled at her she picked him up, cuddled him, smiled back, and cooed at him. In the second part any smile made to her by the infant was given no such response by her; she just

[1] Brackbill, Y. (1958) 'Extinction of the smiling response in infants as a function of reinforcement schedule' *Child Devel.* **29**, 115.

remained still. The effect of her responding to the infants was to bring about a gradual increase in the response-strength of smiling, measured by her in terms of the rate of responding. The effect of her remaining unresponsive, however, was that the rate of smiling gradually declined until eventually the response died out. (She also found that smiling back, picking up the infant, etc., had a reinforcing effect even when carried out irregularly, e.g. at every fourth smile of the infant, and that with the infants treated in this way the response took much longer to extinguish.) It seems probable, therefore, that the increase in response-strength observed in both institution and home infants in our own experimental situation is to be explained in terms of such instrumental conditioning. This, of course, does not take place during the experiment itself but during the natural every-day life of the infant when he smiles at the mother-figure or figures who are caring for him. What is to be seen in the experimental situation are the effects of this natural reinforcement by the mother-figure being generalized on to the face of the experimenter. It seems that during this period of response-increase the faces of people other than the mother-figure are hardly or not at all discriminated by the infant, so that the expectations he learns in relation to the one face are generalized to all other faces. The peak to which the increasing trend of response-strength rises appears to mark the time at which such generalization ceases and discrimination begins.

What then is happening after the peak has been reached (at about 20 weeks with institution infants and about 13 weeks with home infants), when the trend of smiling in the experimental situation gradually declines? There is no reason to suppose that response-strength of smiling to the mother-figure begins to decline at this stage. Although it was not possible, using our particular method, to measure the response-strength of smiling to the mother-figure herself, repeated observations of infants smiling at the people who cared for them during this period indicated that, whether it be mother or nurses, the infants continued to smile at them with the same, if not greater, response-strength as in previous weeks. The decline of response-strength with increasing age in our experimental situation points unmistakably, therefore, to the infant being able to discriminate between the face of the experimenter and that of the mother-figure. Now, it might be thought that the decline in response-strength is due to the fact that once this discrimination begins the experimenter comes to be seen as a stranger. This view would accord with that of most previous observers who have attributed the lack of smiling to strangers from about five or six months of age to a fear of strangers. In my opinion, however, the falling-off of smiling occurring in our experiments is not necessarily due either to fear or to strangeness in all cases. Our evidence suggests that it is more complicated than this.

I have already mentioned Mrs Bernstein's finding that by 26 weeks, and probably before, the smiling of an infant at her is affected by his having learned not to respond to her the week previously. In other words, by this age, although she is discriminated from the mother-figure, she is not seen as a complete stranger. Yet in some cases the more weeks she continues to see the infant, and therefore the less strange she becomes, the less the infant smiles at her. What seems to be happening here is that, as the weekly runs are carried out, the process of learning not to respond to her each week comes to be associated specifically with her face, discriminated as a non-reinforcing one, so that eventually the infant may not smile at her at all even at the beginning of a run. The effect seems to be a long-term process of learning not to respond to a specific non-reinforcing stimulus. This is what I referred to earlier as habituation.

Nevertheless, there is evidence that the waning of the response during this age-period is not dependent only on a learning over the weeks that some particular face or person, viz. Mrs Bernstein, is non-reinforcing in her behaviour. Thus, in the sample observed by me cross-sectionally, the 23-26 week age-group showed a significantly much lower response-strength than did the next younger group aged 20-23 weeks. Since no infant of either group had seen me before, the lower response-strength cannot have been due to their having learned in previous weeks that I was a non-reinforcing stimulus. It appears, therefore, that any face which is discriminated as different from that of the mother-figure in this period elicits smiling at lower response-strength simply by virtue of the fact that it is different. If this is so, it rather suggests that the lower smiling response-strength to me in this period is not due solely to my failure to respond to the infants during a run by behaviour of the sort which Brackbill has shown to be reinforcing. Instead, it seems, the discrimination of a face as being not that of the mother-figure may in itself be non-reinforcing. If this is so, it raises the question of whether perhaps the mere sight of the face of his mother-figure or figures has a reinforcing effect, of itself. What I am suggesting is that the mere sight of the face of the mother-figure may come to have reinforcing effects for an infant simply because it has become familiar to him over the weeks and not just because it is associated with being smiled back at and picked up.

In view of the suggestions of previous observers about the fear of strangers, however, can we be sure that non-reinforcement is the only operative factor? It is here that the smiling-latency measure is able to throw some light. It indicates that, in the period we are now discussing, the falling-off of smiling response-strength during a run can be due to at least two types of factor. One is the building up of inhibitory potential within the response-system of smiling itself through non-reinforcement, as already discussed; the other is the development of interference by some incompatible response system, such as fear.

The basis for this conclusion can be seen in the detailed relations between smiling latency and smiling time per presentation as this wanes over a run of presentations. I said earlier, with reference to the first phase of our study of smiling, that in the grouped results the waning of smiling time appears smooth and continuous. There were, however, individual differences in the detailed manner in which this waning took place: while for some individuals it was smooth and continuous, or monotonic, for others it was irregular or non-monotonic. There were also individual differences between the types of irregularity which occurred. One of the most common was a sudden rapid decline in smiling time at the second or third presentation followed by some recovery at the presentation immediately following, after which waning then continued at a fairly constant rate. I refer to this as an initial valley (Figure 36). Now, those individuals who had monotonic curves of waning also showed a smiling latency which was very low and remained almost constant throughout the run. Those who had waning curves which were non-monotonic or irregular, on the other hand, had smiling latencies which were irregular also. Moreover, these two sorts of irregularity were inversely related to one another: for example, when an initial valley occurs there is also a marked rise in smiling latency. My interpretation of this is that any rise in smiling latency from a low level indicates that smiling is being interfered with by an incompatible response. This means that smiling that wanes smoothly with a constant low latency does so because of an inhibition stemming solely from within the response-system of smiling itself, whereas that which wanes irregularly and with irregular latency does so not only because of this type of inhibition but also because of inhibition arising from interference by one or more other responses. I have

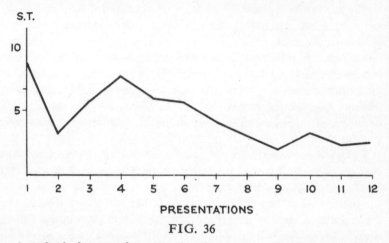

FIG. 36

An individual curve of waning of smiling time per presentation over a run showing types of irregularity of waning: the initial valley and the terminating peak

argued elsewhere[1] that these are likely to be responses either of fear or of curiosity or exploration.

There are two sorts of evidence that indicate that responses such as these which may interfere with the response of smiling are specifically associated with the making of a discrimination, that is, with the discovery in the experimental situation that my face is different from the one (or ones) which are familiar to the infant. One is that in the sample of institution infants observed by me there was a significantly greater frequency of runs showing non-monotonic waning and irregular latency after 18 weeks of age than before. And as I have implied earlier, this is approximately the age at which discrimination between faces may begin to occur in institutionalized

[1] University of London Ph.D. Thesis (1961).

infants. The other is that in runs which show non-monotonic waning and irregular latency, the irregularity most commonly commences just after the beginning of a run. This is the initial valley that I have already described. My interpretation of this is that as soon as the infant has had a chance to have a good look at me in the first presentation and also to discover that I don't respond in the way he has learned to expect, fear and/or curiosity set in. There are individual differences in the extent to which this occurs and also in the number of presentations over which such an incompatible response lasts.

Finally I would like to consider why it is that the peak smiling time per run is so much later for our samples of institution infants, at around 20 weeks, than it is for the sample of home infants, at around 13 weeks (Figures 34 and 35). Such consideration is made difficult by our lack of systematic knowledge about differences between maternal care and institutional care and their effects; as a result it is based at this stage mainly on two clinical impressions we have had regarding some of the differences. One of these is that in the home situation, from the time when smiling starts to occur to the face, it is both more frequently elicited and also reinforced at a higher rate. From this at least two consequences seem to follow. One is that with maternal care instrumental conditioning of smiling is likely to proceed at a faster rate than with institutional care and consequently the response-strength increases more rapidly. The other consequence is that with maternal care conditioning of the classical variety probably also takes place more rapidly than with institutional care, with the result that there is a more rapid learning of the characteristics of the face or faces which elicit smiling. If this is so, it means that the stage when relatively small details of the face are discriminated will be achieved earlier. As a result it may be expected that the discrimination of faces as being different from that of the mother-figure will occur sooner with home infants.

The second difference between home and institution infants which must also contribute to the difference in peak smiling age is the fact that institution infants usually have many mother-figures and not just one or two. Now, if it is the case that with home infants discrimination between different faces commences earlier, then at any given age after this they will have become much more familiar with one face. In so far as the strangeness of any face different from that

195

of the mother-figure is partly a function of the degree of familiarity of that of the mother-figure, then such a face is likely to elicit responses incompatible with smiling, such as fear or curiosity, more strongly than with institution infants. Mrs Bernstein has in fact found this to be the case, and so this seems to be a further reason for the earlier inhibition of smiling to people other than the mother-figure in the case of home infants.

The research was undertaken as part of the work of the Tavistock Child Development Research Unit, which is supported by the National Health Service and by grants from the Josiah Macy Junior Foundation, the Foundations' Fund for Research in Psychiatry and the Ford Foundation, to all of which our thanks are due.

Discussion following Paper by Mr Ambrose

BLAUVELT *It is always very difficult to control all the factors one wishes to when experimenting in the natural situation as opposed to the laboratory. To what extent did environment conditions vary from one testing session to another? Was the baby always in the same position in relation to the light and shade in the room?*

AMBROSE *Any given baby would always be in the same position in the room, but different babies would see different patterns of light and shade.*

GUNTHER *I'd like to ask about a quite different kind of control. Generally speaking, small children smile at other small children very readily, usually more than at adults. Now wouldn't this be a source of difference between your two groups? The home babies would probably be getting their reinforcement from quite different sources than the institution babies.*

AMBROSE *Yes, I am sure that is so. But I haven't done any, very necessary, systematic study of the differences between the effects of home and institutional care on smiling.*

FOSS *I suppose a problem involved here is the extent to which the baby discriminates between faces, or alternatively, generalizes. If it has habituated to one face, will it transfer the habituation to another smiling face?*

HINDE *You suggested that the home baby, because it sees so much of its mother, would discriminate strangers more easily and smile at them less. But one might well say the opposite – that it would generalize to strangers because it has seen so few of them that it has not had a chance to discriminate them.*

RHEINGOLD *Perhaps I could put this in another way? One view says that the more experience an organism has, the less different will the next experience be, and it is less likely to evoke a different response. The other view says that the more experience it has had the more able it will be to discriminate a new experience.*

GEWIRTZ *Of course, in nearly all situations there is discrimination going on all the time. What is generalization? A true generalization gradient is not a gradient at all but a horizontal line. That is, when a response is generalized to a new stimulus, it will be just as strong as to the original stimulus. And in conditioning this is usally to be found only in cases where the organism has not experienced stimuli different from the one it has been conditioned to. The so-called generalization gradients we are usually shown are those representing a response which is progressively weaker as the second stimulus is less like the first. These are really generalization – discrimination gradients, since the organism is clearly discriminating differences between stimuli. For this to happen it must have had previous experience of this range of stimuli. So Dr Hinde's point is a good one. The prediction might be that home-reared babies would smile more at strangers, not less.*

FOSS *But isn't it the case in conditioning that if you condition a response to a single note, say, the more experience with reinforcement the animal has to that single note, the less generalization there is to other notes? So that it looks as if discrimination has built up without experience of other notes.*

RHEINGOLD *This may not be so in an immature organism. You see, a mature organism may already have learnt to discriminate before the conditioning experiment was ever begun.*

AMBROSE *My view is that the baby will begin learning to discriminate various aspects of its mother's face even before smiling has begun. Sometimes this will be associated with rewards, at others with punishment, and yet at others with neutrality. The home infant's earlier discrimination of strangers is possible just because he has so much time with his mother-figure as compared with institution babies. The achievement of actually smiling at one whole, particular face seems to occur at about three months. By that time the baby will have had so much experience of discriminating aspects of faces that it will discriminate strangers more easily.*

FOSS *Perhaps the more important problem is: how does the baby learn that the various rewarding, punishing and neutral aspects of its mother's face in fact belong to one, whole face.*

GEWIRTZ *All that's necessary is that there should be some relatively invariant property of the mother to which all these aspects get conditioned. And that property need not be a configuration. It could be her voice for instance, or the colour of her face or hair.*

* * *

ROSENBLATT *I should like to ask you about a point in your method which may have influenced your results. As I understand it, observation periods of 30 seconds were used interspersed with periods of turning away from the baby to record results. Presumably the baby would sometimes still continue smiling after the moment when the observer turned away. I don't know if you have any data on the lengths of bouts of natural smiling, but I imagine they sometimes last longer than 30 seconds? And if you cut into a bout of smiling, isn't this likely to affect the latency of the responses of the next test?*

AMBROSE *This is an interesting point. I chose a 30-second period for two reasons. One was that I discovered that if I stood in front of the baby for five minutes, the bouts of smiling all occurred at the beginning, practically all within the first minute. There were smiles occurring later, but so infrequently that it would have been very time-consuming to wait to record them. The second reason was that a 30-second period is just about long enough to carry observations in one's head before recording them. I then chose a time interval for recording which would allow sufficient recovery of the response to occur for further observations to be made.*

ROSENBLATT *And therefore you believe the relationship between latency of smiling and response-strength was not in part a result of having interrupted previous bouts of smiling?*

AMBROSE *Yes I do, largely for reasons I couldn't include in this paper. There are many other behaviours of the baby which go with occurrence and non-occurrence of smiling. Things like leg and arm movements of a particular kind, sucking, where it's looking, and so on. Their incidence fits with the interpretation I have given of variations in latency.*

Discussion

ROSENBLATT *There is another point I should like to raise with reference to the question of habituation to a stimulus. Am I right in believing that, when your assistant, Mrs Bernstein, studied the same children day after day, she obtained the same sorts of results that you did when you were looking at several different children of varied ages, and that in both cases it was found that smiling reached a peak at roughly the same age?*

AMBROSE *That is right. I also studied one institutionalized infant over a period of weeks, and found the same sort of trend in smiling, with a peak at about 20 weeks of age.*

ROSENBLATT *Well, in that case would it be necessary to deal with long-term habituation to the observer as a stimulus? Apparently this one infant which saw you successively did not habituate to you.*

AMBROSE *I think it doesn't make much difference whether you use a longitudinal or cross-section method up to about 20 weeks of age with institution babies (13 weeks of age for home babies), that is until the peak in smiling. Then long-term habituation does play a part, and will show up in successive visits if you do not reward the child for smiling.*

FOSS *You said that both habituation and fear might cause the waning of smiling in the older baby. Could you elucidate this?*

AMBROSE *What I was trying to say was that some people, for instance Spitz, have said that after five or six months a fear of strangers develops, and this incompatible drive, fear, results in the disappearance of smiling. Now it seems to me that there is certainly a second factor contributing to waning, and that is habituation – learning not to smile at a face, presumably because the face is not rewarding, or does not lead to reward. There are large individual differences in the characteristics of the waning of the smile during social episodes after 20 weeks of age. In one extreme kind of infant the waning seems to be largely due to habituation; these infants learn not to respond to faces that are different from those with which they are most familiar. Whereas another extreme type of baby seems to develop a strong fear response to strangers, so that smiling, and other behaviour too, is inhibited by this. Most babies of course show a mixture of habituation and fear.*

* * *

ROSENBLATT *May I ask just one more question? You mentioned that*

199

a smile might evoke a smile. On the other hand you talked of a smile as being a reward for smiling.

AMBROSE *Brackbill's experiments suggest that smiling at an infant can be rewarding for the infant's own smiling.*

ROSENBLATT *But why do you need these two separate functions of smiling? Would it not be sufficient to say that a smile is either evoking or it is reinforcing, and leave it at that?*

AMBROSE *There's no doubt that, as soon as a baby is old enough to smile readily, one of the most adequate stimuli to evoke smiling is a face, and it is even more adequate if it is a smiling face. It looks as if an infant's smiling response is an unusual type of response in that an adult's smile can act both as a stimulus which evokes it and as a form of further stimulation which reinforces it.*

* * *

HINDE *Do you think that the events immediately preceding your tests may have influenced your results? Isn't it possible, for instance, that the home babies may have been picked up or attended to more recently than the institution babies, and this would affect their degree of smiling when you come to test them?*

AMBROSE *All I know is what was happening to the babies for a half-minute before testing began. I agree that we should know more about this. The nearest I got to standardizing things was to test the institution babies at about half an hour after their midday feed – which in fact varied from one to two o'clock. But conditions with the home babies must have been very variable.*

BERNSTEIN *Some of them might have just arrived back with the mother from her shopping. Others might just have been fed and played with. And the home might have had visitors before my arrival for testing, which would presumably have a marked effect. But for the last few minutes before testing began, the baby was just lying in its cot.*

AMBROSE *The data for recovery of smiling show that a smile would be elicited very soon after the baby had last been 'visited', but there is no doubt that the extent of smiling would depend on what had been happening to the baby ten minutes before.*

* * *

HINDE *You have described the way in which smiling at strangers reaches a peak, and then declines, giving place to negative reactions, while at the same time the baby will continue to smile at familiar*

200

caretakers. *Do you think the mechanics of this decrease in smiling is likely to be similar in home and institution babies?*

AMBROSE *I don't think they would be quite the same. The home baby has much more experience of one face. Since institution babies are likely to have a multiplicity of caretakers, generalization of the smiling response to strangers will die out more slowly.*

FOSS *One way of putting it is that the home babies have a much better opportunity of learning to discriminate two classes of faces – familiar and strange.*

RHEINGOLD *There may be another reason, which I have tried to suggest, why the institution babies go on smiling at strangers until they are older: that is that smiling is more likely to be rewarded capriciously for institution babies. And such 'variable-ratio reinforcement' is known to be effective in maintaining a response.*

Changes of Responsiveness
consequent upon Performance

Contribution by R. A. HINDE

As I told you, this is under protest, because I have not been working
in the field of mother-infant interaction recently, though I hope to
do so again shortly. However, it would, I think, be relevant to
mention briefly some experiments on changes in responsiveness
consequent upon performance, because I think the principles involved are relevant to the experimental procedures used in some of
the work which has been discussed.

First it must be emphasized that the effects of one response upon
a subsequent one are complex, and probably depend on a number of
different processes in the central nervous system. Thus in a series of
experiments the mobbing response normally given by chaffinches
to predators was elicited by models of an owl and a dog. By making
two presentations, either of the same stimulus repeated or of two
different stimuli in succession, it was possible to study the effect of
the response to one stimulus upon that to the next. By varying the
lengths of the initial presentation and the interval between presentations some progress could be made in analysing the various processes
underlying the changes in response-strength consequent upon performance. It was found that the initial presentation might cause an
increase or a decrease of the response on a subsequent occasion, the
nature and magnitude of the effect varying with the lengths of the
initial presentation and the rest interval, the similarity and relative
effectiveness of the two stimuli, the initial response strength, and
various other factors. It seems possible to classify the underlying
processes according to whether they cause an increase or decrease
in response strength, the extent to which they are specific to the
eliciting stimulus, and their decay period. Such results are important
here, I think, in that a number of the tests described depend on

203

successive presentations of the same stimulus in different situations, or of different stimuli in the same situation. The response in the second test may be influenced by the first test, and thus prove misleading about the factors under investigation.

The second point I would like to make is that these sorts of effects change with age and with the sort of environment in which the animal has lived, and I quote here an experiment by Margaret Vince of the Department of Psychology at Cambridge. She trained birds in a successive discrimination task, in which they were given one of two dishes, one with a black cover and the other with a white one. The dish with the white cover contained food, but the black one did not; the birds had to learn to take the white cover off and ignore the other one. She discusses her results in Pavlovian terms and regards the latency of the response to the empty cup as a measure of internal inhibition; you can call it experimental extinction or a decremental effect on the response to the empty cup or whatever you like. She found that this internal inhibition was less stable in young birds than in older birds. In other words, young birds which have learned not to respond to the empty cup one day, often forget about not responding the next day. And furthermore, she found that in birds reared in a deprived environment the internal inhibition was less stable than in those reared in a rich environment. She used birds brought up in three different environments – hand-reared birds brought up in restricted conditions inside a cage where they had little experience of the world; other birds which were reared by their own parents in a fairly large aviary, and third, birds which were reared in the wild and subsequently trapped. She found that the richer the environment, the more stable this internal inhibition was – that is, the less likely they were to forget that they must not respond to the empty cup.

I think this is possibly relevant to Tony's work where he measures the waning of the smiling response and uses as his criterion the total amount of smiling in a given time. It is possible that changes in the initial strength of the response and the rate at which it wanes will compensate for each other and not be revealed in a measure of total time smiling. I'm sure Tony checked this, but he did not mention it in his talk.

REFERENCES

HINDE, R. A. (1954) 'Factors governing the changes in strength of a partially inborn response, as shown by the mobbing behaviour of the chaffinch (*Fringilla coelebs*)' III *Proc. roy. Soc. B*, **159**, 398-420.

VINCE, M. A. (1960) 'Developmental changes in responsiveness in the Great Tit (*Parus major*)' *Behaviour* **15**, 219-243.

Discussion following Dr Hinde's Talk

AMBROSE *I have not looked into this last point. It is a very interesting hypothesis and does account for the fact that sometimes smiling response-strength does start very much higher than at other times and drops very much more quickly.*

HINDE *Can you correlate that with anything?*

AMBROSE *We might be able to, we probably have got data to do it.*

FOSS *I think probably the unstable inhibition also shows up in irregular waning curves, doesn't it?*

AMBROSE *Yes, it shows up there all right. But it is questionable whether the age range I am studying, between two months and five months, would provide the difference in age between young and old that Robert is talking about.*

HINDE *It is a pretty important age range for the development of faculties and I have no doubt that which age is important depends on what sorts of faculties.*

Well, if I can say one final thing about deprivation experiments. Dr Prechtl pointed out to me yesterday that deprivation can mean two different things. On the one hand one may be dealing with a homeostatic mechanism. This is the way in which 'deprivation' is commonly used in experiments on learning – an animal is deprived of food and it has some sort of homeostatic mechanism which causes it to show a certain type of behaviour which is likely to lead to food. On the other hand there is the sort of deprivation that one is talking about when one isolates an infant in an institution. Various factors present in the normal environment of the infant are absent, but the consequences cannot all be regarded as due to the functioning of a

205

homeostatic mechanism tending to end the deprivation. Rather, the organism/environment relations have been changed so that the organism develops along a different course – perhaps a pathological one.

BOWLBY *I am sure that both these situations obtain in the area which we are concerned with. In the early weeks and early months, it seems to me, it is an impoverishment of the general environment such that the ordinary relationships do not develop in the normal way. But after a certain age, one can say conservatively at five to six months, there is 'searching for' going on. For instance, Rudolph Schaffer's work[1] makes it clear that in healthy infants sent to hospital there's a sharp difference in behaviour before the age of 28 weeks and after it. I think both of these different meanings of the word 'deprivation' come into our work and need sorting out with the greatest care.*

HINDE *The last thing worth my while saying concerns this second class of deprivation in which we are dealing with development in an abnormal and impoverished environment. There are many different effects of development in an impoverished environment and I do not think anyone has made much progress in sorting them out. For instance, Dr Kaufman of Boston has recently been working at Cambridge on the 'cheeping' of chicks – a response call normally given by chicks when they are separated from their mother. He was interested to see what happened to this response when he reared his chicks in isolation from each other, instead of in a social group. If you rear chicks in a social group and then you take one of the chicks out and put it by itself, it cheeps at loss of social contact from the others. One might think that chicks reared in isolation, never having had experience of social contact, would not show this response. However, Dr Kaufman found that the response of chicks reared in isolation to being moved to the test pen depended very much on the precise conditions of rearing. Chicks isolated from each other in a hut in which there are people passing to and fro, noises around, and a fairly rich inanimate environment showed quite a different type of behaviour in the experimental situation from those which were isolated from each other in a soundproof room.*

That brings me to another point. When you isolate young

[1] Schaffer, H. R. (1958) *Brit. J. med. Psychol.* **31**, 174-183; Schaffer, H. R., & Callender (1959) *Pediatrics,* **24**, 528-539.

animals they normally always show a disorder of some sort in their fear responses, but it is very unpredictable which way this will go. Sometimes isolation leads to a great increase in the response strength to fear-provoking stimuli, but sometimes the animals become quite unresponsive to any kind of fear stimuli. This again seems to depend on the richness of the environment. One suspects, though I have absolutely no evidence for this, that there are psychological effects involved in the nature of the functioning of the adrenals. Perhaps if you bring animals up in a moderately impoverished environment, so that they get sufficient variety of stimuli to have fear responses elicited sometimes, then learning (habituation) may bring about a reduction in responsiveness, but if you bring them up in a very impoverished environment, it may be the adrenal mechanism which is responsible for an abnormally low responsiveness to fear-provoking stimuli.

ROSENBLATT *It is also true that whether an infant learns or does not learn to make discriminations in its early life may not matter at a later age, since this early learning may not be carried forward in later stages of development. That is, some early learning may be discrete and time-limited in its influence, important at the time it is present, but not of direct importance at later periods. In kittens olfactory discriminations that are important in early nest-returns are apparently not so important after vision appears and orientation occurs on a different basis. Even in the early period, Harlow has shown that very young monkeys can form discrete visual discriminations but that each successive discrimination is learned separately and the process of learning is not changed by the experience of having learned visual discrimination in a similar way.*

HARLOW *The usual way in which learning sets show up is when an animal progressively improves in discriminating between pairs of objects, one of which stands for food and the other does not. After a rhesus has been presented with many such pairs it will learn the trick, and get the discrimination right from the first or second attempt. There is positive transfer between such discrimination problems – as though the animal learns how to learn. But with the very young rhesus, although a single discrimination can be solved, there is none of this progressive improvement. The monkey seems not to profit by experience, so to speak, at least not in this kind of problem.*

BOWLBY *Which in a sense goes counter to much of what we assume –
that early learning does matter greatly in developing an organism's
repertoire of responding. If the early environment doesn't call for
discriminations, then the repertoire will be limited. Perhaps we need
much more information about the age ranges where transfer of
learning of various kinds is possible.*

BLAUVELT *It is my impression that the sustained attention that
mothers give their babies in the first few days postpartum is often
followed by quick ability to interact with the baby, responding to its
cues. Such interaction, initiated by the infant in this way, may be
followed by a long train of events in response to the baby and
stimulating it in varied ways. In the nursery, some of these cues
draw response from the nursing staff also. But here, the interaction
may last only briefly until the baby seems comfortable. Institution
babies may have much experience of these beginnings of interaction,
but babies at home have more experience of later stages of interaction.*

RHEINGOLD *On the other hand, for institution babies each sequence
of interaction is much less predictable, since several caretakers are
likely to be caring for the child. So that in this sense, of unpredict-
ability of events, the institution baby has a much more varied and
stimulating life.*

BOWLBY *The moral of all this seems to be that we should never say just
'deprived' about a baby, but 'deprived of what, at what time, and in
what conditions'. We must be more precise about this term.*

SUTHERLAND *Would I be right in interpreting Hinde as saying that an
early richness of experience leads to a building-up in the uncom-
mitted part (so to speak) of the nervous system of something which
can later act as an essential inhibitory force during learning
processes? Would this build up of inhibition assist later in the
general efficiency of the animal? I'm interested, because this whole
idea reminds me of the psychoanalytic concept of the Ego.*

HINDE *I don't think I would say that, because there would be dangers
of going on to say that there is a special part of the brain concerned
with inhibiting unreinforced responses – or something like that.
I would prefer to say that, if there is a richness of the environment,
inhibitory effects are more easily and stably produced.*

GEWIRTZ *I think the analysis of all this must be taken a stage further.
These studies have shown that there is a correlation between the*

richness of an animal's early environment and its later behaviour. But what exactly does the animal in a rich environment learn, which the deprived animals don't learn? One of the things that can happen is that they simply learn not to respond to a great variety of stimuli. On the other hand the availability of stimuli makes it possible that many of the stimuli become associated with responses, and the consequences of responses, that occur in their presence. So that the probability of a child behaving in a certain way will alter with the discriminable stimuli which are present at any given time. The mistake we are making is in assuming that the sheer availability of stimuli, in their number and duration, is sufficient in itself to make this difference in the reactions of the organism. As Robert Hinde has shown, stimuli may be plentifully available, yet the organism may not be responsive to them. This might be because the responses would occur only if they were maintained by a yet quite different set of stimuli. It seems to me that the analysis must be made in this kind of detail if the richness – deprivation dimension is going to be useful.

HINDE *I think if you go through the literature on deprivation you will find many reasons given to explain why an animal reared in an impoverished environment does not produce responses which a normal animal would show. There are cases where the response does not occur because the animal has not learned that the stimuli which are present are appropriate for eliciting the response; or the animal may have learned other responses which are in competition with those you are expecting; or perhaps it's just the motivation that's lacking. And I'm sure one could think of yet more explanations. If what you're saying is that one should analyse at each stage in the response what has gone wrong, then I agree with you.*

BLAUVELT *The results of deprivation in young children and animals are often defined in terms of changed capacity to interact appropriately with the individual who cares for them, and with their social groups. When the deprivation is maternal-infant separation, both mother and baby are deprived, and there may be double opportunity for changed behaviour. Our behaviour farm laboratory studies with goats and sheep indicate that when the behaviours of mother and young are not complementary, move out of phase so to speak, interaction may function in unexpected ways. This is also shown in Thelma Rowell's study of hamsters.*

ROWELL *The sort of thing which can go wrong is that the mother of a young litter may try to carry older pups to her nest, but they misinterpret her behaviour as an attack and run away. The result is that the female then attacks them. Or again, when her own litter is older, and the female finds a strange newborn pup in her cage, she may eat it.*

ROSENBLATT *We have a related observation of a female cat that had given birth to a litter which was immediately removed and placed with a foster mother for rearing. This mother lived without her kittens, but periodically one was presented to her and she acted somewhat maternal toward it without nursing it, of course. However, it occurred to us that presenting only a single kitten to this mother was unfair to the other mother cats that were rearing three or four kittens; we therefore presented her with three kittens, two weeks after parturition. While she could tolerate one kitteen, three were too much: she immediately went into a panic, attacked the kittens and was anything but maternal toward them. Thus the mother must be in continual contact with her young if she is to remain maternal toward them and no doubt the young exert a strong influence on the hormonal basis of maternal behaviour in the female.*

HUNTER *Perhaps this corresponds to the little girl who is ready to take care of one younger brother, but panics if presented with more than one?*

BOWLBY *One thing is plain. We need a much clearer idea of maternal behaviour and under what conditions it becomes operative. It seems probable that the female of any species is more prone to show maternal behaviour than the male. One question is, is this physiologically determined, or the result of identification, or both.*

PART IV

A Theoretical Approach

A Learning Analysis of the Effects of Normal Stimulation, Privation and Deprivation on the Acquisition of Social Motivation and Attachment*

JACOB L. GEWIRTZ

Note: Superior figures throughout the text refer to Notes in Appendix, p. 283.

Introduction

The problem I have set for this paper is to attempt an analysis of some key issues in the conceptualization of the processes of acquisition of *social motives* and *attachments* by man. At the same time, I shall outline a simple, plausible theory of the origins in human infancy of these behavior patterns. The theory emphasizes the availability of environmental stimuli, particularly from social sources, and the process of instrumental learning for the developing infant as well as for his caretakers. This process is inherent in the conditions of intensive, continuing interaction between the infant and his caretaking environment. At the same time, my analysis can provide considerable leverage upon the reciprocal issue of the various deficiency patterns of environmental stimulation in early life which effect aberrant outcomes in the social and attachment behaviors of the child. These deficiency patterns typically have been labelled emotional 'privation' and 'deprivation'.

* Many of the notions detailed in this paper were first advanced in a paper titled 'Social Deprivation and Dependency: A Learning Analysis' which I delivered at the 1957 annual conference of the American Psychological Association.

In recent years, I have had many useful and stimulating discussions with a number of colleagues on some of the issues I have raised in this paper. I wish particularly to acknowledge my debt to D. M. Baer (with whom I first began to explore the concept of childhood 'deprivation'), and to C. B. Ferster, Hava B. Gewirtz, M. Glanzer, L. Kohlberg and W. S. Verplanck. To each of them, many thanks.

213

The basic assumption of my analysis is that, in order to understand the development of human social motivation under both normal and deficiency conditions of stimulation, it is not sufficient simply to focus on which, or on how many, stimuli[1] are provided the infant. (Such an approach would seem to imply an homeostatic drive for stimuli, a model, as I will show, which cannot possibly order the phenomena in question.) Rather we must take account of the circumstances under which given stimuli are made available to him, and in particular, whether these stimuli are functional, and with his behaviors enter effective contingencies for learning.

I shall restrict myself to considering the earliest developmental characteristics of those behavior ('motivational') systems which appear to be directed solely toward bringing forth positive social responses (as reinforcing stimuli) from other persons and are not instrumental for the child in the setting. They are labelled attention, approval, affection and the like, and ordinarily would be classified under the heading of 'emotional dependence'. As yet, little is known about the antecedents, or the dimensions, of these behavior systems. I will also consider the possibility of extending the analysis of these systems to the case where initiations for such positive social responses (and other responses) are made primarily or uniquely to one other person, as is implied in the concept 'attachment' (relationship, bond or tie).

An analysis of these behavior organizations is fundamental for an understanding of the key controlling attributes ('motives') of human social life generally. Such an analysis promises a basis for bridging the wide gaps existing at present between three areas of knowledge: (1) basic learning and behavior concepts and principles; (2) theories of social development and action, such as psychoanalytic theory, with their rich concepts and traditions; and (3) the actual conditions of earliest parent-child interaction.

In recent years we have been witnessing the basis of a significant evolution of ideas in psychological thought. A number of research and conceptual advances have been made. At the same time, there has been an ever-deepening realization that our best conceptualizations of the properties of events which have traditionally fallen under the motivational rubric have been far from adequate. This conceptual weakness would apply not alone to the factors thought to control the complexities of human social behavior which concern

214

us here, but also to the motivational factors which control even the simplest behaviors of the lower animals. In this paper I shall attempt briefly to pull together some trends of current research and thinking in several areas of psychology. Some of these have not as yet been fully articulated into motivational thought. At the same time I shall examine ways in which these trends may be relevant to a conceptualization of the beginnings of human social motivation and attachment, under conditions of adequacy and deficiency both.

THE THEORY OF ACQUIRED DRIVE AND ATTACHMENT BASED ON PHYSIOLOGICAL NEED SATISFACTION

In recent years the theory most generally held for the acquisition of social motivation and attachment, particularly of the child's tie or bond to his caretaker-mother, has emphasized as its central concept the conditioned (generalized) reinforcing stimulus. This stimulus acquires and maintains its reinforcing value as a function of being paired with the unconditioned reinforcing stimuli that satisfy what, in conventional thought, are taken to be the biological needs of the child. The stimuli which can become conditioned reinforcers would include the attention or unique physical and behavioral appearance characteristics of the caretaker. The term 'drive' may be gratuitous in this formulation, since the behaviors of the child which are generally taken to reflect his motivation and attachment could be accounted for completely in terms of the control of the conditioned reinforcing stimuli operating.

This has been the theory of cathexis and object formation held by Freud (c.f. Freud, 1938; Fenichel, 1945) through the years (though 'sexual' stimuli would appear also to belong in the reinforcer class that can produce attachment for him) and by Anna Freud (1954). In its essentials, it has also been the standard learning approach to conditioned (derived, acquired, secondary) drives and attachments (e.g. Miller and Dollard, 1941; Mowrer and Kluckhohn, 1944; Dollard and Miller, 1950). These two theoretical approaches, with such different origins but with concepts basically very much alike, are appealingly simple, and because together they have been providing the focus for consideration of the issue of social motivation and attachment in the literature for a sufficiently long period, their main points are generally known; hence, I shall not dwell on the details of their similarity here.

In recent years, the adequacy of this theory has come to be questioned increasingly from different directions, as relevant research data have been accruing from diverse fields of inquiry. The results stemming from two distinct areas of thought and research are particularly relevant to the question how social motives and attachments are acquired.

From the field of *ethology* and animal behavior have come important research discoveries based on studies of lower species, unlearned (instinctual) species-specific behavior patterns, releasing stimuli, and the process of imprinting (see, e.g., Tinbergen, 1951; Bowlby, 1957; Hinde, 1959). It is on the basis of a careful evaluation of this literature, as well as of an extensive literature from child development, social learning, and psychoanalysis, that Bowlby (1958) has recently concluded that attachment is not formed through learning, as the traditional theory holds. Instead, he postulates that three instinctual (unlearned species-specific) behaviour patterns of the infant (sucking, clinging, and following), which become integrated, and become through learning focused on the mother, constitute the infant's attachment to her. At the same time, he assumes, the basis of the mother's reciprocal tie to her child is provided by her instinctual behaviors to him, which are released by stimuli provided by his crying and smiling.

And from diverse research during the past decade in the field of *learning* and performance, there have come two important realizations, that: (*a*) there may be potent reinforcing stimuli for both animal and human behavior which do not seem at all relevant to the organic needs of the organism; and (*b*) that the organism may be in active interaction with his environment even when those needs are satisfied. While otherwise continuous with the traditional learning approach to social motivation and attachment based on organic need satisfaction, the theory I am advancing in this paper takes account of these trends in recent psychological thought. Further, it attempts to reconcile this learning approach with ethological concepts generally, and in particular with Bowlby's provocative theory of attachment based on ethological principles.

Jacob L. Gewirtz

The Simplest Model for the Learning of Social Motivation and Attachment

From all that we have discovered to date, it is reasonable and profitable to conceive of social behavior as following general behavior laws, except for the fact that the relevant environment, particularly discriminative and reinforcing stimuli, is mediated by the behavior of other persons. On this basis, the investigation of human social behavior would proceed in the same way as would investigations (at the molar level) of all classes of behavior, by analysis of the controlling variables in the environment, both of the present and the past. At the same time, the concepts of learning and of adaptive behavior generally seem to provide a model that is simple and at the same time sufficiently flexible for ordering the complexities of the behavior patterns which characterize the development of social 'motivation' and attachment in the child, as functions of differences in the conditions of environmental stimulation. The changing capacities of the child in the earliest phases of life through developmental processes such as those which are indexed by the terms 'organismic maturation', species-specific behaviors, and the like, would only qualify this model, but would not change its essential features. Further, allowing for differences in language and in an occasional assumption, I think that most learning approaches to the issue would be rather similar at the molar level of analysis which is emphasized in this presentation.

The traditional concepts of Pavlovian conditioning seem minimally to apply to the learning of the varied and subtle behavior patterns, almost constantly and sometimes rapidly developing in complexity, which characterize social motivation and attachment in the early years of life. Rather, these emerging social behavior systems seem better (though not perfectly) ordered at present under the concepts of *instrumental* or *operant* learning and adaptive behavior (see, for example, Skinner, 1938, 1953; Keller and Schoenfeld, 1950; Verplanck, 1957; Ferster, 1958), with emphasis on the development and functioning of conditioned reinforcing stimuli. These concepts can order the case under which (the components of) unconditioned responses of the child which occur (either reflex or 'voluntary') are differentiated out and shaped (i.e. conditioned) by some of their immediate environmental consequences, which function as reinforcing stimuli. While occurring non-reflex responses are typically the ones conditioned under this case, it is also possible for components of what appear originally to be reflex behaviors, such as crying and sucking, to become conditioned on this basis by reinforcing stimuli in the environment. Thus, the child may cry initially only as a reflex response to hunger or to some other internal distress; but subsequently he may learn to cry also to bring his caretaker to him, to gain attention, or in other ways to manipulate his environment to attain what are for him reinforcing stimuli. It is in such processes as these that originally neutral stimuli provided by the reinforcing agent can acquire reinforcer value because of their key positions in behavior sequences leading to one or more important reinforcing stimuli for the child. It is on this basis of utility that the adaptive learning paradigm of instrumental conditioning is given a basic role in the analysis which is to follow.

The evoking stimulus, the discriminative (cue) stimulus which stands for the relevant environment controlling behavior, the instrumental or operant response, and the reinforcing stimulus which stands for the factors which sustain responses, are concepts which can facilitate the analysis and ordering of behavior which seems to be directed, that is, employed to attain some event from the environment. In this analysis we shall focus on the roles these concepts play for infant behavior.

THE EVOKING-AROUSING ROLE OF STIMULI FOR INFANT BEHAVIOR

One critical role of environmental stimuli would be to *evoke* or arouse the behavior of the infant. The biologically satisfied infant is quite the opposite of the passive and unresponsive being he is pictured to be by the widely held theories of Freud (e.g. Freud, 1938; Fenichel, 1945) on infant development and of need-reduction learning and behavior (e.g. Hull, 1943, 1952; Dollard and Miller, 1950). These theoretical approaches have for some time set the tone for thought on the topic of the impact of the environment on infant behavior. Rather, it seems far more reasonable to assume that the highly responsive infant is in active interaction with his environment, regularly and for extensive periods, even when his organic needs are satisfied. He would seem to behave as if he seeks stimuli which are ever more complex as he moves to each higher stage of development.

Indeed, the infant sometimes behaves as if he seeks to maximize stimulation.

From the earliest phases of life, even before any learning will have occurred for the infant, he will exhibit a great variety of behaviors, many of which will not appear to constitute simple responses to those environmental stimuli which can be identified by the observer. Such stimuli may be thought to make more probable, in the period immediately following their presentation, the subsequent occurrence of various free behaviors of the infant, and may be termed evoking stimuli. Unlike the highly specific eliciting stimulus for the unconditioned reflex response, the evoking stimulus is thought to operate by increasing the likelihood of occurrence, in the immediate setting, of such behavior as might be characterized by terms like active approach, reaching for, interest, curiosity, investigation, exploration. Alternatively, evoking stimuli may be thought to raise the infant's level of general responsiveness, i.e. to effect 'arousal'. When thus evoked, the behaviors of the infant would be in position to be differentiated and maintained by the potent reinforcing stimuli which can be provided by the environment's responses to the infant.[2]

(Another consequence of the availability to the infant of diverse unconditioned stimuli early in life will be considered in a later section dealing with the apparently complete habituation of what seem to be innate emotional responses.)

THE REINFORCING ROLE OF STIMULI IN CHILDHOOD SOCIAL LEARNING

Reinforcement is the basic process by which operant behavior is generated and maintained (i.e. learned): hence, it is central to any analysis of the effects of the environment on the developing individual from the earliest phases of life onward. Any stimulus event which, when it follows directly an identified response, systematically increases some index of that response (e.g. the rate of its occurrence, or its amplitude), is termed a *positive reinforcing stimulus*, or simply a positive reinforcer. In this context, then, for an analysis of a recurring behavior of the child, we would examine its effect on the environment to determine what consequence sustains its occurrence. *Unconditioned Reinforcing Stimuli* – It remains an empirical question which of the myriad stimuli in the infant's environment emerge at each stage of development to function as unconditioned (i.e.

'primary') positive reinforcers for his behavior, to effect learning. Even so, it would seem that a large variety of stimuli can function in this way,[3] in addition to those which are said to meet the 'organic needs' of the child, i.e. food, water and those provided by the removal of aversive cutaneous stimuli, such as involve pain, cold and wetness. These are the positive reinforcing stimuli which to date have been emphasized most in social learning theories; still they are only relatively well understood.

It is likely that the removal of aversive stimulation, unconditioned or conditioned, can provide some most potent positive reinforcers for children. Other potential unconditioned reinforcing stimuli, many perhaps even more potent than food and water, remain still to be studied for the case of earliest human learning. The most potent reinforcers initially are likely to be kinesthetic,[4] involving skin contact (as might be provided, for example, by the stroking of particular body areas) and warmth. (In this connection we recall that Freud [1905] speculated in his early writings on the 'sexual excitation and satisfaction' from his erotogenic zones that the infant may associate with the caretaker who provides it by stroking, kissing and rocking him.)

Further, Piaget's (e.g. 1952) observations of infant play and environmental manipulation, a variety of more recent researches on animals[5] and humans including Rheingold's current observational studies of infants (that are reported in this Conference), and my own current experiments on identifying both evoking stimuli and positive reinforcing stimuli which can effect instrumental learning in early infancy (which will be reported elsewhere) all suggest that the environmental consequences of infant behavior that can function as reinforcing stimuli are likely to be provided also by diverse tactile, olfactory, visual and auditory stimuli. These might include the simple answering responses of a caretaker to a child (as when she mimics, or answers him vocally or behaviorally [Rheingold, Gewirtz and Ross, 1959]. Finally, reinforcers may be provided by as yet incompletely understood dimensions of environmental change, such as changes in the direction of novelty or complexity (e.g. through approaching, reaching and manipulating, behavior we sometimes call 'curious' or 'exploratory').[6, 7]

Conditioned Reinforcing Stimuli – Stimuli which signal that a response, if emitted, could be followed by a functioning reinforcer (or simply precede in the chain of events leading to a reinforcing stimulus), are termed *discriminative* or *cue* stimuli. Such stimuli, originally neutral in reinforcer value, can acquired (conditioned) reinforcer value for the organism after having systematically preceded (or, more generally, after having been presented contiguously in time and space with) a functioning reinforcing stimulus, unconditioned *or* conditioned; and they would continue to function as reinforcing stimuli for as long as their relationship to the functioning reinforcing stimulus maintains.[8] The conditioned reinforcer functions, as it were, as a 'promise' that the reinforcer it stands for will follow. It was assumed earlier that a large variety of environmental stimuli will function as unconditioned reinforcers for the child, to transform cue stimuli originally neutral in reinforcement value (when made directly contingent upon behavior) into conditioned reinforcers, when paired systematically with them.

There exists further the possibility of pairing regularly a cue stimulus with more than one reinforcing stimulus (and of maintaining that pairing arrangement under typical caretaking conditions, which would preclude the extinction of the acquired reinforcer value of that stimulus). These events may be said to function as conditioned reinforcing stimuli because they represent occasions on which the probability is high that behaviors can be reinforced by many other reinforcing stimuli important to the organism, some of which would depend on particular deprivation conditions. Conditioned reinforcers so established would be powerful and effective under a wide range of conditions, and have been labeled *generalized* reinforcers by Skinner (1953). It is assumed that the effectiveness of such reinforcers would not be limited, for example, to the circumstances under which there are present the deprivation states that control the efficacy of some of the functioning reinforcing stimuli on which their acquisition of reinforcer value is based.[9]

The human infant is immature and helpless relatively longer than are the infants of other species. His helplessness requires that he receive care for a long time, making it possible relatively early for his approach and dependent behaviors to become conditioned by the reinforcing stimuli provided through that care. Moreover, the infant, who is most attractive to the average adult, will be responded to or 'answered' (e.g. through mimicry) even when he does not exhibit an apparent 'need', as when he has emitted a response which delights the adult, or at times simply because the caretaker thinks him to be so charming. Hence, on this basis also, a variety of the behaviors of the baby (which constitute the occasion for adult responding to him) will be reinforced, initially by the unconditioned reinforcers and later also by the conditioned reinforcers provided through those caretaker responses. These conditions lead to the acquisition of strong reinforcing power by discriminative stimuli provided by a caretaker, for example, her near presence, her attention, her approval, even her smile. These stimuli are incidental to but concomitant with the care she gives the child, or the other attentive responses she makes to him. Thus the stage is set very early for the conditioning of generalized reinforcers, and their growth would seem limited only by the capacities of the developing child at any given maturity level, for example, by his ability to discriminate stimuli and to relate them, as cues and as consequences, to his behavior.

Stimuli, like attention, approval and affection are conceived to function as basic generalized conditioned reinforcers. As they are supplied through the positive social responses of others, we would also label them *social* reinforcers. It is a basic assumption of this analysis that social life, particularly for the young child, is for the most part made up of behavior systems directed at, or maintained by, a variety of such conditioned reinforcers.

The effectiveness of these conditioned reinforcing stimuli would be relatively independent of the stimulus characteristics of the particular reinforcer dispensing caretaker, excepting, of course, that the particular stimulus complex which stands for, e.g. attention or approval, may include some stimulus elements unique to a particular caretaker (or interactor). (In a later section I shall consider in detail attachment learning, in which the unique appearance characteristics of another person acquire conditioned reinforcer value for the child.) Even so, through the process of *equivalence learning* the child will come to learn first, that the stimuli in the behavior complex characteristically denoting say, attention or approval, from a particular caretaker will not be uniform, and may vary in some component stimuli from occasion to occasion; and, second, that somewhat different stimulus complexes, as those provided by different reinforcing agents, are all functionally equivalent (as discriminative and reinforcing stimuli). Thus, for example, the child will learn that while approval from a caretaker typically involves her smile, it need not always; and that the stimulus complex denoting approval as provided by others will sometimes involve their smiling and sometimes not.

Conditioned generalized reinforcing stimuli like attention are usually provided contingent upon socially acceptable behaviors, that is, under circumstances in which the dispenser of those stimuli is cooperative. Sometimes, however, in cases where an environment provides a very low rate of such social reinforcement to a child, and there is no available alternative environmental context which will provide reinforcement for his behavior (as in the case of the young child whose reinforcing environment consists entirely of his parent, in the case of the institution child in the care of a few busy caretakers, or in the case of an older child in a restrictive classroom setting), the child may force the parent (or teacher) to provide attention (e.g. by deviating, annoying), even though the attention he thus receives might be mixed with contempt or punishment. Even when it is mixed with such negative reinforcement, in environments which control most of the child's behavior, attention can function as if it were a most potent positive reinforcing stimulus for such behavior.

Before proceeding, I wish to point out that I am here emphasizing primarily the positive functioning of reinforcing stimuli, both unconditioned and conditioned, and of attachments. Except as they enter into the analysis of emotional privation and deprivation in childhood which follows in a later section, a detailed examination of issues dealing with the actual or threatened removal of positive reinforcing stimuli and the conflict aspects of attachments must be put off to another occasion. In passing, we may observe in this connection that, based on its implications as a cue stimulus for the withholding of a variety of positive reinforcing stimuli important to the child which it not infrequently would precede, the withholding of generalized reinforcers by the caretaker-parent can be an unusually effective technique of aversive control for child behavior. This would be particularly so in cases where the caretaker controls most of the important reinforcing stimuli (e.g. food) which ordinarily maintain the behavior of the child and the child has access to no other reinforcing environments.[10] Still, there may be other behavioral consequences of employing frequently such techniques of control;

for example, in the extreme case, an over-dependent and emotionally insecure child might be the result.

Reinforcement and Development – The focus of any developmental analysis of instrumental learning generally, and social learning in particular, must be twofold: First, it must examine the development of reinforcing stimuli, either through organismic maturation or through their acquisition of reinforcer value as functions of the key roles they play in behavior chains important for the child. And, second, it must identify the increasingly complex behavior repertories of the child, acquired through continuous shaping by the emerging reinforcing stimuli, and limited only by his behavioral capacity at each maturational level. Clearly, these joint foci of a developmental analysis are not independent.

On the first point, some of the potential reinforcing stimuli listed in the immediately preceding sections, unconditioned and conditioned both, must surely exhibit the beginnings of their effectiveness at different times in the course of a child's development. Further, as the infant develops, some reinforcing stimuli may drop out functionally, to be superseded by others. Or their importance for him relative to other reinforcers may change. In this way, for example, food may decrease in reinforcing effectiveness relative to environmental change. Thus, also, it is likely that the essential nature of the event pattern which constitutes the reinforcing property of certain stimuli for the infant changes as he moves from one developmental level to the next. To illustrate, those stimulus changes which could be effected by rather gross movements of his hands or fingers (e.g. interfering with light sources), originally the most complex behaviors of which the infant was capable, might become increasingly less effective as reinforcing stimuli in the context of his increasingly complex response repertory. Thus, also, to give an illustration for conditioned social reinforcing stimuli, the reinforcer of attention may be superseded in importance by that of approval (to be attained from the caretaker-parent by successively more complex performances) in restricted settings in which the caretaker's approval response mediates the receipt by the young child of most of the reinforcing stimuli which are important for him.

On the second point, a reciprocal and not entirely independent focus of a developmental analysis would be on the identification of the increasingly complex behavior repertories developing in the child through the differential reinforcement by the emerging reinforcing stimuli (unconditioned and conditioned both) of successive approximations of more complex responses, limited at each stage only by the level of maturation reached by the child. Thus, whichever stimuli are reinforcing for an infant, his many responses in almost every developmental stage will be continuously shaped through differential reinforcement in the direction of more efficiently attaining such positive reinforcing stimuli (independent of the actions of caretakers), and these responses once shaped will be maintained by those reinforcers. At first, these performances will have only limited effects on the environment, but they will develop gradually through approximations of increasingly complex and efficient responses to have increasingly direct reinforcing effects.

THE IMPACT ON THE INFANT OF HIS MOTHER'S ATTENTION AND LOVE UNDER THE MODEL

The basic assumptions of the simple motivation-learning model have been presented. They point to the learning contingencies provided to the infant through the behaviors of his caretaking agency as the basis for the acquisition by him of patterns of social behavior and of social reinforcing stimuli. Hence, instead of focusing solely on the simple fact of which, how few, or how many stimuli of each class are provided to the infant, our analysis focuses also on whether the particular stimuli available to the infant are functional, and with his behaviors enter into effective contingencies for learning.

Specifically, the questions we must ask about the stimuli which are made available to the infant are the following: (a) Are potential eliciting, evoking, or reinforcing stimuli actually provided, and if they are, can they be discriminated by him? (b) If eliciting stimuli are provided for behaviors of the (presumably unlearned) emotional-startle complex, does the pattern of their occurrence allow the relatively complete habituation of those behaviors? (c) If potential evoking stimuli are provided, is it at a rate and in a pattern which increases the likelihood of occurrence of the behaviors they can effect? (d) If potential reinforcing stimuli are provided, are they made effectively (i.e. immediately) contingent upon his behaviors (particularly those which are defined as social by the reinforcing community) so that they might be conditioned? (e) Do these possible reinforcing stimuli follow effectively originally neutral cue stimuli

P   225

(e.g. a caretaker's attention or appearance), so that those cues might acquire reinforcer value (which could maintain for as long as such pairings continued)? And, lastly, (f) are there background conditions, contemporary or of the immediately preceding past (e.g. satiation for a stimulus repeatedly presented or fatigue of a response repeatedly employed), operating to qualify for him the effectiveness of the stimuli provided, in their evoking, reinforcing or cue roles?

In the section which follows, some focused implications of the assumptions of the learning model are spelled out for the case in which the infant receives from his mother-caretaker such stimulus qualities as attentive care, mothering, affection or love. (The term 'love' will stand for all such abstract stimulus qualities in the analysis which follows.)

1. Stimulus qualities like love can only be dispensed as physical stimuli; that is, they must be made up of visual and sound patterns, skin contact, odors and the like. Hence, from the earliest phases of life their component stimulus elements may operate as *unconditioned* eliciting (releasing), evoking, or reinforcing stimuli for diverse behaviors of the infant who receives love from his caretakers. Some eliciting stimuli would drop out functionally as the infant's behaviors to them become completely habituated.

2. Aside from the possibility that its component stimulus elements may provide unconditioned stimuli for his behaviors, a stimulus complex like love should have no meaning for the inexperienced infant except as it has been involved for him in effective learning contingencies.

3. Further, there appears to be no evidence for the proposition that the human infant is born into the world with built-in 'needs' for love, mothering, and the like, which, if frustrated, would lead to dire consequences for him. Rather, the infant's responsiveness, particularly to social stimuli, would be maintained primarily by unconditioned and conditioned reinforcing stimuli dispensed by people, and not by such innate 'needs'. Of course, the infant may not thrive in the relative absence of stimuli to support his behavior and learning. In addition, the discriminative stimuli dispensed through the 'loving' behavior of his caretakers, most of which were originally neutral, would acquire reinforcing value for him according to the conditioned generalized reinforcer paradigm.

4. On this basis, the stimulus complex involved in love would

differ in composition and value from child to child as a function of differences in the conditions of their early learning. Thus, when offered by different people, love stimuli could have quite different value for the young child, and might effect his behavior differentially (at least until equivalence learning occurs for him). But when offered to a child by his mother or primary caretaker, the stimulus complexes involved could be most adequate and potent as reinforcers. For then they would most likely be constituted of precisely those component stimuli which were involved in the original acquisition by the love complex of reinforcing value, and they would likely be offered at the same rate as well.

Thus, in behavior settings different from the one in which the child's basic learnings occurred, various stimulus complexes which are labelled love, and are intended to represent love for the child by the dispensing agency, would not operate as reinforcing stimuli simply because they have not been conditioned as such for him. Further, children would differ on the relative importance for each of them of such a conditioned reinforcing stimulus, on what constitutes a sufficient supply of it, and on the rate at which they have learned to receive it.

Hence, the possible consequences when such reinforcing stimuli as love are offered by different people in different settings could include the following: (*a*) the child of whom different aspects of a learned behavior are required to gain reinforcement initially might exhibit variations on that behavior, very likely at a more rapid rate; (*b*) the reinforcing agency might learn from the behavior of the child what the definitions of the appropriate reinforcing stimuli are for him, and then provide such stimuli; (*c*) the child might adjust to the new setting, acquiring new conditioned reinforcing stimuli which then could maintain his behavior there; (*d*) when his responses are not reinforced as was customary in a setting, the frustrated child might emit emotional behaviors of various sorts and intensities, as is often the case in early phases of experimental extinction; (*e*) if, in the new setting appropriate reinforcing stimuli are offered on a different schedule than usual, for instance, more frequently, the child might adjust to this fuller schedule and emit behavior at a correspondingly higher rate.

5. From the above emphasis on the differential meanings and consequences of conditioned reinforcing stimuli like love provided

in different settings, it follows that there would be no simple general formula for giving children 'enough' love or attention, as is implied in some sources as a remedy for the inadequacy (privation or deprivation) in earlier life of love and similar commodities.[11]

6. The very conditions of providing 'enough' love or attentive care to a child, if repeated sufficiently often and sufficiently clearly in given relationships to his behaviors, could constitute contingencies for entirely new learning, or for changes in existing habit systems (i.e. relearning or competing learning). Hence, paradoxical as it might appear under non-learning models for social motivation which seem to emphasize only the simple fact of the provision of stimuli like love, the conditions under which the stimulus commodities are provided could create in the child a *new* or changed 'need' (i.e. responsiveness) for those very stimuli, or for different ones. Further, assuming that the conditioned reinforcing stimulus class provided is actually the same as the one to which the child is most responsive (i.e. the one he 'needs' most), then in a new behavior setting, brought on perhaps by a move from one home to another or by entry into a therapeutic setting, different discriminative stimuli can come to control the occurrence of behaviors for that conditioned reinforcing stimulus class.

7. It follows that stimulus cues of no inherent reinforcer value, which are *un*correlated with subsequent opportunities for the child to receive or to be denied reinforcement, even when they are associated with intense affect responses (e.g. affection or anger) of a caretaker, will be ineffective in their impact on the child's behavior in so far as they cannot provide either positive or aversive control over it.

8. The final assumption of the learning model focuses the earlier assumptions, and is not independent of them. It provides the key to my analysis of the origins of social motivation and attachment which emphasizes stimulation provided through mother-infant interaction, as well as to the analysis of the consequences of emotional privation and deprivation with which this paper will conclude.

We have seen that the learning contingencies available to the child are critical for the development of response patterns and conditioned reinforcing stimuli characterizing social motivation and attachment. Hence, parents could provide efficient conditions for their child's social learning if their behavior were to fit in with (i.e. if they were to 'understand') the contingencies for optimal learning. This, indeed, they usually do not. Most parents, like most theorists in the area, seem to emphasize the importance alone of the simple fact of giving a commodity, like food or love (assumed to be indispensable for every child), and do not emphasize, in addition, the circumstance under which such stimulus events are provided through their behavior, and in particular, how, as potential discriminative and reinforcing stimuli, these events could relate to the child's behaviors. This latter emphasis would necessarily provide the basis for the greater part of the child's social learning.

Therefore, there may be a low correlation between such dispositional abstractions (for the behavior of parents) as would be labelled 'love', 'indifference' or 'rejection', and the learning contingencies provided by their behavior to their children. Thus, a parent labelled 'loving' by his community might dispense stimuli which would appear to him and to his community to indicate love and attentive care, but which may have little or no effect on his child's behavior; indeed, these might sometimes function as frustrating, even noxious stimuli. The result, in the extreme case, might be an inadequate, even asocial, child. On the other hand, the apparently indifferent parent in the eyes of his community may respond sparingly to his child, but the stimuli provided could enter with the child's behavior into effective contingencies for learning, constituting for him discriminative and positive reinforcing stimuli. The result of such interaction might be an acceptable, social child.

Factors which may Qualify the Learning Model

CONTEMPORARY BACKGROUND CONDITIONS MAY DETERMINE THE
EFFECTIVENESS OF STIMULI IN BEHAVIOR AND LEARNING

It is likely that the effectiveness of many (but not necessarily all) non-aversive stimulus events, in their roles as evoking or eliciting stimuli, as discriminative or cue stimuli, and as reinforcing stimuli for the awake infant, are governed by background[12] conditions which operate on him in the present or the immediate past. Among these conditions would be many of the classical determinants of 'attention' and 'motivation'. I am assuming here that these background conditions operate directly on stimulus factors to produce their effects in behavior, and not on response factors, as for example through fatigue or reactive inhibition.

229

In particular, the effectiveness of many reinforcing stimuli may be under the control of operations of deprivation (recovery from satiation or from short-term habituation) and of satiation (short-term habituation). These conditions determine the rate at which a stimulus is presented to an organism in the immediately preceding period (whether or not it is made contingent upon its behavior). That is, the effectiveness of each of these stimuli in its several roles will be raised after it is made unavailable to the organism for a sufficient period, and it will be lowered after it is made available to him in abundance for a sufficient period. Indeed, on this basis the possibility exists that food and water may be the exceptional rather than the typical stimuli, in the sense that for them we have relatively simple models (e.g. size of the stomach for food) for the physical constraints which would appear to limit their intake for an organism, and hence to control their reinforcing (and other stimulus) qualities (Gewirtz, 1959). For the more typical stimuli under deprivation-satiation control, the characters and limits of the operations, and the forms of the functions relating them to effects in behavior, must yet be determined.[13]

COMPLETE HABITUATION

The decrease in strength of a response through its repeated elicitation may be termed long-term or complete *habituation* when there is little or no subsequent recovery of response strength; for example, when the decreased likelihood of occurrence of the response holds for a long period. Sometimes recovery does not take place during the entire life of the organism. In the case of unlearned responses, this process apparently involves learning not to respond to a stimulus or stimulus class, which appears otherwise to be unimportant for the organism, through repeated occasions of responding to it (Humphrey, 1933; Thorpe, 1956). In an environment which provides a large variety of stimuli in abundance, the complete habituation of the responses elicited by many of these stimuli, particularly by intense sudden stimulation, e.g. involving noise, would be likely to occur early in an infant's life. Hence, for example, the components of the emotional, startle, defensive or aversive response complexes that are habituated-out would be unlikely to occur subsequently, and so would not be in position to be associated with, or reinforced by, stimuli in the infant's environment. Further, such infants, being less responsive to those disorganizing stimuli which would otherwise be without significance in their lives, would operate more freely in their environments; and as their early learning experiences would be encumbered minimally by competing unlearned emotional behaviors of the startle, fear and flight pattern, we would expect their developmental learnings to occur both more rapidly and in a wider sample of life settings.

Thus, also, habituation could be effected readily in cases where the infant is 'handled' frequently and intensively, as, for example, when he is held, rocked or fondled. His relaxation responses produced in this process would be incompatible with such emotional, startle or defense responses, or generally with responses which involve high levels of excitement, as might occur during the handling. Further, when a child is handled frequently and intensively, those of his emotional responses which occur will be associated with some of the regularly occurring familiar and conditioned reinforcing stimuli provided during the handling interaction. These responses would then not be likely to develop as regular aversive or defensive responses to, e.g. startle stimuli, and could habituate rapidly. This process would seem very much like that involved when a laboratory animal is 'tamed' by the intensive handling it receives from its trainer. That is, it ceases to respond emotionally or defensively to most of those incidental stimuli which regularly elicit such responses from untamed species mates. This habituation-as-taming process would not be inconsistent with Ribble's (1943, 1944) loosely stated contention that 'plentiful fondling' is critical for the infant's development.

For unlearned behaviors to startle and certain novel stimuli which are experienced by the infant, the process of habituation or taming probably operates through a relatively wide time period in early life. Even so, this process which provides the context of much of social learning would seem likely to play its most important role in the first six or eight months of the infant's life.[14] While the concept of the habituation of various 'unnecessary' behaviors of the child would seem to provide one of the keys for understanding the background conditions of his early social development, and can be put forth for that purpose even now, much more would need to be known about the young child before we might employ the concept in a more articulate way than I have done here.

THE PLACE OF SPECIES-SPECIFIC BEHAVIORS, SOCIAL RELEASERS,
AND DEVELOPMENTAL SEQUENCES IN A LEARNING APPROACH

Focused as it is on the instrumental learning contingencies that are provided by the temporal relationships prevailing between environmental stimuli and behaviors, the approach outlined in this paper is entirely open with respect to possible social releasing stimuli or species-specific behavior patterns, both for infants and for their caretakers. Indeed, it would be important for this theoretical approach (as for any other one) to take account of such facts as the following: that particular response sequences of human infants might be most likely to occur at a given developmental level, and more in some environmental contexts than in others; that some of these behaviors might be evoked with a high probability in a species when no apparent learning process has been involved; that the evocation of one given behavior would be a precondition for the evocation of another behavior, either on a concurrent or on a developmental-sequence basis; or that particular responses of the infant would uniformly elicit particular responses from the reinforcing environment, or function as reinforcers for those responses. Such information would be particularly important for a learning analysis, for it is the behavior which occurs with some frequency initially, whatever its basis, that would be in a position to be reinforced; and such behaviors would mediate the acquisition by the child of social response patterns and the conditioned reinforcing stimuli which control social motivation generally.

In this connection, we have noted that Bowlby (1958) believes that infant smiling and crying behaviors, as stimuli, function as social *releasers* of unlearned behavior patterns in mothers – agreeable behavior to smiling and behavior characterized by concern to crying. Regardless of whether these stimuli function as innate releasers, as Bowlby suggests, or whether they operate thus through a process of learning which caretakers have experienced uniformly, what would be important for a learning analysis of the process of parent-child interaction is the fact that the cessation of an infant's crying or the onset of his smiling may represent highly effective positive reinforcing stimuli for a caretaker-mother's behaviors that these events follow. Hence, these stimuli would determine the learning contingencies her behavior provides for the child, as well as the ways in which the mother, in turn, may be conditioned and generally controlled by the infant whose responses constitute these potent reinforcing stimuli for her behavior.

Infant Crying and Smiling as Releasing Stimuli – But now to move on to a more detailed consideration of Bowlby's assumption that the human infant's responses of crying and smiling provide innately determined releasing stimuli for adult caretaking behavior. This assumption would be difficult to validate, for it requires that we exercise a sufficient degree of control over the histories of human adults to rule out the possibility that the control exercised over caretaker behaviors by the stimuli provided by infant smiling and crying is not a function of experience and learning. Nevertheless, on the basis of an abundant literature which indicates that, relative to lower animals, a rather large proportion of human adult behavior systems would seem to be determined by experience and learning, it is at least equally plausible to assume that the possibly homogeneous aversion of parent-caretakers of both sexes for infant crying or their uniform delight with infant smiling could be products of learning. This learning may reflect the nearly universal value orientations placed on these behaviors of infants by world society. Or at a different level of analysis, the adult responses to infant crying and smiling might be determined by the learning involved in identification, either with one's own parent or with the succorant infant as a function of once having been one, as plausibly as they might be unlearned, innate responses to releasing stimuli for the species.

But there would seem to be an even more compelling reason for thinking that the effect on adult behavior of infant crying is not a simple function of its innate releaser qualities. It is a characteristic of the human that auditory stimuli with the physical properties of high pitch or loudness and long duration are noxious to him (a fact which would apply as well to stimuli of social origin). Hence, in so far as crying would often involve sounds high in pitch, loudness and duration, it should generally be noxious to the listener, who would then attempt in varying ways to terminate it. On this basis alone it would seem unnecessary to postulate the specific releasing effect of crying for caretaker behavior.

Other possible reasons for the reinforcing effectiveness of infant smiling and crying for caretaker behaviors follow: First, the human infant is, generally speaking, an enigma to his caretakers. Very much like an animal pet, he would be poorly understood. His smiling and crying (which come close to the responses of adults in similar contexts), can serve to communicate to them important information about his overall well-being which greatly concerns them. Thus, his crying may reflect many kinds of unknown problems which would have to be set right. Further, when the infant smiles at his caretaker, she may interpret it to mean that he likes and appreciates her, recognizes her, or prefers her to strangers – all of which could be rewarding to the adult involved. Smiling may also indicate to the adults that other interesting and charming reinforcing stimuli may be forthcoming, such as vocalizing or reaching for them (as objects). Crying, on the other hand, may suggest to the caretaker blame, or withdrawal of love.

Attachments

THE CHARACTERISTICS OF ATTACHMENTS

I have discussed in detail the possibility that the *general* characteristics of a caretaker or mother-figure, e.g. attention, incidental to the many reinforcing stimuli provided during the interaction of caretaking, could develop as conditioned generalized reinforcing stimuli for the child. This reasoning may be extended to the process underlying the development of attachments. But first, an important distinction must be made for this analysis: the fact that a child's behavior is employed 'for' (i.e. is maintained by) such conditioned generalized reinforcing stimuli as attention does not in itself constitute attachment behavior with reference to the person dispensing those stimuli. Rather, attachment behavior, and an attachment generally, would be involved only when a wide variety of behaviors of the child, including strong orientation, approach or following responses, are supported by the unique discriminative appearance characteristics (both physical and behavioral) of a particular ('object') person, functioning as generalized reinforcing stimuli. On this basis, it would seem reasonable to say that a child has an attachment to a particular person in cases where he consistently 'seeks' from that person various reinforcing stimuli, ranging from food through such conditioned reinforcers as attention or approval, even at such times as apparently identical stimulus events are available also, or only, from other persons.

This distinction between the functioning of conditioned generalized reinforcers based on the *general* characteristics shared by a mother-figure with many other caretakers and other persons and the *specific* appearance characteristics which are unique to the particular mother-figure would separate social *dependence* (unspecific) on people generally from an *attachment* to some particular person. I failed to emphasize this important distinction in an earlier focused analysis of social dependence (Gewirtz, 1956), as Sears *et al.* (1953) also did not do in their more general analysis of dependence. The distinction I emphasized in my earlier analysis was between 'instrumental' dependence and 'emotional' (i.e. social) dependence.[15]

As the basis for attachments, we can focus on two intimately correlated processes: the development of specific appearance characteristics of the parent-caretaker or mother-figure, and of that 'object' person in her entirety, as conditioned generalized reinforcing stimuli; and the development in the child's response repertoire of strong orientation, approach and following behaviors with respect to that mother-figure, which subsequently come to be maintained by those conditioned generalized reinforcing stimuli.

During the very early phases of life when the child is essentially helpless, and even afterwards when he becomes more self-sufficient, the caretaker-parent is the central medium providing almost all of the stimuli which are important to him, and which can serve as reinforcers when made contingent on his behaviors. On this basis, the near presence of the caretaker would be a precondition for those stimuli, whether or not they are offered as potential reinforcing stimuli. Hence, such aspects of the caretaker's physical appearance as hair color, facial features, type of smile, size, odor and such aspects of her behavioral appearance as gait and other characteristic movements would come to function as discriminative or controlling stimuli for the child's behavior. All of these stimuli occupy, in the chain of events leading to the unconditioned reinforcing stimuli dispensed through caretaking, even more remote positions than do the stimuli provided through attention or affection. Indeed, we may speak of the over-all appearance of the caretaker-figure as the major discriminative stimulus for reinforcement of the child, as it provides an occasion on which any of a large number of his responses is likely to be reinforced by any of a large number of potent reinforcing stimuli. That is, the sight of the parent becomes an occasion when the child's smiles, vocalizations or reaching responses are likely to

235

be reinforced by various reinforcers, as for example those provided through similar responses of the parent, or by being hugged, petted, kissed and the like. Thus, as we have seen earlier, the general and more specific characteristics of the caretaker's physical appearance both come to function as conditioned generalized reinforcing stimuli which can maintain many of the behaviors of the child under a great variety of conditions.

At the very same time as the conditioning of the appearance of the mother-figure as a generalized reinforcing stimulus is taking place, the child is learning directly to approach, to follow and to orient toward that parent-caretaker. At first, when the infant is completely helpless and immobile, it is likely that simple orientation and attention responses, such as following with its eyes or perhaps smiling, are reinforced by a variety of stimuli dispensed by this large object, the caretaker. Then, in keeping with the developing capacities of the child, diverse motor approach and following behaviors, as well as more general proximity responses which would preclude the caretaker from getting out of sight or of earshot, are reinforced by the large variety of stimulus events provided by that caretaker. (These responses would include clinging and following, which represent two of the three species-specific behavior patterns that Bowlby [1958] proposes as the basis of the attachment of the infant to his mother.)

In addition to acquiring attachments to their primary caretakers, children might also become attached on this basis to other adults, and even to children, with whom they have intensive contact over long periods. This is because these persons could also become, as objects, discriminative for a large variety of reinforcing stimuli which they may provide.[16] And these stimulus complexes functioning as reinforcing stimuli for the child would maintain a very large number of responses, including such response patterns as orientation to, moving toward, following, or being with, the attached person.

In this connection, Anna Freud and Dann (1951) present an unusual case that can serve to illustrate the possibility of children forming seemingly strong primary attachments to one another, apparently on the basis of the positive reinforcing stimuli provided through constant interaction (and the likelihood that each child was sometimes instrumental in removing conditioned negative reinforcing stimuli for some of the others), and minimally because of positive reinforcement provided through (mutual) caretaking. They

236

studied a group of six children, three to four years of age, whose caretakers, for years, never remained with them for long periods. These children, who provided the only constant companionship for each other from earliest life, were found to care greatly for, and to have formed very strong attachments to, each other, apparently caring for no other person or thing.

It is unlikely that the child of the typical family, during his earliest years, would develop more than a very few all-encompassing attachments in addition to the one to his constant caretaker-interactor, i.e. mother-figure. No other interacting person aside from the mother could have provided so many different and so many potent reinforcing stimuli to the child, contingent on so many of his behaviors, from the earliest learning occasions. Thus, the child's early and subsequent learning opportunities would have been most effective and uniform in so far as few competing learning opportunities, contingencies or conditioned responses would have been involved to retard them. Moreover, since the mother will have been involved in these learning experiences of the child from the very beginning, she will have molded them. Thus, she is likely to be highly sensitive to her child's responses, and as a simple continuation of those very learning experiences, she should provide to him at a most satisfactory rate precisely those discriminative and reinforcing stimuli which would constitute satisfactory support conditions for his behavior systems, social and nonsocial both.

SUBSTITUTE ATTACHMENTS

On this basis, if on no other, it would seem likely that in a normal family (or in similar contexts) a child will develop one all-pervasive attachment in early life to his mother-caretaker who mediates most of the important environmental consequences of his behaviors; and while he may independently develop attachments to other individuals on equivalence learning or other bases, these are likely to be less strong, and hence secondary. Still, the child may develop substitute or new attachments according to any one of several possible cases. Three such heuristic cases, which are not completely independent of each other, follow:

Substitute Attachments through Stimulus Generalization – According to the basic behavior principle of stimulus generalization, the child could exhibit to some other persons responses like those he exhibits to the object figure to whom he has his primary attachment, in proportion to the physical and behavioral similarity along relevant stimulus dimensions between those persons and the person to whom he is attached. And if reinforcing stimuli important for the child were forthcoming contingent upon these responses, a primary attachment could develop to that originally substitute person.

But while it would be theoretically possible alone on this basis of shared stimuli and similarity along very many relevant stimulus dimensions for the child to develop a satisfactory 'substitute' attachment to a new object person, in the sense that he would respond to that new person indistinguishably from the way he responded to the person to whom he was attached, this would seem a most unlikely happening: there are many dimensions in terms of which similarity could be gauged, and under ordinary circumstances it would seem a practical impossibility for such transfers in attachment to occur, except in those cases where the critical discriminative characteristics of the caretaker for the child are at the same time few and shared with many others in the population.

It would seem that one set of conditions under which substitute attachments might be facilitated on this basis (perhaps together with some of the other bases which are listed in the sections which follow) theoretically could occur in institutional settings. Under this case a caretaker-interactor, regularly present in the child's environment and to whom he has become attached, leaves him, and is replaced by an equally approachable caretaker who follows rather similar institutional routine and may dress similarly as well. On the basis of stimulus similarity, the child may exhibit similar behaviors to this new caretaker, who in the institutional setting would share a number of critical discriminative characteristics with the previous attached caretaker. And the somewhat different overall appearance of the substitute caretaker would develop conditioned reinforcer value for the child. This attachment process could be facilitated where the substitute caretaker-interactor adapts her behavior as necessary to provide in a consistent manner the eliciting, discriminative and reinforcing stimuli functionally important for the child (i.e. that could maintain his behavior), a possibility which is detailed in the next section.

Substitute Attachments through the Adjustment of the New Caretaker –
In general, it would seem more likely that substitute attachments

could be effected readily in a context in which a new (potential object) caretaker *learns* to provide (at the optimal rate) most of the discriminative and reinforcing stimuli already functionally important for the child, contingent on his responses with reference to such stimuli. I shall not consider in much detail the general principles governing the adjustment required by a move from a relatively stable environment to a new, very different environment, as when a child is separated from the adult to whom he has a primary attachment and is placed in the care of one (or perhaps more) different adults. (I shall attempt this in a later section on emotional deprivation – separation in childhood.) It is perhaps sufficient for our purpose here to note that, aside from the necessity for the child to adapt to the novel events in the new environment (which process in itself would for a period tend to disrupt his behavior patterns), the major principle governing the effects in the behavior of the child of such a change will be the degree of functional similarity between the former environment and the new one. Hence, whether or not the child's behavior repertory is under the close discriminative control of conditions in the earlier environment, if that environment is *similar* to the new one the child should adjust to the change with a minimum of difficulty. Further, this adjustment should be particularly easy for him when his behaviors are *not* under the close control of conditions in the earlier environment.

However, if a child's behavior repertory is under the close control of the earlier environment, and there is a shift to an environment that is very different, then the emission of the responses in his repertory under these new conditions will depend on the degree to which they are adapted to provide (*a*) appropriate cue and evoking stimuli, to make more likely the emission by the child of repertory behaviors and of novel behaviors as well, and (*b*) effective reinforcing stimuli which, when provided contingent on those behaviors, will condition them, making more likely their occurrence in the presence of the available cues.

When a new and very different environment does not adapt itself to the child whose behavior is under the close control of stimuli provided by his earlier envrionment, he may respond at a substantially reduced rate there. In cases in which an extremely different environment does not adjust itself to him, he may cease responding completely. This would be because in his earlier environment this child would have learned *not* to respond in the presence of certain discriminative stimuli. That is, most of the unique behaviors he has employed with invariable success to attain from his parent-caretaker reinforcers of unique importance to him would *never* have been reinforced there in the presence of those cue stimuli. (For example, particular children may have learned not to respond in the presence of complete strangers who appear occupied, or of peers.) Hence, this child would very likely be functionally without responses in stimulus contexts closely associated with non-reinforcement; and he may be hindered initially from adapting to them by learning responses appropriate in the changed circumstances in which he finds himself.

Ordinarily, however, the child is enabled to make a smooth transition to a new different environment. Cue and evoking stimuli are typically made available to him there, and reinforcing contingencies are so adjusted that almost any of his behaviors, particularly those high in his existing repertoire, might effect reinforcing consequences. Even so, under certain circumstances a pathological outcome may be the result. Let us consider the case of a child functioning in one environment only, whose response repertoire is under the close control of stimuli there, and in whose life an extreme environmental shift occurs. His response repertoire will be considerably 'weakened' by the shift, in the sense that he is more likely to emit simpler or 'primitive' behaviors relative to his earlier repertoire. If, for example, the reinforcing rules in the new environment are such that a child of his age must employ either more complex behaviors to attain reinforcement or behaviors which are entirely different from those the child has exhibited or is likely to exhibit, then conditions are such that his behaviors will never be reinforced. On this basis, there would be little chance for that child's responses to become fashioned into a substitute repertory comparable to the one he exhibited in the earlier environment. And, with the passage of time, there would be increasingly less likelihood that an adequate response repertory could develop for that child, as long as such reinforcement contingencies maintain.

Substitute Attachments through New Attachment Learning – It is also theoretically possible that the development of a substitute attachment might be facilitated for the young child through *new* learning, in which discriminative and conditioned generalized reinforcing stimuli and orienting, approach and following responses become conditioned for him with respect to a new caretaker-interactor. We have already taken note of the fact that, relative to recent or current learnings, earlier or earliest learnings are highly stable and resistant to change. As derivatives of all earlier learnings in that sector of the child's life, his attachment behavior pattern would be most strong and pervasive. Further, new learnings often would occur only with some difficulty under this case. For, the stronger the attachment, the more it would approach the case where the child's attachment response repertory is under the close control of the earlier environment (i.e. of stimuli provided by the attached person), which was considered in the immediately preceding section. On this basis, then, substitute attachments should develop only with considerable difficulty, except under very special conditions.

One set of conditions under which, theoretically, the development of substitute or new attachments might be facilitated on the basis of entirely new learning is that where the potential substitute figure mediates (i.e. controls) almost all the unconditioned and conditioned reinforcing stimuli which are important for the child (in that they maintain his ongoing behaviors). This would be very much like the situation in the first two or so years of a child's life, during which the parent-caretaker controls nearly all the important reinforcing stimuli for his behavior. But in this period also the child will be young enough still so that the reinforcing environment will reinforce the simple forms of behavior which very likely would be emitted by him when his response repertory is much weakened by a shift in the stimuli which control his behavior. Implicit in this limited environment (particularly after the child has experienced, as will all children surely, the accidental withholding or withdrawal of reinforcing stimuli) is the possibility that the caretaker can withhold at will nearly all of the reinforcers she provides; and the threatened or actual withholding of generalized reinforcing stimuli can be a most potent control technique. However, as the child grows he gains access to reinforcing environments outside his home; hence, the problem of actual or possible loss of reinforcement at home could become increasingly less critical for him.

By this reasoning, new generalized reinforcing stimuli and orienting, approach and following responses, which provide another basis for (substitute) attachments, should be established more readily and strongly in early life in relatively closed environments, where the new caretaker-parent mediates nearly all the important reinforcing stimuli for the child's behavior, than when the child has access to reinforcement from other environments, as when he is older. Further, this outcome might be expected even when the child has had an earlier attachment, in that the learning conditions outlined should be sufficiently effective in the closed environment to override the limitations inherent in competing against the earliest attachment learning. This theoretical possibility seems compatible with the observation of Anna Freud and Burlingham (1944) that substitute attachments of children for new parent-caretakers can develop rapidly, as when opportunity is offered through formation of artificial family groups.

Attachments formed by Children in Institutions – The attachment outcome for the child raised in the typical institution on the theoretical bases outlined may conceivably be quite similar to that for the child reared in the typical family household.[17] If in the first year or two of life as one of a relatively small group the child is in the constant care of one (or possibly two, but very few in all) caretaker-interactors, then very possibly a close, primary attachment could develop between that child and one or two of his caretakers. In addition, less focal, secondary attachments might well develop among some of the children in an institution group on the basis of reinforcing stimuli dispensed independently of caretaking.

The attachment outcome might take a different form in an institution where many caretaker-interactors share responsibility for the young children in their care, are rotated frequently and have in their individual charge relatively many children. There, the child would not seem likely to develop a strong attachment to any of his caretakers. That is, the child might develop an attachment of a sort, but one unspecific as to object, to a generalized caretaker as it were, based on only those stimulus characteristics caretakers in an institution share in common. This is the same as saying that a child reared under the institutional conditions outlined is likely to become responsive only to conditioned generalized reinforcing stimuli, and particularly to attention but perhaps also to approval, which would be *independent* of the unique physical and behavioral stimulus characteristics of his particular reinforcing agents. Functioning as conditioned generalized reinforcing stimuli, such unique stimuli are the very essence of attachments. It is important to note that the behavior outcome discussed in this section would not be limited to the type of institution setting described, but might occur also in those family settings which involve similar caretaking conditions.[18]

Attachments among peers would seem possible particularly in cases where children, who do not compete for the parent-caretaker as would siblings, are constantly together from early life onward, though we would not expect such relationships to be as powerful as the attachment of a child to his caretaker-parent. This would be because peers are not likely to mediate nearly all the important environmental consequences of the child's behavior through such a long period in early life as parent-caretakers typically do. Still, as was earlier illustrated by the case reported by Anna Freud and Dann, attachments among peers occasionally are found which appear to be as strong as the typical attachment of the child to its mother.

ATTACHMENT LEARNING AND IMPRINTING

Imprinting – For a short while following hatching, the young of many species of birds and fowl will tend to follow closely, at a more or less constant distance, almost any moving object to which they are exposed. The exposure of the young of these species to such an object (usually sound-emitting) during a brief and apparently critical period in the early hours of life (e.g. within the first 54 hours for one species of fowl [Jaynes, 1957], and within the first 32 hours for another [Hess, 1959]), can establish these behaviors in great strength. This provides the opportunity for them to repeat frequently the initially occurring but weak response of following, and otherwise to orient to characteristics of that object. The process involved was first described systematically by Spalding (1873) and William James (1890). On the basis of the rapidity with which it occurs in many avian species, and its stability once established, the process was given the name 'imprinting' by Lorenz (1935). The response complex of following (and remaining near) the object is typically employed as the index of the strength of imprinting. Once established, this complex is highly resistant to change.

The object imprinted is usually the originally nearby mother, but could also be an organism of a different species, or even an originally 'inanimate' object, for example, one that is made to move (Jaynes, 1956, 1957) or that is associated with visual flicker (James, 1959).

243

Subsequently, even if the imprinted object is not a member of its own species, the young bird will show a preference for its company. He will usually attempt to mate with, and otherwise respond to, members of the object class in the same manner as other members of its own species ordinarily respond toward one another.

The following-behavior then seems to become restricted to the class of objects initially followed, with respect to which the animal remains tame, by a somewhat later appearing incompatible tendency which may be species-specific (Hess, 1959). This tendency is to fear and to flee from objects which were never followed. These objects would be unfamiliar ones, of the same general class as initially excited following as well as of all other classes. This later process would be incompatible with responding to those objects which had not been followed prior to the appearance of the fear and flight behavior pattern in the early life of the organism. Hence, its onset would effectively define the end of the 'critical' period for imprinting in the particular species.

Recent preliminary observations have suggested that imprinting may occur also in some mammals, for example in the guinea pig (Gray, 1958; Hess, 1959). In this context, it is small wonder that imprinting has provided a provocative model to some for the development of early, strong and lasting human attachments, such as that between the child and his mother (e.g. Gray, 1958; Scott, 1960).
The Formation of Primary Relationships by Social Animals – Comparative studies with mammals and other species by Scott, his associates, and others (summarized by Scott, 1960) have been interpreted by him to indicate that imprinting is but a special case of the process of the formation of primary (positive) social relationships with a group of familiar individuals which develop early in the history of all gregarious species. As with birds which imprint there may be critical periods during which such 'primary socialization' takes place with the times and behavioral mechanisms involved differing from species to species. Soon afterwards, there come into play 'behavioral mechanisms' involving fear and avoidance of unfamiliar individuals of the same or different species, which seem to prevent social relationships from developing with strange animals or with other species.

Scott illustrates this process with the typical infant dog (puppy) who begins to attend to stimuli in his environment at about three weeks of age. While his initial response to strange persons or animals is fear and avoidance, the puppy cannot locomote far; hence, if a person maintains 'contact' with him for even a short time, the puppy's fear and avoidance responses disappear (i.e. they habituate completely), and he 'develops' an attachment to and tolerance for that individual, Thus, the puppy establishes positive relationships on the basis of contact alone. Scott reports that some puppies will develop an attachment to their handler even when he punishes their social advances to him. Further, experiments with puppies raised together, but away from humans, indicate generally that a puppy can be taken out of the group and quickly made into a pet until about seven weeks of age, when it may take several days before he will recover from his initial fear. Scott reports that puppies taken at 12 weeks or older never become completely satisfactory pets, and always show more attachment to dogs than to humans.

Scott's report of the formation of primary social relationships in animal species other than birds and fowl, and the protection of these relationships by initial fear and avoidance behaviors to strangers, provides gross descriptive data for mammals which dovetail nicely with the imprinting findings on birds. However, there is missing from Scott's description a focused analysis of the details of the process of acquisition of the primary social relationship by the animal (for example, what does the 'contact' variable actually involve?), just as there has been lacking a focused analysis of the imprinting process itself in many of the writings on imprinting in birds. It is hoped that the attachment learning analysis which is presented in this paper would provide some useful leads for filling in the details of the two apparently overlapping processes, the acquisition of the primary social relationship that Scott has surveyed, and imprinting.

Imprinting as Learning – Several writers, including Fabricius (1951), Hinde, Thorpe and Vince (1956), Jaynes (1956) and Verplanck (1955) in his incisive analysis, have suggested that rather than a special process, imprinting may represent simply a form of early stimulus-response learning occurring under rather special conditions. This line of reasoning is compatible with existing research, but must await more definitive empirical data before it can stand as conclusive. It runs very much as follows: an initially weak though relatively probable response in the unlearned repertory of the inexperienced young animal, to approach and follow discriminable (usually moving) objects, is strengthened by repetition, presumably by a variety of the potent reinforcing stimuli which are provided contingent on the instrumental behaviors which comprise the locomotor act of following in that environmental context. These reinforcing stimuli could include visual stimulus changes as might be produced by movement or rapid fluctuations in illumination, auditory changes and the like.[19] (Indeed, it is possible also, as H. James [1959] speculates, that the visual stimuli provided by the movement of the object may on an unconditioned basis regularly elicit or release and maintain approach and following behaviors in young organisms of many species.)

On this basis, learning should be effected rather quickly for the young organism, as the response complex of following would be frequently and potently reinforced in a relatively short time span, in the complete absence of competing response systems. Thus, the organism's initial response of following an object: (*a*) would become strong very early in his life; (*b*) would be protected from change by the subsequent onset of the fear-flight behavior pattern to strange objects; (*c*) would be the earliest basis of subsequent learnings in this behavior sector, which would constitute an ever-increasing number with time; and (*d*) for these reasons, the response could be pervasive, and for all purposes, permanent and irreversible, even though the essentials involved are learning processes, and, hence, should be extinguishable under the proper conditions.

Imprinting and Human Attachment Learning – It is hardly surprising that the assumptions advanced in the earlier sections as one of the bases of attachment learning, specifically the learning of orientation, approach and following responses with respect to an object person, are very much those which would receive emphasis in any attempt to approach imprinting as a possible instance of early learning. For, the orientation-following behaviors are generic, as are the learning assumptions employed. When applied to the case of earliest human learning, these assumptions can account for its primacy and pervasiveness in so far as earliest learning determines later behavior and learning. Even so, the imprinting literature highlights two important issues which are relevant to the analysis of human attachment learning presented in this paper; one relates to the nature of the infant response pattern which would mediate attachment learning; and the other relates to the appearance of a fear of strangers pattern which might limit and protect from change the behavior pattern learned.

Our point of departure for the first issue is provided by Verplanck and Gray. We note that Verplanck (1955) has speculated that imprinting (as a learning phenomenon) should be found in all social species whose young are capable of locomotion shortly after birth (or hatching), which would preclude the possibility of human imprinting. On the other hand, Gray (1958) has proposed a theory of human imprinting independent of learning in which, between the ages of one and one-half and six months, the smiling response functions in the imprinting of the human infant as does the response of following in the imprinting of lower animals.

Alternatively, the model for human attachment learning favored in this paper emphasizes that the human infant in the early months of life, incapable of the locomotion in space of which many of the lower species are capable, still can make a variety of responses with respect to attending persons in his vicinity which would seem to be functionally equivalent to the response of following in some avian species. In effect, these responses of the infant could control the behaviors of the caretaker so as functionally to keep her near by, at a more or less constant distance, while she is 'followed' and interacted with by the infant. Thus, many of the infant's behaviors, e.g., his smiling and laughter (whether or not they function as releasing stimuli), his crying, his glances and stares, his reaching and manipulating, his vocalizing, can bring in reply reinforcing responses from the near by caretaker and others, at the same time as they can serve to reinforce the behaviors made to the infant by those attending persons, while keeping them in the immediate vicinity. In this way, the infant and his caretaker could often engage in long sequences of interaction.

These and similar behaviors of the infant constitute functionally orientation, approach and following responses with respect to the stimuli provided by persons in his perceptual field. In this way, very much as would seem to be the case for the young bird being imprinted whose sequences of following behavior, under an instrumental learning model, are assumed to bring about conditions of reinforcement, these orienting and following behaviors of the human infant seem capable of being reinforced by a variety of potential, potent reinforcing stimuli. Hence, neither a locomotor response, like following which Verplanck proposed, nor necessarily the response of smiling which Gray proposed, would be critical for the attachment learning model outlined in the paper. Rather, any response class that consistently maintains contact in the reinforcing interchange early in life with another individual could mediate attachment learning, which imprinting seems to represent. On this basis, the key concept for such learning is not that of following (or locomoting); rather it is that of maintaining contact with the object, in the sense that responses made with respect to the (stimuli provided by the) object would be reinforced frequently and potently during a relatively short-time span early in the life of the young infant, who then would not be encumbered by competing response tendencies based on earlier learnings.

We have seen that Gray has suggested that the smile of the infant functions as the behavior that mediates human imprinting. And, as is detailed elsewhere in this paper, Bowlby has proposed that the infant's smile is a key releasing stimulus which activates the mother's positive behavior to her infant, and serves to bind her reciprocally to him. The reader will recall that it is also my point in this paper that the infant's smile is very likely to be a key response in mother-infant interaction. However, I have proposed a different two-phase mechanism for its operation: First, the smile can gain for the infant a variety of potent reinforcing stimuli from the mother; hence, various incidental stimuli provided, for example, by the appearance of the mother, can acquire reinforcer value, which would be an important basis for the acquisition by the infant of an attachment to his mother. And, second, her infant's smile can function as a most potent reinforcing stimulus for a mother's behaviors with reference to the child, causing them to be maintained, and providing a basis for the acquisition of her attachment to him.

Our speculations about the possible conditions for learning that may be the basis for the special process of imprinting also highlights a second important issue for the attachment learning model proposed; it involves the emergence of fear and avoidance responses to objects of the same general class as those which were followed earlier but which were never followed themselves, as well as to other classes of strange objects. These fear responses, incompatible as they are with the responses of following, effectively serve to define the end of a critical period for imprinting and to limit the imprinting that has taken place (to objects of the specific class as the one earlier followed), as well as effectively to prevent imprinting from occurring if it had not already taken place.

The literature contains reports (e.g. Bridges, 1932; Shirley, 1933; Gesell and Thompson, 1934; Spitz, 1950) that many infants raised in normal homes, typically after five or six months of age, begin to show avoidance-withdrawal responses, sometimes together with intense emotional reactions as well as crying and whimpering, to unfamiliar adults ('strangers'), and to unfamiliar animals or objects. Thus, Shirley (1933) reports that about 25 per cent of the 25 infants she visited regularly for observations from birth onward exhibited fear of her for the first time during the fifth or sixth month. And Gesell and Thompson (1934) who observed 107 infants at monthly intervals during the first year of life, found that, by the fourth month, 92 per cent of the infants 'knew' their mothers and 56 per cent 'sobered' at strangers. At the same time, the incidence of 'acceptance' of strangers by the infants started dropping regularly from 80 per cent in the fourth month to 18 per cent in the twelfth month, with a peak at close to 60 per cent in the five to seven month interval; and the incidence of 'withdrawing' from strangers by the infants started rising from 19 per cent in the fourth month to a peak close to 50 per cent in the 8 to 11 month interval, after which it dropped to below 30 per cent at 12 months. From what we can glean from such data as these, the 'fear of strangers' pattern is not to be found in all infants, nor does it appear in the same degree in the infants in which it is found. Further, it is likely that this pattern would be found more in infants who are cared for by very few persons and have had little experience with other persons or objects, than in infants who are sometimes cared for by others and from the beginning have had wide experience with people, animals, and objects. In this connection, we note that Hebb (1958a), who with Riesen (1943) observed that this fear of the strange may occur in the infant chimpanzee beginning at four months of age, thinks that it is produced by events that combine the familiar with the unfamiliar, and not by the unfamiliar event alone.

Nevertheless, this fear response pattern in human infants would seem homologous to the pattern occurring in animals of some species. We have seen that in species which imprint, fear-avoidance responses to unfamiliar objects (i.e. those which had not elicited following before the appearance of fear, including objects of the same general class as those followed) appear in most animals after an apparently homogeneous period of fearless approach to or following of objects. These avoidance behaviors, incompatible with the social responses of approach and following, can effectively limit the opportunity for additional imprinting experiences.

If we take this not infrequent 'fear of strangers' pattern in human infants to be independent of the quality of the attachment which develops between an infant and its caretaker(s) and to be relatively resistant to modification, then, as in the case of animal species which imprint, this avoidance response pattern would be incompatible with any one of the responses constituting the pattern of orienting to, approaching and following, in short with exhibiting attachment behavior to potential object persons. Hence, avoidance behaviors would restrict those attachment responses to the object or object class to which they were made earlier. In this way, new attachment(s) for the infant would be precluded, and earlier ones protected from change.

THE LEARNING OF ATTACHMENT TO THEIR INFANTS BY PARENTS

It would seem useful at this juncture to focus briefly on two most important reciprocal learning processes; (*a*) the conditioning of the behaviors of his parent-caretaker *by* the infant, and (*b*) the learning of attachment to their infants by these parents. These two processes, reciprocal to the learning of the infant, are only too seldom treated in analyses of the early social growth of the infant. Yet they would be equally as important as are the processes of infant conditioning and attachment learning for an understanding of mother-infant interaction, which, after all, must involve a two-sided learning process.

Infants can provide most adults with almost endless entertainment and pleasure, even while requiring continual dedication and care. A variety of the responses of the infant, such as his smiling, laughter, vocalizing (many of which delight adults), can provide potent positive reinforcing stimuli for the behaviors of his parents (and of adults of both sexes generally) when made contingent upon them. And by the same token, the crying responses of the infant can be highly aversive for his parents and adults generally; hence, stimuli provided by the cessation of the infant's crying can function also as very potent positive reinforcing stimuli for adult behavior.

Jacob L. Gewirtz

Let me illustrate this point. The typical infant may shape (through differential reinforcement) and subsequently control a variety of the behaviors of his caretaker-parents, for example, those of their responses which are aimed at getting the infant to emit such vocal responses as 'goo goo' or 'da da', to smile, or to stop crying. In this way, the young child can effect gradual changes in the behavior of his caretakers, in the direction of responses likely maximally to produce effects in the child's own behavior which are reinforcing for the parents' behavior. Thus, the 'foolish' movements of facial grimaces and body contortions, and the similarly 'foolish' sounds of baby talk, all may enter gradually the parents' behavior repertories as functions of the differential reinforcement provided by their infants. Of course, some of these foolish responses, especially the vocalizations we call 'baby talk', may at first have been made by the caretaker simply as repetitions, or in mimicry, of the 'cute' responses of the baby.

On this basis, also, an attachment to the infant in her charge may be acquired by the parent-caretaker on the same conditioned reinforcer basis that is involved in the acquisition of the child's attachment to its parent. But because she does not depend on her infant for all the stimuli which are important for her, and because she would already have other attachments, the attachment she forms to her infant would not be as all-encompassing and strong as would be the attachment to her formed by her infant.

Is 'Mother Love' a Learned Attachment? – While on the subject of the attachment learning of parents to their infants, it is tempting to explore briefly the possibility that what is called a mother's 'love' for her infant may itself be the product of learning, perhaps even of recent origin in the very caretaking setting in which it is seen for the first time. In the context of our assumptions about the acquisition of attachments, it is plausible to propose that the love of a human mother for her child (and parent love generally) for the most part may be a product of learning. In preceding sections we have noted the possibility that many infant behaviors, for instance his smiles, may provide some most potent positive reinforcing stimuli for the behaviors of caretaker-mothers. (The observer who is not sensitive to this process of control by the infant of those behaviors of his mother which could be judged to reflect 'warmth' might conclude from their occurrence that the mother being observed was 'warm' from the beginning.) We have noted also that some of these stimuli might be reinforcing for the mother on an unconditioned basis and that others might have acquired reinforcer value through earlier learning, like that involved in the process of female sex-typing.

However, it is possible that the special attachment behavior pattern of a caretaker-mother which would be taken to reflect 'mother love' is learned rapidly under highly favorable conditions which exist in the very interaction setting in which the pattern appears for the first time, that is, after the infant is placed in her care. If a caretaker who is well-intentioned and otherwise unencumbered in her caretaking role has the primary responsibility for the care and well-being of an infant for a length of time, she could become increasingly committed to him through a process of learning. She would be continually and unambivalently attentive to the infant. While witnessing the successive developmental stages through which the infant's behavior systems move, and being charmed and otherwise reinforced by his changing behaviors at each level, the caretaker would come to appreciate small, subtle changes in these behaviors as well as to become capable of being reinforced by ever-increasing numbers of them. On this basis, and because of the increasingly complex reinforcing stimuli for her behavior that the infant can dispense at successive points in his development, the caretaker could become increasingly committed to, and fond of, the infant in her care.

The process can be supported by the complementary process wherein the caretaker-mother may come to think herself appreciated and loved by the infant. The infant early exhibits a non-specific responsiveness, particularly delightful smiles, to a large variety of stimulus objects and persons in his immediate environment. Thus, he will often respond and smile to his caretaker-mother, who spends a good deal of time with him and provides complex and interesting stimuli. Her infant's smiles and other positive responses may be appreciated by the caretaker-mother, not as reflex responses that are initially made to almost anything or anyone, but as 'loving' smiles made uniquely to her, which would be most flattering and could function as potent reinforcing stimuli to modify and control her behaviors. (This attachment process would be expedited in cases where the biological mother of the infant holds the belief that there is a natural affinity between an infant and its true mother.) A process

Jacob L. Gewirtz

of this type would, of course, strengthen the attachment of a parent-caretaker to her infant even before the infant actually becomes motivationally dependent on her, after which his smiles and other responses will actually be made more selectively to her than to other non-social or social stimuli.

It is in some such way as this, with the evergrowing parent commitment to her infant, and the potent reinforcers the child can provide for caretaker behavior through some of its 'cute, interesting, flattering, and changing' behaviors, that the caretaker-parent very early in the life of her infant can rapidly acquire an attachment to him – she acquires, as some would put it, 'a mother's love for her child'.

THE RELATIONSHIP OF THE THEORY OF ATTACHMENT LEARNING
PROPOSED TO BOWLBY'S ETHOLOGICAL THEORY

Bowlby (1958) has recently questioned the adequacy of the 'Secondary Drive' theory of the child's tie to his mother, which according to both standard social learning theory (e.g. Dollard and Miller, 1950; Mowrer and Kluckhohn, 1944) and Freud's psychoanalytic theory (Freud, 1905, 1938; Anna Freud, 1954) has been based on the association of physiological need satisfaction with stimulus characteristics of the caretaker-mother.

In its place Bowlby has proposed a theory which holds that the attachment exhibited by the child to his mother is made up of a number of unlearned component 'species-specific behavior patterns' (he also labels them 'instinctual responses') which mature at different times and develop at different rates during the child's first year, and which are originally independent of each other. Of those he believes he can identify, the ones in which the infant is the active partner and which require only a limited reciprocal response from the mother are: (*a*) sucking, (*b*) clinging and (*c*) following (i.e. not letting her out of sight or earshot). In the normal course of development, these three behavior patterns become integrated, focused through learning on a single mother-figure, and form the basis for attachment behavior which reflects the bond or tie of the infant to his mother. The remaining two behavior patterns, in which the infant's responses provide releasing stimuli to activate or evoke the unlearned instinctual behavior patterns of the mother, and to bind her reciprocally to the child, are: (*d*) crying and (*e*) smiling.

The theory of attachment learning outlined in this paper is open with respect to the identities of the stimuli involved in the formation of attachment, in particular, the reinforcing stimuli likely to condition aspects of the mother-figure as conditioned reinforcing stimuli. It is open as well with respect to the attachment behaviors (e.g. orientation, approach and following responses) which come to be maintained by those conditioned reinforcing stimuli. Hence, releasing stimuli or species-specific behavior patterns, both in infant and mother, might be involved. Further, this learning model does emphasize the potential reinforcing efficacy of stimuli provided through skin and other contacts (e.g. through clinging), the response of following (e.g. environmental changes) and the like. Hence, on these issues, Bowlby's ethological theory would complement the learning approach proposed, and would seem completely compatible with it, given the current level of specificity of both theories.

It is to be regretted that Bowlby does not present the conditions for the emergence of attachment under his theory in sufficient detail to show decisively that learning is *not* involved in any important way in the development of attachment; also, he leaves unclarified the developmental mechanism involved. An abundant research literature exists which suggests the countless ways in which learning (in the sense of a systematic increase in the incidence of an identified behavior in a setting) readily can be effected by recurring environmental conditions. And mother-infant interaction, particularly in the settings indexed by the species-specific infant behaviors which Bowlby emphasizes, namely sucking, clinging, following, crying and smiling, very likely involves an abundance of such recurring conditions for learning. Thus, for example, a variety of behaviors and sequences must surely be involved in the complex act of clinging. When these occur, they would be in position to become conditioned by the potent reinforcing stimuli (e.g. those provided through physical contact) that a mother can provide contingent upon them. And these reinforcing stimuli could, at the same time, establish those appearance characteristics of the mother which have become discriminative for reinforcment as conditioned reinforcing stimuli, in this way providing the basis for attachment learning.

Indeed, regardless of how correct or fruitful Bowlby's theory of attachment (or a learning theory for that matter) ultimately proves to be, by highlighting some of the key settings for interaction between mother and infant, the assumptions of his theory provide guide lines which point to conditioning possibilities that a learning approach to attachment must ultimately detail. Hence, it would be most important for a learning approach such as ours to give close attention to the details of all settings for intensive interaction between infant and parent in early life, including those emphasized by Bowlby as the basis of his ethological theory of attachment, but including many other interaction settings as well. For it is a fundamental assumption of this approach that, while some such unlearned behavior systems of the human infant or of his mother might well be involved as Bowlby suggests, they would but set the stage (or the limits) for the social motivation and attachment learning of the infant, and of its mother, but are not likely in themselves to produce, or even to represent, attachment.

Emotional Deprivation in Childhood

My main attempt up to this point has been to present an analysis of the different roles environmental stimulus events can play in early human development, and to relate some of the antecedent conditions such stimuli can provide to selected consequences in children's behavior. The view I have taken is that there is every reason to assume that early social motivational development consists for the most part of learnings by the child that his behaviors can serve instrumentally to bring about reinforcing events (unconditioned and conditioned both) as consequences; and that this process is always qualified by earlier learnings and the everchanging, maturing capacities of the child. Thus, much of what I have presented thus far has been general and simple, but may fall short of doing justice to the full richness of the social life which is at issue.

For the purpose of illustrating further the utility of some of the elementary conceptions I have presented, as well as to make a plausible explanatory case for some of the conditions that may be operating, I shall in this last section extend the conceptualization outlined earlier in the paper to the beginnings of an analysis of a most important issue of social development in childhood, namely emotional 'deprivation' ('privation'). My approach to this important area of emphasis will be different from the way it has been conceptualized to date. Further, it will necessarily be incomplete on some of the issues it will touch; for, there will surely be other consequences of conditions of emotional deprivation than those I deal with here, as well as alternative theoretical models that could order the conditions and their results. However, this effort seems worth while, for at the very least it may point to gaps in current approaches to the problem which must be filled in. And, of course, it may stimulate the development of alternative, and better, conceptual schemes.

This deprivation analysis will be general and could stand independent of those special issues and assumptions I have considered in earlier sections of this paper. For example, with regard to the nature or identities of positive reinforcing stimuli, my analysis could contain the traditional 'physiological need' reinforcement case, in which food, water and the removal of noxious stimuli are taken to be the key positive reinforcing stimuli operating, but it could contain also the case which includes in addition stimulus change reinforcers, as well as the possibility proposed that almost *any* stimulus which is discriminable to the organism might function as a reinforcer of behavior. Of course, the analysis becomes most powerful for this case of childhood deprivation if emphasis is placed on two assumptions: that a large variety of stimulus events, unrelated to the organic needs of the infant, may function as evoking and reinforcing stimuli; and that the effectiveness of stimuli in their various roles may be a function of background conditions operating for the infant in the present and immediate past, such as short-term deprivation and satiation for those stimuli.

THE BACKGROUND

In recent years, due primarily to the work of Levy (1937), Bakwin (1942, 1949), Bowlby (1940, 1944, 1951), Goldfarb (e.g. 1945a, 1945b, 1955), Ribble (1943, 1944) and Spitz (1945, 1946a, 1946b, 1949, 1954), the concept of 'deprivation' has occupied a central role in formulations which have attempted to relate deficiency conditions in early childhood, as antecedents, to aberrations in later behavior patterns of the children. (As the concept of 'privation' has been used interchangeably with that of 'deprivation' in the literature, I shall employ only the latter term in this brief survey of background factors). Generally, the concept of deprivation seems to involve the assumption that, if young children receive an inadequate supply of essential stimuli from their caretaking environments, this could lead to atypical patterns of responsiveness to non-social stimuli, of adaptive behavior generally, as well as of social and attachment behaviors. These behavior patterns would include developmental arrest, depression and apathy in the younger children; and in others, no requirements, or apparently insatiable, and sometimes indiscriminate ones, for the deficient commodities (e.g. attention, affection) and a limited capacity for relationships.

Reports from many and diverse sources seem to concur on a general deprivation syndrome in the presence of apparently adequate physical care. However, it is not a simple matter, when examining this deprivation literature, to evaluate either the nature of the assumptions advanced or the reliability of the observations reported (though Bowlby [1951] has made an admirable beginning in this regard): For one, the operational meaning of the concept, or, for that matter, of the entire theoretical formulations of which it is the key, is never stated explicitly. Thus, we are unclear about the identities of the required or indispensable stimulus commodities, of what constitutes an adequate supply of them, about the importance of a relationship with a caretaking person, and similar issues. Further, there has tended to be ambiguity in the reporting of the behavioral effects of assumed conditions of deprivation. And, lastly, it is not always clear which set of antecedent deprivation conditions leads to which resultant deviant behavior pattern.

Still, those who have theorized about child development under deficiency conditions would seem to be emphasizing, in itself, the simple fact of giving stimuli to infants (and sometimes also the frequency or duration of the stimuli offered). Such stimuli would appear to be included as (are involved in) 'love' and 'emotional interchange' which might be provided by people through attentive or affectionate care, but for some theorists physical stimuli which are not necessarily associated with human agencies seem also to be included. The deficiency model of these theorists appears to be based on the assumption that these stimuli are indispensable for infants, very much as are food and water. Indeed, one implicit motivational analog of this model is that of *hunger*. We recall in this connection that Levy (1937), in his pioneering study, coined the phrase 'primary affect hunger', and that Spitz (1949) has written of 'emotionally

R   257

starved' children. This presumably analogous homeostatic hunger drive model usually has been applied in other contexts to order the *periodic* requirements of organisms for such indispensable stimuli as food and water. However, an analysis of the hunger model indicates that it cannot possibly order the reported conditions and results of regular, long-term deprivation: It operates only through hours, or at most a very few days; and it implies complete satiability after periodic deprivation, with *no* residual effects that could cumulate in time, and manifest themselves in systematic changes in behaviors for the events of which the organism was earlier deprived.

A rather different drive model may also be contained in the writings on deficiency environments of the theorists cited. It is one which seems to order through months and (more typically) years, not periodic but *cumulating* effects of recurring conditions of deprivation in the early life of the child, which result in systematic changes in some of his behaviors with reference to the stimulus commodities deprived. Thus, this model emphasizes a 'need for stimuli' which can through time grow in strength if unrequited, i.e. if less than some (unspecified) adequate level is supplied to the infant over relatively many occasions (trials) through the longer term, on either a regular or irregular basis. The 'need' which builds-up in this way may later on lead to the child exhibiting apparently insatiable requirements for (and even the hoarding of) the stimulus commodities earlier provided to him in deficient supply, but sometimes to apathy or other aberrant behavior outcomes.

But this formulation of the deficiency model which attempts to order the effects in children's behavior of long-term deprivation is as inadequate for that purpose as is the drive model for periodic hunger. For it is little more than a simple restatement, in a different set of terms, of the empirical relationships assumed to be involved, but a restatement that is limited by the fact that the drive term carries excess (i.e. irrelevant, even misleading) meaning which derives from its usage in contexts which are in their essential properties quite different from those in which the term 'childhood deprivation' has been applied.

It is at such theoretical junctures as this one that the concepts of learning and adaptive behavior seem better suited for the required analysis. For, undeveloped as some of these concepts may be, they (and not, e.g., motivational concepts) were evolved to order through long time spans systematic changes in behavior effected by recurring environmental conditions. And this task is precisely what my analysis indicates that the deficiency drive model has been implicitly, and awkwardly, attempting. On the other hand, motivational concepts (like the hunger drive model) have been useful, in the main, for ordering the effects in behavior of conditions of the environment operating through rather short[20] time spans – less than 100 hours typically – where the behavior index returns rapidly to the base level after the drive conditions are removed, and there are *no* residual effects which cumulate in time.

Thus, also, as long as it appears that there are recurring environmental conditions which can determine (if only in part) the responsiveness of the infant to environmental stimuli, we must inevitably come to this conclusion: It is by failing to recognize the circumstances under which stimuli are provided, and by focusing only on the simple fact of which or how many are provided the child, that the deficiency drive model formulation must miss the essentials of, and perhaps even obscure, the processes involved. (An exception here, of course, would be emotional response habituation which could be effected by the availability of particular classes of eliciting stimuli.) For example, it would be of crucial importance to know whether or not stimuli provided through attentive care were contingent upon an identified behavior of the child. For these conditions constitute the bases on which behaviors become conditioned in given settings. Hence, if one such behavior is subsequently taken by the observer to constitute a 'natural' index of the importance of the stimuli (provided earlier) to the individual, then even if he has focused simply on the fact of which or how many stimuli were provided and not on how they related to the behavior index, he must inevitably (though inefficiently) be assessing the learned basis of that behavior index.

On these bases[21] my analysis of emotional deprivation will focus, not just on which stimuli, or how few or many of each, are provided to the infant. As in the analysis outlined in earlier sections of this paper, it will focus, in addition, on whether those stimuli are functional and enter with his behaviors into effective contingencies for learning. Hence, on the basis of an analysis in terms of such instrumental learning concepts, we could expect the outcomes in the social and attachment behaviors of the child sometimes to be quite different from (and even the very opposites of) those which would be expected under a model for emotional deprivation which emphasizes only the provision of stimuli to the child.

PRIVATION VS. DEPRIVATION

In terms of the conceptual analysis presented of the role of stimulation in earliest social learning, it appears that the key phenomena that have been listed under the heading of emotional deprivation in childhood can be ordered under (at least) two independent general cases: one involves the dimension of *availability of stimuli* which could support the early behavior and learning of the child; and the other involves the dimension of *change in behavior setting* from one which supported the earlier and basic learnings of the child, and in which he had been adjusted.

Under the first general case, the dire behavior outcomes appear to be due to stimulus *privation*. From the earliest phases of life the child's environment provides a paucity of all, or of particular classes of, functional stimuli, far fewer than would be available in normal environments. In this case the available stimuli would be insufficient to support the early, basic learnings of the child, *at the very time* those learnings would ordinarily occur.

Under the second general case, the dire behavior outcomes appear to be due to stimulus *deprivation* which is conceived to involve the effects of a continuing state of frustration brought on by an extreme and lasting change in the controlling environment for the key behavior systems of the child. Specifically, key cue and reinforcing stimuli become unavailable to the child, *after* most of these stimuli have acquired important meaning for him through learning.

Several heuristic sub-cases for each of these general cases are outlined in the sections which follow. These depend on the availability to the infant of diverse stimuli, and can illustrate the plausibility of ordering many childhood deprivation phenomena in terms of the basic concepts of instrumental learning and adaptive behavior, as well as to suggest the potential fruitfulness of the approach. For these reasons, I shall attempt neither to list all the simple prototypes possible in theory nor to keep those listed from overlapping. When the many deprivation phenomena considered are approached from the standpoint of the conception of instrumental learning (with or without the assumptions that a large variety of environmental stimuli can function as evokers of behavior, as reinforcing stimuli for behavior and to establish conditioned reinforcing stimuli), the following proto-typic cases, which are possible in theory, fall into relief.

Privation

The first general case into which childhood deprivation phenomena fall has been labelled long-term *privation*, for it focuses on the possi-bility that a child's environment from the earliest phases of life may contain little functional stimulation. The basic learnings of the child, both social and non-social, should be severely limited by stimulus privation conditions, as is illustrated by the sub-cases outlined in the sections below. Aside from the role of stimuli in effecting learning, the availability in an infant's environment of some of the uncon-ditioned eliciting stimuli for responses in the startle-avoidance complex could make possible the relatively complete habituation of some of them (with reference to those eliciting stimuli). This would make possible a subsequent adjustment of that infant which would be less encumbered.

TOTAL PRIVATION

From the earliest phases of life, the infant's environment may provide relatively few environmental stimuli, and hence few functional stimuli for behavior and learning, justifying the label 'total privation'. Specifically, caretaking and related interaction ('mothering') might be inadequate in the sense that: (a) very few potential evoking or discriminative stimuli are provided, (b) very few potential reinforcing stimuli are provided, and these are rarely presented under conditions where they could function effectively to reinforce the infant's behavior to effect learning, and (c) very few social stimuli are avail-able for pairing with (or to stand as discriminative for) those few reinforcing stimuli as might be presented, hence precluding the establishment of effective conditioned social reinforcers for the infant. As a consequence, children developing in such a limited, isolated environment would be expected to be relatively unresponsive to unconditioned as to conditioned stimuli, to be unaffected by most of the usual social reinforcers, and hence to appear passive (vege-table-like) and asocial. Further, as these children will have had but minimal opportunity to become habituated to stimuli which elicit startle and avoidance behavior complexes, they should remain responsive to such stimuli.

This case can illustrate the possibility that if infants develop with a relatively small amount of attentive care, which would constitute an environment providing few effective cue and reinforcing stimuli, adequate learnings would be unlikely to develop, either social or non-social. This would seem likely only in the poorest institutions or households, very likely including the 'Foundling Home' which Spitz (1945) has described. We would imagine that this case is relatively infrequent these days, but might sometimes occur in those institutions in which very few caretakers are responsible for very many infants, or which follow uncritically antiseptic hospital routines, or in settings in which caretakers, for whatever reason, are completely indifferent to, or even dislike, the children in their care.

FUNCTIONAL PRIVATION

It seems useful to separate two possible cases of 'functional privation': One case involves a paucity of *all* classes of stimuli required for learning, and the second case involves only a dearth of effective cue stimuli which are specifically social.

Functional Privation of All Stimuli – The possibility exists that while, from earliest life, the infant's environment may contain even a relative abundance of potential stimuli, few of these events provide *functional* stimuli for effective learning contingencies; hence, the label 'functional privation'. In this case, the potential (unconditioned) evoking stimuli provided by caretakers do not occur frequently or intensely enough, or in the most effective patterns in given periods to constitute discriminable occasions for the infant's behavior. When they occur, these behaviors would be in the position to be reinforced. But even more important for this case, when stimuli are presented which could function as reinforcers if they followed immediately those behaviors which the infant exhibits, typically they would not follow those behaviors immediately. Hence, adequate conditions for learning would not be present, behaviors and relationships among stimuli would not be learned, and the child would be relatively unresponsive to environmental (including social) stimuli, even despite an apparent abundance of environmental stimulation. However, relative to the infant raised under 'total privation', the stimuli provided should make it possible for this infant to become habituated for many stimuli which originally could elicit startle, avoidance, and emotional responses. Still, the possibility would exist under this case that, by chance, associations might be formed for the infant between elements of this 'emotional' response complex and originally neutral cue stimuli, such as might be provided by people in the environment.

Functional Privation of Specifically Social Cue Stimuli – Of equal importance to the preceding case is the possibility that, even if a good number of evoking and reinforcing stimuli are presented to be effective, caretaking and related interaction may be inadequate in that most of the social stimuli ordinarily afforded by the caretakers *incidental* to caretaking are *not* presented as discriminative for reinforcement frequently or clearly enough to establish them as positive conditioned reinforcers. As a consequence, infants from such an environment should be unaffected by most of the usual social reinforcers, and hence would appear asocial, even autistic. Nevertheless, such infants might well develop to be responsive to, and even highly competent in coping with, non-social stimulus events in their physical environment; and they might respond as well to social stimuli as if they were non-social. (In this connection, the autistic child described by Kanner [e.g. 1949] comes to mind as a possible instance of the functional privation of specifically social cue stimuli.) We would expect these infants to have become habituated to many unconditioned startle and avoidance eliciting stimuli, like those reared in normal environments. And relative to the case of 'functional privation of all stimuli', there likely would be fewer associations for these infants between the startle-avoidance response complex and environmental cues.

Both of the preceding privation cases would seem best to characterize those settings in which babies receive 'impersonal' care and minimal interaction from people, as, for example, when caretaking follows a rigid institutional routine (i.e. more according to the clock or the apparent group need and less according to the behavior of the individual infant), or simply when there are just too few caretakers adequately to care for the many infants in their care. It would seem also to characterize settings containing well-meaning, 'warm' caretakers who, because they are limited in 'empathy' for the children in their care or are inept for other reasons, do not provide effective stimulus contingencies for learning to occur. (We may note parenthetically at this point that stimuli provided through such impersonal care would likely function not infrequently as frustrating or negative reinforcing stimuli, which would tend to produce learnings *not* to respond, or to respond by escape or avoidance, in the presence of particular environmental stimuli.)

NON-PRIVATION

At this point it may be profitable briefly to detail typical conditions for development in normal environments, to provide a baseline for the three theoretically possible privation prototypes outlined. Under both of the 'non-privation' or normal cases which are here detailed, relative to the preceding privation cases, there would be abundant opportunity for the habituation of behaviors in the startle-avoidance complex. Also, it is likely that few associations would be formed between elements of that complex and incidental cues provided by caretaker-adults.

Abundant and Regular Stimulation – For this non-privation case it is assumed that, from the very beginning, there would be available to the infant a substantial number of not unpleasant environmental events which provide functional stimuli, both evoking and reinforcing, which with his behaviors could enter into effective contingencies for learning. These stimuli need not be available in great abundance. (Indeed, as the next heuristic case will illustrate, the more abundant the available stimuli, the less effective they may be.) Specifically, such stimuli are discriminable, reinforcing stimuli typically follow effectively such responses as are emitted, and social stimuli afforded incidental to caretaking (and other interaction) are provided with sufficient frequency and clarity to establish them as effective conditioned reinforcing stimuli.

As a consequence, infants from such an environment should develop as responsive both to non-social and to social stimuli, and might show greater adequacy in coping with unexpected events and frustrations than would infants from the privation environments listed. On this basis, for example, it would be possible to explain, at least in part, some of the reported differences in responsiveness to, and the ability to cope with, events in both the physical and social environments, and intellectual functioning, between infants raised in inadequate institutions and infants raised under normal family conditions (see, e.g., Goldfarb, 1945a).

Highly Effective Functional Stimulation through Short-term Deprivations of Stimuli – In the immediately preceding analysis, some of the consequences of emotional deprivation in childhood were ordered under the concept of *privation*. Thus, differential responsiveness of the child to physical and social stimuli were referred to the simple fact of the availability in his environment of functional stimuli which could enter with his behaviors into learning contingencies, for significant periods of time, in the early months of life. On the basis of the assumption that the effectiveness of many stimuli may be governed by short-term deprivation and satiation conditions which operate on the organism in the immediately preceding period, it is possible to order still other consequences of what have been called conditions of childhood deprivation. This case, which is compatible with the general learning case of the more rapid acquisition of responses under distributed rather than massed practice trials, constitutes something of a paradox when considered against the conventional deficiency formulation of childhood privation. As we have seen, that formulation generally appears to emphasize that a deficiency 'need' for particular stimuli develops cumulatively in the infant as an inverse function of the availability of those stimuli to him in the past.

It has been suggested that the effectiveness of many stimuli, in their evocative, discriminative or reinforcing roles, may be enhanced by deprivation operations and lowered by satiation operations. (Allowing limited or no access to those stimuli for a period would constitute relative deprivation, and providing an abundance of access to them for a period would constitute relative satiation.) Let me illustrate this point in terms of the reinforcing role of stimuli alone. If reinforcing stimuli are generally dispensed to an infant at a rate such that recovery from satiation will not have taken place before each new occasion (trial), those stimuli would be relatively less effective as reinforcers (and sometimes even frustrating) for that infant. Hence, the behaviors they maintain would be emitted relatively infrequently, and they would be less likely to support new learnings. Alternatively, if the value of these reinforcing stimuli were allowed to recover from satiation for an infant (through deprivation), they would be maximally effective in maintaining his behaviors, and in effecting new learnings.

On this basis, for example, assuming that effective learning con-

265

tingencies prevail in both cases, we would expect that reinforcing stimuli provided to children reared in institutions generally would be far more effective (i.e. potent) than those provided to children reared in normal households. The assumption on which this would be based is that contact between caretakers and children is both less frequent and of lesser duration in institutions than in normal households, say for 5 rather than for 30 consecutive minutes each hour that the infant is awake. Because of this, we would expect institution infants more effectively to have learned responses of all sorts, and for the conditioned social reinforcers to which they are responsive to be more potent. On this basis alone, then, institution children might exhibit a greater incidence of behaviors for such conditioned reinforcers, thus possibly giving the appearance of having been 'starved' for affectionate contact to those observers who utilize a hunger-deficiency theory. For under that theory, emitting behaviors for such stimuli would be interpreted to reflect having received them in deficient supply in the past.

Deprivation

The second general case into which childhood deprivation phenomena fall has been labelled long-term *deprivation*. This case focuses the possibility of an abrupt and continuing change in what earlier was a satisfactory pattern of availability of (important) cue and reinforcing stimuli to a child, *after* these stimuli have been conditioned as such for him. The child's experience with stimuli would determine the behaviors he employs in given settings as well as the controlling social events which have become conditioned as cue and reinforcing stimuli for him. These learnings would of course depend on conditions in the earlier environment of the child, and would differ for children from different environments, for example, from normal families, broken homes, institutions and the like.

After the key behavior patterns will have reached a stable level for a child, there may be occasions or a continuing situation in which some of the relevant controlling stimuli for these behaviors are no longer offered. Specifically, the relevant discriminative stimuli which define the occasion when the child's behaviors will be reinforced are not made available, and when he employs a response for reinforcement, the relevant reinforcing stimulus may not be forthcoming. On

Jacob L. Gewirtz

any single occasion, this interference with responses or response sequences, as in the early stages of extinction (a sudden thinning out of the rate of reinforcement) or frustration (a forced break in the response sequence), might result in the child emitting a greater number of responses for the reinforcer than he did in the immediately preceding period. On the same basis, there may be a rise generally in other responses of his repertory. (Hull's theory [1943] and its later versions might explain this as due to a rise in generalized drive [D] level.) On any given occasion, the interference with the child's learned behavior patterns brought about when the relevant discriminative and reinforcing stimuli controlling them are no longer offered (and the extraneous stimulation thus provided), may also result in the child exhibiting various irrelevant emotional (often angry) responses. When these emotional responses occur, they would constitute further interruptions in the earlier interfered with response patterns. Moreover, they would preclude the occurrence of possible behaviors alternative to the one interfered with which could make new learning and adjustment a possibility in the setting. On a continuing basis, if the disruptive emotional behaviors in rather young children go on occurring after a major change in the controlling environment, a reasonable adjustment to the new behavior setting would become progressively less likely, and serious pathological outcomes (e.g. progressive withdrawal, depression) might result in extremely disrupted cases. Some of these possible outcomes of deprivation as continuing frustration are discussed in a section which follows, on the effects of deprivation brought on by separation.

In earlier sections, when the operating characteristics of the motivation-learning model and the principles that would govern the acquisition of substitute attachments were listed and illustrated, I detailed some of the general points which it would be necessary to take into account in any attempt to predict the consequences in a child's behavior of an extreme shift in environment. Hence, only a brief summary of the main points is required here before I list the considerations which are specifically relevant to the issue of cases of deprivation brought about by extreme shifts in behavior setting.

It is axiomatic that the child will bring to a new environment those behavior systems that have been acquired and maintained in the environment from which he comes, particularly if it constitutes the context of his earliest learnings. On this basis, the child's initial behavior in a new environment will be a function of its similarity to the context in which he was earlier adjusted, as well as of his rate of habituating to novel stimulus conditions, sometimes a slow process with disruptive effects. In most of the cases being considered here, the child's previous environment will be his earliest, that is the one in which his behavior repertory was originally acquired.

In addition to the factor of similarity of the new environment to his earlier one, and his rate of habituation to novel stimulus conditions, other factors on which the adjustment of the child in the new environment would depend are likely to include such conditions as: whether the new caretakers learn from the child's behavior what the appropriate reinforcing stimuli are for him, and then provide those stimuli; and whether the child, through new learning, acquires responses and reinforcing stimuli appropriate to the new setting. Further, as was earlier suggested also, a sudden and extreme shift from an environment in which the child's behavior systems are under close stimulus control to an environment which is quite different may lead to a considerable weakening, deterioration or even cessation of those behaviors. That is, because the controlling stimuli are no longer available, if the child exhibits behaviors at all in the new setting, many of them may be less complex, even primitive, relative to his repertory which was specific to the previous environment. In the extreme case, if the reinforcing agency in the new environment is not flexible in reinforcing successively more appropriate instances of originally simple behaviors to make it possible for the child to acquire a substitute behavior repertory there, then conditions would exist that might eventuate in a pathological outcome. This would be particularly so if a substitute behavior repertory is not readily acquired by the child, at the same time as his behaviors are expected by the reinforcing agency to advance in complexity as appropriate for his advancing age.

DEPRIVATION BROUGHT ABOUT BY MOVES TO NEW ENVIRONMENTS

The first and more general sub-case of deprivation that can be identified deals with the behavioral consequences of a significant *change* between an earlier and the contemporary behavior setting. Under this general case, it appears possible to explain a variety of the changes in the young child's behavior as being due simply to the extreme change in maintaining environment brought about, for example, by his move from an institution to a foster home (or from one foster, or adoptive, home to another).

A move of this type could result in many possible, sometimes radical, changes in reinforcement conditions, especially if the move is from the context of the earliest social learnings of the child. Hence, it is on the basis of the effects of the radical environmental changes which could be involved and the consequent necessity for the child (and for the new caretaker for that matter) to 'reshape' old learnings in the new setting, rather than to some type of early privation, that some of the atypical ('problem') behavior patterns reported by Goldfarb and others may be explained. This would be particularly so if the observations of the children were made *after* they were moved to the new behavior setting but *before* they had fully adjusted to it, i.e. before their behaviors had become stable there. Indeed, some of these 'problem' behaviors may themselves represent a reasonable adjustment of the child to the new setting. For example, extreme attention-getting behavior may be heavily reinforced in the new setting; or attention may be, effectively, the only class of social reinforcing stimuli provided there.

The circumstances under which a child enters a foster home from an institution would often be like those in the early stages of experimental extinction, where a response he characteristically would employ is not reinforced. (It has already been noted that various intense and disruptive emotional behaviors may be one consequence of this change.) As in the early phases of extinction, over-all repertory behavior rate may rise, and the child may exhibit qualitative and quantitative variations on the originally learned behaviors to gain reinforcement. For her part, the new caretaker may reinforce a *different* manifestation of a behavior than the one conditioned, for example, its amplitude rather than its frequency; or she may reinforce a different behavior entirely, for example, behaviors for approval and not those for attention. Also, the conditioned reinforcers she provides may differ on a number of dimensions from the conditioned reinforcers important for the child, which were available in his earlier environment. Thus, she may typically smile or give tacit approval rather than hug or caress; or she may exhibit a different degree of 'warmth' in her responses than was typically exhibited in the previous institution setting.

Further, the *schedule* on which the new caretaker dispenses reinforcers may differ from the earlier one. Thus, if the stimuli provided through caretaking and other interaction have been relatively infrequent, as in a busy institution, then behaviors for a social reinforcer like attention may show the characteristics of behavior on some 'thin' interval (or possibly even some ratio) schedule; if, later, in an adoptive home environment, the reinforcer were to be delivered more frequently to the child, his behaviors for it could be emitted at a higher rate. This would be still another way of accounting for the more frequent and apparently 'insatiable' attention-seeking of formerly institutionalized children after their placement in foster homes.

Deprivation brought about by Separation – In the preceding section I outlined generally some of the possible consequences in children's behavior of deprivation effected by a drastic change in the reinforcing environment. A frequently occurring sub-case of change in the maintaining environment merits particular emphasis here. It focuses on the consequences when the change involves those unique appearance characteristics of the 'object' person which, functioning as conditioned reinforcing stimuli to maintain many of the child's behaviors, are the basis of an attachment. It is the possibility of a child being put under a condition of long-term deprivation, in the sense of a continuing state of frustration, which is brought about by his being *separated* from an object person to whom he is strongly (and perhaps uniquely) attached, typically his mother. This condition would involve at the same time many radical changes in the conditions of reinforcement (if substitute persons are not able to provide the relevant stimuli equally well), which would produce simultaneously a number of vast changes in the response systems of the child, perhaps causing a continuing extreme, disruptive emotional behavior pattern in him.

Hence, on a long-term basis, unless a relationship to some substitute person develops so that the particular discriminative and reinforcing stimuli which are important to the child are forthcoming, or new learning occurs so that the new response repertories and new discriminative and reinforcing stimuli are conditioned with reference to another attached person, a pathological condition might be the consequence. In extreme instances the child might develop a listlessness and progressive withdrawal reaction, perhaps even an apparently irreversible depression, as has been noted by Spitz (1946b). And his withdrawal would limit the possibility for the child to establish new relationships. This would be another way of accounting for the 'lack of capacity for emotional attachment' which many of the children studied by Goldfarb, Levy and others exhibited, aside from the earlier considered possibility of referring the outcome to a privation etiology.

Summary

In this paper I have attempted to propose a simple yet plausible theory of the learned origins in human infancy of social motivation and attachment. My analysis has focused on the availability to the infant of different classes of environmental stimuli, and has emphasized the contingencies for effective learning they could enter together with the behaviors of the infant. In this process, I have examined the learning outcomes in patterns of adaptive behavior, social motivation and attachment of conditions of normal stimulation, as well as aberrant outcomes of the deficiency patterns of stimulation provided by emotional 'privation' and 'deprivation'. The key assumption of my analysis has been that, in order to understand the acquisition of human social motivation and attachment, under both normal and deficiency conditions of stimulation, it would be of little use simply to focus on which, or how many, stimuli are provided to the infant. Rather, it is that we must, in addition, take account of the circumstances under which given stimuli are provided to him, and, in particular, whether, with his behaviors, these stimuli enter effective contingencies for learning.

In addition to the standard concepts of instrumental learning and adaptive behavior I have employed in a close examination of the process of mother-infant interaction, several assumptions derived from recent behavioral research were emphasized. These took account of the growing body of data on the evoking and the reinforcing properties of stimuli, and their implications for the behavior of the infant. Thus, the biologically satisfied infant was conceived to be quite the opposite of the passive and unresponsive being he is pictured to be by widely held theories of environmental impact on infant behavior, for example, that of Freud on infant development and object cathexis and that of need-reduction learning. It was thought here to be more reasonable to assume that the highly

271

responsive infant is in active interaction with his environment, regularly and for sizable periods, even when biologically satiated. Further, the important possibility was entertained that many evoking, cue and reinforcing stimuli for the infant may be raised in effectiveness by background conditions operating in the setting, and, in particular, when these stimuli have been unavailable to him for some sufficient period (deprivation), and lowered when they have been available to him in abundance for some sufficient period (satiation).

REINFORCEMENT AND LEARNING

In this context, a variety of stimuli would seem to function, in the brief period immediately following their presentation, to make more likely the occurrence of various free behaviors of the infant, i.e. to *evoke* them. At the same time, a large variety of stimuli would function to *reinforce* (i.e. condition) these and other occurring behaviors when they follow them directly. Reinforcement is the basic process by which adaptive, 'non-reflex' behavior is generated (through differential reinforcement) and maintained; hence, it is central to any instrumental learning analysis of the effects of the environment on the behavior of the developing child. Any stimulus event which effects a systematic rise in the output rate of a defined response it (or its removal) follows is termed a positive reinforcer. While it remains an empirical question which of the myriad stimuli in the infant's environment emerge at each stage of development to function as unconditioned positive reinforcers for his behavior, it would seem that a large variety of stimuli can function in this way, in addition to those which meet the 'organic needs' of the child, i.e. food, water and the removal of aversive stimuli (cold, wetness). Some of the most potent reinforcing stimuli initially for infant behavior are likely to be kinesthetic, involving skin contact and warmth. Recent research indicates that reinforcing stimuli are likely to be provided also (e.g. through exploration or manipulation) by environmental changes, such as changes in the direction of novelty or complexity, and by different tactile, auditory, visual and olfactory stimuli, including the simple answering responses of a caretaker to a child (as when she mimics him).

In this context, several questions would be at issue for a learning analysis both of the acquisition of social motivation and attachment and of the effects of the conditions of privation and deprivation.

These questions, mainly about the characteristics of the stimuli which are made available to the infant, are:

(*a*) Are potential eliciting, evoking, or reinforcing stimuli actually provided, and if they are, can they be discriminated by him?

(*b*) If eliciting stimuli are provided for behaviors of the (presumably unlearned) emotional-startle complex, does the pattern of their availability allow those behaviors to habituate?

(*c*) If potential evoking stimuli are provided, is it at a rate and in a pattern which increases the likelihood of occurrence of the behaviors they can effect?

(*d*) If potential reinforcing stimuli are provided, are they made effectively (i.e. immediately) contingent upon his behaviors, particularly those which are defined as social by the reinforcing community, so that they might be conditioned?

(*e*) Do these reinforcing stimuli follow effectively originally neutral cue stimuli (e.g. a caretaker's attention), so that those cues might acquire reinforcer value?

And lastly, (*f*) are there background conditions, of the present or of the immediate past (e.g. satiation for a stimulus presented repeatedly or fatigue of a response employed repeatedly) which operate to qualify for him the effectiveness of the stimuli provided, in their evoking, cue, or reinforcing roles?

ACQUISITION OF SOCIAL MOTIVATION AND ATTACHMENT

If one or more such reinforcing stimuli are effectively paired often enough with a relatively neutral (preceding or otherwise contiguous) stimulus, that stimulus can become conditioned as a reinforcer, and in the simplest case can function as such as long as the pairing which underlies its reinforcer value is maintained. In most learning approaches to the development of social motivation and attachment, the conditioned reinforcing stimulus would be the key (controlling) concept which generates and maintains a variety of the behaviors of the child with reference to another person. In the case of an unspecific social motive, e.g. dependence, the conditioned reinforcing stimulus would be the general characteristics shared by, and hence available from, many persons (e.g. their attention or approval), and various behaviors of the child could be maintained by that reinforcing stimulus. In the case of an attachment, however, the unique appearance characteristics of the object person, physical and behavioral, would be the ones which as conditioned reinforcing stimuli maintain different behaviors of the child, including orientating to, approaching and following the object person.

The assumption that a wide variety of environmental events can in early infancy function as reinforcing stimuli for behavior and for the conditioning of reinforcers, would appear to provide a more satisfactory basis for the acquisition of social motives and attachments than one based only on the reinforcing stimuli which 'meet the organic needs' of the child, inherent both in earlier learning approaches and in Freud's writings (though for Freud sexual reinforcers function also to produce attachment).

After tracing the process of human attachment learning, three theoretically possible ways in which *substitute* attachments could be acquired were considered. More than one of these might provide the basis for a substitute relationship. These would be through: (*a*) stimulus generalization, (*b*) the adjustment by the new caretaker (as potential object person) to the child, and (*c*) new attachment learning.

The process of imprinting was examined as a possible case of earliest attachment-learning, in which the response of following-approaching may be reinforced frequently and potently during a brief initial period, in the complete absence of competing response systems, by reinforcing stimuli provided by the object of imprinting. This earliest learning process is then protected by the later appearance of the fear and flight pattern to strange objects, and would provide the basis for all subsequent learning in that sector of the animal's life. The implications of imprinting-as-learning for human attachment learning were then considered, after which the general attachment-learning model advanced was contrasted to Bowlby's theory of attachment based on ethological principles.

An analysis was then made of a rarely considered but most important process, namely the conditioning by infants of their parents' behaviors, as well as the correlated process of attachment-learning by parents to their infants. In this connection, the possibility was considered that 'a mother's love for her child' may be acquired through learning. Further, it was suggested that this learning might even be of recent origin, and occur very rapidly under highly favorable conditions which might exist in the very settings in which that pattern seems to appear so dramatically.

EMOTIONAL DEPRIVATION

Lastly, the attempt was made to illustrate the utility of the learning model outlined (and perhaps to make a plausible case for some of the conditions that might be operating there) by applying it to the beginnings of an analysis of some of the behavior outcomes of emotional 'deprivation' in early childhood, which has generally been taken to represent deficiency patterns of environmental stimulation.

The concept of emotional 'deprivation' has occupied a key role in formulations about the effects of long-term deficiency conditions in childhood. These conditions have been thought to lead later on to aberrant outcomes in the adaptive behaviors of the children, both non-social and social, as well as in the patterns of social motivation and attachment they show. Thus, for example, deprivation conditions have been thought to lead to developmental arrest, apathy, or to no requirements, or to apparently insatiable ones, for the earlier deficient commodities. While neither conclusions about the operational meaning of the deprivation concept, nor the reliability of its effects, can be clearly drawn from the formulations in this literature, the homeostatic hunger model which elsewhere has been applied to the organism's periodic requirements for indispensable stimuli is implicit there. An analysis of this stimulus hunger model indicates that it cannot order the reported conditions and consequences of long-term deprivation: It operates only through hours rather than years; and it implies complete satiability after periodic deprivation, with no residual effects that could cumulate in time later to manifest themselves in systematic changes in identified behaviors for the earlier deficient events.

As the concepts of learning and adaptive behavior were evolved to order through long time spans systematic changes in behavior effected by recurring environmental conditions, they (and not, for example, motivational concepts) would seem more satisfactory for ordering at least some of the reported effects of childhood deprivation. On this basis, the attempt was made heuristically to order deprivation phenomena under (at least) two independent general cases: Under the first case, termed *privation*, the outcomes appear due to a dearth of all, or of particular classes of, functional stimuli in the early environment of the infant, insufficient to support either his basic learnings or the habituation of emotional-startle responses,

275

at the very time these processes would normally occur. Hence, the relevant analysis would focus on whether stimuli are functional and could enter into effective learning contingencies, not just on which, or how many, stimuli are available. Under the second case, termed *deprivation*, the outcomes appear due to a continuing state of frustration, brought on by an extreme, lasting change in the controlling environment for the key behavior systems of the child. Specifically, critical cue and reinforcing stimuli become *un*available to the child (and responses he had employed to attain them are no longer appropriate) *after* these stimuli have acquired important meaning for him through learning.

Several heuristic sub-cases of privation, which depend on the availability to the infant of diverse stimuli, were outlined to illustrate the utility of applying instrumental learning concepts to privation phenomena: Under *total privation*, the environment provides few stimuli which might evoke or reinforce behavior. Hence, neither learning nor emotional response habituation would occur, and the infant would develop as unresponsive to stimuli (i.e. passive and asocial), except to those eliciting emotional-startle behaviors. Under *functional privation*, there may be abundant stimuli, but, because they are not discriminable or in proper timing or sequence relationships, they rarely function effectively. Some emotional behaviors may habituate, but little learning would occur. Hence, the child develops as unresponsive to stimuli generally, despite an abundance of access to them. Under the *functional privation of specifically social cue stimuli*, abundant stimuli for effective learning contingencies are provided, but without discriminable social cues. Like the normal child, he can become habituated for most emotional responses and generally responsive to stimuli, but not as such to social conditioned reinforcers and cues available from people (i.e. he would appear 'autistic'). For the *normal* child, there would be available from the beginning evoking, cue, and reinforcing stimuli for behavior, functional for effective learning. These stimuli need not be available in great abundance. In this case, the child's emotional behaviors habituate and he becomes responsive to his environment and oriented toward attaining conditioned social reinforcers.

For deprivation, the general case of a major shift in reinforcing-maintaining environment (e.g. from a home to an institutional environment) was illustrated; after which the sub-case of an extreme environmental shift which *separation* from an attached (object) person constitutes was considered.

ASSUMPTIONS ABOUT NON-LEARNING DETERMINANTS

It has *not* been necessary, for my analysis of the origins of motivation and attachment in man, to make any of the assumptions which follow:

(*a*) That the child is born into the world with fully developed instinctive social 'needs', such as for mothering or social contact. (Indeed, it was thought gratuitous to postulate such 'needs', for the term 'need' would add nothing to explain the effectiveness on infant behavior and learning of the unconditioned reinforcing stimuli which operate.)

(*b*) That certain environmental conditions are necessary for the 'blossoming' or unfolding of biologically determined social behavior patterns.

(*c*) That dramatic processes like 'imprinting' (a non-learning process, as some theorists have thought of it) account for his social and attachment behavior. (Indeed, imprinting was approached as a plausible instance of earliest instrumental social learning, under conditions conducive to efficient, rapid learning.)

At the same time the important possibility that unlearned social releasing stimuli or species-specific behavior patterns could be involved in parent-infant interaction was left entirely open. It was thought that such unlearned patterns, as well as the emergence of different behaviors and the developmental changes they could go through, would qualify, but would not change in any important respect, the learning model for social motivation advanced in this paper.

REFERENCES

ALLPORT, G. W. (1937) *Personality: A Psychological Interpretation* New York: Holt

BAKWIN, H. (1942) 'Loneliness in infants' *American Journal of Diseases of Children*, **63**, 30-40

BAKWIN, H. (1949) 'Emotional depri ation in infants' *Journal of Pediatrics*, **35**, 512-521

BALDWIN, J. M. (1906) *Mental Development in the Child and the Race: Methods and Processes* New York: Macmillan

BEACH, F. A. (1945) 'Current concepts of play in animals' *American Naturalist*, **79**, 523-541

BERLYNE, D. E. (1950) 'Novelty and curiosity as determinants of exploratory behaviour' *British Journal of Psychology*, **41**, 68-80

BOWLBY, J. (1940) 'The influence of early environment in the development of neurosis and neurotic character' *Int. J. of Psychoanal.* **21** (2), 154-178

BOWLBY, J. (1944) 'Forty-four Juvenile Thieves: their characters and home life' *Int. J. of Psychoanal.* **25**, 19-52 and 107-127

BOWLBY, J. (1951) 'Maternal Care and Mental Health' *Bull. World Health Organization*, **3**, 355-534. Also published separately, Geneva: World Health Organization, 1952

BOWLBY, J. (1957) 'An ethological approach to research in child development' *British Journal of Medical Psychology*, **30**, 230-240

BOWLBY, J. (1958) 'The nature of the child's tie to his mother' *International Journal of Psychoanalysis*, **39**, 350-373

BRIDGES, K. M. B. (1932) 'Emotional development in early infancy' *Child Development*, **3**, 324-341

BUTLER, R. A. (1953) 'Discrimination learning by rhesus monkeys to visual-exploration motivation' *Journal of Comparative & Physiological Psychology*, **46**, 239-241

BUTLER, R. A. (1957) 'The effect of deprivation of visual incentives on visual exploration motivation in monkeys' *Journal of Comparative and Physiological Psychology*, **50**, 177-179

DOLLARD, J. & MILLER, N. E. (1950) *Personality and Psychotherapy* New York: McGraw-Hill

FABRICIUS, E. (1951) 'Some experiments on imprinting phenomena in ducks' *Proceedings Xth International Ornithological Congress*, 375-379

FENICHEL, O. (1945) *The Psychoanalytic Theory of Neurosis* New York: Norton

FERSTER, C. B. (1958) 'Reinforcement and punishment in the control of human behavior by social agencies' *Psychiatric Research Reports*, **10**, 101-118

FREUD, ANNA (1951) 'Observations on child development' *Psychoanalytic Study of the Child*, **6**, 18-30

FREUD, ANNA (1954) 'Psychoanalysis and education' *Psychoanalytic Study of the Child*, **9**, 9-15

FREUD, ANNA, & BURLINGHAM, DOROTHY (1944) *Infants Without Families* London: George Allen & Unwin

FREUD, ANNA, & DANN, SOPHIE (1951) 'An experiment in group upbringing' *Psychoanalytic Study of the Child*, 6, 127-168

FREUD, S. (1905) 'Three contributions to the theory of sex' Pp. 553-629 in A. A. Brill (Translator), *The Basic Writings of Sigmund Freud* New York: Modern Library, 1938

FREUD, S. (1938) *An Outline of Psychoanalysis* London: Hogarth

GESELL, A., & THOMPSON, H. (1934) *Infant Behavior: Its Genesis and Growth* New York: McGraw-Hill

GEWIRTZ, J. L. (1956) 'A program of research on the dimensions and antecedents of emotional dependence' *Child Development*, 27, 205-221

GEWIRTZ, J. L. (1959) 'Discussion of the use of operant conditioning techniques in children' Pp. 127-136 in S. Fisher (Editor), *Child Research in Psychopharmacology* Springfield, Illinois: Chas. C. Thomas

GEWIRTZ, J. L., & BAER, D. M. (1958a) 'The effect of brief social deprivation on behaviors for a social reinforcer' *Journal of Abnormal & Social Psychology*, 56, 49-56

GEWIRTZ, J. L., & BAER, D. M. (1958b). 'Deprivation and satiation of social reinforcers as drive conditions' *Journal of Abnormal & Social Psychology*, 57, 165-172

GLANZER, M. (1953) 'Stimulus satiation: an explanation of spontaneous alternation and related phenomena' *Psychological Review*, 60, 257-268

GOLDFARB, W. (1945a) 'Psychological privation in infancy and subsequent adjustment' *American Journal of Orthopsychiatry*, 15, 247-255

GOLDFARB, W. (1945b) 'Effects of psychological deprivation in infancy and subsequent stimulation' *American Journal of Psychiatry*, 102, 18-33

GOLDFARB, W. (1955) 'Emotional and intellectual consequences of psychologic deprivation in infancy: a revaluation' Pp. 105-119 in Hoch, P. H., & Zubin, J. (Editors), *Psychopathology of Childhood* New York: Grune & Stratton

GOLDSTEIN, K. (1940) *Human Nature in the Light of Psychopathology* Cambridge, Mass.: Harvard University Press

GRAY, P. H. (1958) 'Theory and evidence of imprinting in human infants' *Journal of Psychology*, **46**, 155-166

HARLOW, H. F. (1950) 'Learning and satiation of response in intrinsically motivated complex puzzle performance by monkeys' *Journal of Comparative & Physiological Psychology*, **43**, 289-294

HARLOW, H. F. (1953) 'Motivation as a factor in the acquisition of new responses' Pp. 24-49 in *Current theory and Research in Motivation*. I. Lincoln: University of Nebraska Press

HARLOW, H. F. (1958) 'The Nature of Love' *American Psychologist*, **13**, 673-685

HARLOW, H. F., HARLOW, MARGARET K., & MEYER, D. R. (1950) 'Learning motivated by the manipulation drive' *Journal of Experimental Psychology*, **40**, 228-234 ;

HARLOW, H. F., & ZIMMERMANN, R. R. (1959) 'Affectional responses in the infant monkey' *Science*, **130**,421-432

HARTMANN, H. (1939) *Ego Psychology and the Problem of Adaptation* (Translated by D. Rapaport). New York: International Universities Press, 1958

HEBB, D. O. (1958a) *A Textbook of Psychology* Philadelphia: Saunders

HEBB, D. O. (1958b) 'The motivating effects of exteroceptive stimulation' *American Psychologist*, **13**, 109-113

HEBB, D. O., & RIESEN, A. H. (1943) 'The genesis of irrational fears' *Bulletin Canadian Psychological Association*, **3**, 49-50

HENDRICK, I. (1942) 'Instinct and ego during infancy' *Psychoanalytic Quarterly*, **11**, 33-58

HESS, E. H. (1959) 'Imprinting' *Science*, **130**, 133-141

HINDE, R. A. (1954a) 'Factors governing the changes in strength of a partially inborn response, as shown by the mobbing behaviour of the Chaffinch. I. The nature of the response and an examination of its course. II. The waning of the response' *Proceedings of the Royal Society. B.* **142**B, 306-331; 331-358

HINDE, R. A. (1954b) 'Changes in responsiveness to a constant stimulus' *British Journal of Animal Behaviour*, **2**, 41-45

HINDE, R. A. (1959) 'Some recent trends in ethology' Pp. 561-610 in S. Koch (Editor), *Psychology: A Study of a Science*. Vol. 2. New York: McGraw-Hill

HINDE, R. A., THORPE, W. N., & VINCE, M.A. (1956) 'The following response of young coots and moorhens' *Behaviour*, 214-242

HULL, C. L. (1943) *Principles of Behavior* New York: Appleton-Century

HULL, C. L. (1952) *A Behavior System* New Haven: Yale University Press

HUMPHREY, G. (1933) *The Nature of Learning in Its Relation to the Living System* New York: Harcourt Brace

JAMES, H. (1959) 'Flicker: An unconditioned stimulus for imprinting' *Canadian Journal of Psychology*, **13**, 59-67.

JAMES, H. (1960) 'Imprinting with visual flicker: Evidence for a critical period' *Canadian Journal of Psychology*, **14**, 13-20

JAMES W. (1890) *Principles of Psychology* New York: Holt

JAYNES, J. (1956) 'Imprinting: The interaction of learned and innate behavior: I. Development and generalization' *Journal of Comparative and Physiological Psychology*, **49**, 201-206

JAYNES, J. (1957) 'Imprinting: The interaction of learned and innate behavior: II. The critical period' *Journal of Comparative and Physiological Psychology*, **50**, 6-10

KANNER, L. (1949) 'Problems of nosology and psychodynamics of early infantile autism' *American Journal of Orthopsychiatry*, **19**, 416-426

KELLER, F. S., & SCHOENFELD, W. N. (1950) *Principles of Psychology* New York: Appleton-Century-Crofts

LEVINE, S. (1960) 'Stimulation in infancy' *Scientific American*, **202**, 80-86

LEVY D. M. (1937) 'Primary affect hunger' *American Journal of Psychiatry*, **94**, 643-652

LORENZ, K. (1935) 'Der Kumpan in der Umwelt des Vogels'. Translated as 'Companionship in Bird Life,' pp. 83-128 in Claire H. Schiller (Ed.), *Instinctive Behavior* New York: International Universities Press, 1957

MILLER, N. E., & DOLLARD, J. (1941) *Social Learning and Imitation* New Haven: Yale University Press

MONTGOMERY, K. C. (1951) 'The relation between exploratory behavior and spontaneous alternation in the white rat' *Journal of Comparative and Physiological Psychology*, **44**, 582-589

MOWRER, O. H. (1950) *Learning Theory and Personality Dynamics* New York: Ronald Press

MOWRER, O. H., & KLUCKHOHN, C. (1944) 'Dynamic theory of

personality' Pp. 69-135, in J. McV. Hunt (Ed.), *Personality and the Behavior Disorders*. Vol. 1. New York: Ronald Press

MYERS, J. L. (1958) 'Secondary reinforcement: A review of recent experimentation' *Psychological Bulletin*, **55**, 284-301

PIAGET, J. (1952) *The Origins of Intelligence in Children* New York; International Universities Press

PREMACK, D., COLLIER, G., & ROBERTS, C. L. (1957) 'Frequency of light contingent bar pressing as a function of the amount of deprivation for light' *American Psychologist*, **12**, 411 (Abstract)

RHEINGOLD, HARRIET, GEWIRTZ, J. L., & ROSS, HELEN, W. (1959) 'Social conditioning of vocalizations in the infant' *Journal of Comparative and Physiological Psychology*, **52**, 68-73

RIBBLE, MARGARET A. (1943) *The Rights of Infants* New York: Columbia Univ. Press

RIBBLE, MARGARET A. (1944) 'Infantile experience in relation to personality development' Pp. 621-651, in J. McV. Hunt (Ed.), *Personality and the Behavior Disorders* New York: Ronald Press

SCOTT, J. P. (1960) 'Comparative social psychology'. Chapter 9, pp. 250-288, in Waters, R. H., Rethlingshafer, D. A. & Caldwell, W. E. (Eds.) *Principles of Comparative Psychology* New York: McGraw-Hill

SEARS, R. R. (1951) 'A theoretical framework for personality and social behavior' *American Psychologist*, **6**, 476-483

SEARS, R. R. *et al.* (1953) 'Some child rearing antecedents of aggression and dependency in young children' *Genetic Psychology Monographs*, **47**, 135-234

SHIRLEY, MARY M. (1933) *The First Two Years: A Study of Twenty-Five Babies. Vol. III. Personality Manifestations* Minneapolis: University of Minnesota Press

SKINNER, B. F. (1938) *The Behavior of Organisms* New York: Appleton-Century

SKINNER, B. F. (1953) *Science and Human Behavior* New York: Macmillan

SPALDING, D. A. (1873) 'Instinct: with original observations on young animals', reprinted in *B.J. Animal Behaviour*, 1954, **2**, 2-11

SPITZ, R. A. (1945) 'Hospitalism: An inquiry into the genesis of psychiatric conditions in early childhood' *Psychoanalytic Study of the Child*, **1**, 53-74

Jacob L. Gewirtz

SPITZ, R. A. (1946a) 'Hospitalism: A follow-up report' *Psychoanalytic Study of the Child*, 2, 113-117

SPITZ, R. A. (1946b) 'Anaclitic depression' *Psychoanalytic Study of the Child*, 2, 313-342

SPITZ, R. A. (1949) 'The role of ecological factors in emotional development in infancy' *Child Development*, 20, 145-156

SPITZ, R. A. (1950) 'Anxiety in infancy: A study of its manifestations in the first year of life' *International Journal of Psychoanalysis*, 21, 138-143

SPITZ, R. A. (1954) 'Unhappy and fatal outcomes of emotional deprivation and stress in infancy', in Iago Galdston (Ed.), *Beyond the Germ Theory* New York: Health Education Council

SPITZ, R. A., & WOLF, K. M. (1946) 'The smiling response: A contribution to the ontogenesis of social relations' *Genetic Psychology Monographs*, 34, 57-125

THORPE, W. H. (1956) *Learning and Instinct in Animals* London: Methuen

TINBERGEN, N. (1951) *The Study of Instinct* Oxford: Oxford University Press

VERPLANCK, W. S. (1955) 'An hypothesis on imprinting' *British Journal of Animal Behaviour*, 3, 123

VERPLANCK, W. S. (1957) 'A glossary of some terms used in an objective science of behavior' *Psychological Review* (Suppl.), 64, No. 6, Part 2

WOODWORTH, R. S. (1958) *Dynamics of Behavior* New York: Holt

ZIMMERMAN,, D. W. (1957) 'Durable secondary reinforcement: Method and theory' *Psychological Review*, 64, 373-383

APPENDIX

NOTES

1. In this analysis I shall follow these conventions in labelling stimuli: an unconditional stimulus, which in the brief period immediately following its presentation increases the likelihood of occurrence of one or more categories of apparently free or operant behaviors (but not reflex responses) relative to a condition when such a stimulus is absent, is termed an *evoking* stimulus; an unconditioned stimulus which elicits a given unconditioned reflex response is termed an *eliciting* stimulus; and a stimulus which increases systematically the occurrence of a response when made immediately contingent upon it is termed a (positive) *reinforcing* stimulus.

2. This conception, that the organism is full of life and responsive *to* and *for* a large variety of unconditioned (and conditioned) stimuli which have no apparent survival value where the traditional biological drives are concerned, is not a new one. Concepts very much like it have been advanced through the years by various psychological theorists, many of whom represent quite different fundamental approaches to psychological issues. Thus, this notion would hardly surprise Piaget (1952) and others who have written on the origins of intelligent and adaptive behavior in humans, particularly children's play. And Skinner (1938, 1953) early in his work emphasized a conception of this sort in the field of experimental learning, as has Woodworth (1958), and those who have emphasized the transformation of energy in ego psychology (e.g. Hartmann, 1939), and the concept of active mastery and actualization (Goldstein, 1940; Hendrick, 1942). Indeed, J. M. Baldwin (1906) appears to have advanced a similar notion (his Law of Dynamogenesis) at the beginning of the century.

Nevertheless, the growing readiness at this time to accept this conception of the characteristics of the developing child would seem to be based more on the evidence accumulating from diverse researches and observations in recent years (mostly with lower animals and infra-human primates in a variety of behavior settings), than on the conceptual climate surveyed above. These studies have employed a variety of experimental operation and observations under such headings as curiosity (Berlyne, 1950), exploration (e.g. Montgomery, 1951), intrinsic motivation (Harlow, 1950, 1953), manipulation (Harlow, Harlow and Meyer, 1950), play in young animals (Beach, 1945), stimulus satiation (Glanzer, 1953), and instrumental learning where simple auditory or visual stimuli function as reinforcers of behavior (e.g. Butler, 1953, 1957; Premack, Collier, and Roberts, 1957). They direct our attention quite forcefully to the implication that stimuli of the environment may evoke and maintain behaviors of the young child. In particular, they underline the possibility that various environmental changes in the direction of novelty, variety, complexity, or simply various discriminal consequences which can be referred back to action by the child, may function as reinforcing stimuli for the child's behaviors if they occur directly contingent upon them. And the effectiveness of such stimuli as reinforcers would be independent of the reinforcing stimuli, like food and water, relevant to the biological needs of the child.

3. It is possible that further analysis and research on the functioning of stimuli generally will provide us with a quite different picture of the basic mechanism underlying the operation of positive reinforcing stimuli than even the one which receives emphasis in this paper. I think we may find that almost any non-noxious stimulus to which an organism will respond regularly (on either an unconditioned or a conditioned basis) will function as a reinforcing stimulus if made properly contingent upon his behavior. To be sure, as is the case for the stimuli of food and water, a variety of background conditions which can effect the organism at the time of observation may qualify the operating characteristics of these positive reinforcing stimuli. Some of these qualifying conditions will be discussed in a later section.

4. Is it useful to postulate innate drives 'for' such reinforcing stimuli in infancy? It is relevant to emphasize parenthetically in this connection that, since the functioning of such potential unconditioned reinforcing stimuli as the ones listed here (and of the conditioned reinforcers which will be considered next) can be explained in terms of reinforcing stimulus control *alone*, it would be gratuitous

to attempt to explain their functioning (as some frequently quoted theorists of early development appear to have done) by invoking hunger-like instinctive 'needs' of the child, as for example an 'innate need for contact with the mother' (Ribble, 1943, 1944). Of course, such motivational terms might still be employed in cases where drive operations as typically defined (e.g. deprivation-satiation and similar manipulations) are found to control the effectiveness on behavior of stimuli, particularly reinforcing stimuli. However, even in such cases these motivational terms typically provide no more explanatory power than would a simple statement of the class heading under which the experimental manipulation falls, or, for that matter, than would a brief statement of the experimental manipulation itself. (See the section which follows, on contemporary background conditions which may determine the effectiveness of stimuli in behavior and learning, for some further speculations on this point.)

5. If we take into account work on imprinting with avian subjects, and Harlow's (1958, 1959) most interesting result on the clinging of his Rhesus monkey infants, the possibility comes to mind that reinforcing stimuli may be more specific to the species variable than we had heretofore thought. Thus, visual stimuli might be relatively the most potent as reinforcers for birds generally, stimuli provided by touch and body feel the most potent reinforcers for the Rhesus monkey, visual and sound stimuli (or some combination of body contact, sight, sound, even smell) the most potent reinforcers for the human infant, with still other reinforcing stimulus hierarchies holding in other species.

6. While sometimes the infant may find some of the above list of possible positive reinforcing stimuli aversive (whether or not they occur as consequences of his behavior), it is sufficient for our purpose here to note that under normal conditions they can constitute potential positive reinforcing stimuli for an infant's behavior. One likely condition under which the infant may find a positive reinforcing stimulus to be aversive is when he is well-satiated for that stimulus, whether it be food, a light or a sound, and cannot avoid 'receiving' it (through his mouth if food or through his receptors if light or sound). The infant may sometimes be able to cut out particular stimuli. Frequently, however, he would not be able to manage this, in which case the stimuli involved would begin to function as aversive events.

7. The possibility remains that upon further analysis some of the stimuli which have appeared to function as reinforcers on an unconditioned basis for the infant would be found to have acquired and maintained their reinforcer values through conditioning. Thus, for example, the possibility exists that even the conditions of the sight of food or of environmental change, each may be effective as reinforcing stimuli not on an unconditioned basis, but rather as conditioned generalized reinforcers.

In this connection, there comes to mind particularly aspects of stimulus objects the reinforcing effectiveness of which appear to be under the control of periodic, homeostatic conditions, as food and water. In the case of *food*, for example, the stimuli provided by the sounds accompanying its presentation, the sight of it, its smell, and its taste each may have acquired reinforcer value for behavior solely on the basis of its position in the usually invariant sequence of events which leads ultimately to some terminal unconditioned reinforcing event. And they should be extinguishable as reinforcing stimuli if the sequence in which they constitute an important occasion for behavior could be broken at some point. This possibility fits generally with the informal observations made by a number of workers;

for example, Professor Harry Harlow has observed that rhesus monkeys must learn (and rather slowly at that) to eat food.

Further, *environmental change* may be conditioned as a reinforcing stimulus. As the child grows, an increasing number of his responses will become reinforced by a growing number of both unconditioned and conditioned reinforcing stimuli provided by the increasingly direct effects of his ever-increasing success in operating on the environment. As a function of its having occurred contiguously with a large variety of potent reinforcing stimuli (perhaps even before most conditioned reinforcing stimuli have developed as such for a child), it is possible that the fact of environmental change *per se*, or simply the immediate effect of a change in the environment, will develop as a conditioned generalized reinforcing stimulus. On this basis, it would function as a most potent reinforcer capable of controlling the behaviors of the child within a wide range. This possibility would, of course, question the interpretation that stimulus change functions as an unconditioned reinforcing stimulus class; and this would parallel the possibility that the sound, sight, smell and taste of food may function as conditioned reinforcing stimuli.

Thus, also, some of the stimuli provided the child through contact-holding, as when he is picked up to distract or otherwise quiet him at times when he is in apparent pain, or for feeding and other caretaking, stimuli which have generally been thought to operate as unconditioned reinforcers, may have acquired some or all of their reinforcing power through conditioning. This could be because of the association for the child of these contact stimuli with the potent reinforcing stimuli provided by the disappearance (through distraction) of the pain, by 'interesting' environmental changes, or by feeding and caretaking.

8. While there is some controversy about whether a stimulus need be discriminative in order to acquire conditioned reinforcer value (see particularly Myers [1958] and Zimmerman [1957] in this connection), such an assumption will be made for the purposes of this presentation. In any event, the eventual outcome of this controversy is not critical for us here. Also not critical for our purpose here is the fact that our understanding of the variables governing the acquisition by stimuli of reinforcer value is far from complete.

However, it would be most important for my point here to consider some technical issues raised by the conditioned reinforcer model. Some have argued (e.g. Allport, 1937) that the attempt to conceptualize social motivation and attachments on the basis of the descriptive concepts of a reinforcement learning theory and focally the concept of the conditioned reinforcing stimulus must fail because even in simple laboratory experiments conditioned reinforcing stimuli have been but fleeting in their effectiveness. The limited power of these stimuli follows from the fact that in the usual laboratory situation the pairing (on a 100 per cent basis ordinarily) between the conditioned reinforcer and the original reinforcing stimuli which have given it its value typically is discontinued once testing for the effectiveness of the conditioned reinforcer begins, i.e. the tests generally are conducted under extinction conditions. But such laboratory conditions are far removed from the life situations being considered here. For in actual life settings pairings between conditioned reinforcers and a variety of functioning reinforcers would continue regularly, if at times infrequently, and effective extinction conditions for the conditioned reinforcing stimuli should rarely, if ever, maintain.

Moreover, positive conditioned reinforcers which in life depend on the mediation of another cooperative person, who is not infrequently otherwise occupied or deliberately uncooperative in her role of socializer of the child, may be assumed to develop under conditions of intermittent reinforcement. Further, once conditioned reinforcers are developed, they would be made available on an intermittent basis, for some of the same reasons. Such intermittent reinforcement conditions ordinarily can generate rather stable behavior output rates which are highly resistant to extinction, probably in part because they are not readily discriminated from extinction conditions. Zimmerman (1957) is one of the few who have made this important point; he did so while demonstrating the possibility of establishing conditioned reinforcing stimuli which were resistent to extinction to an extent not previously known.

9. This consideration of the functioning of conditioned social reinforcers would be less than complete if note were not taken of the important possibility that the stimuli of proprioceptive or sensory responses, including the stimulus components of those learned responses which move forward in a sequence to become anticipatory (c.f., e.g., Sears, 1951), may acquire conditioned reinforcer value. These stimuli would occupy in the stimulus-response chain positions closer to the terminal reinforcing stimuli which maintain it than do the potential conditioned reinforcing stimuli which were discussed earlier. Even so, it is the concept of the chain which is the crucial one here, and there are clear advantages in attending to observable stimuli of the class earlier discussed, rather than to such unobservable events as sensory stimuli. Further, the correlation between the two types of stimuli should approach unity.

10. On this basis, the effective control of the child's behavior by the withholding of generalized reinforcers would be less effective when the child is either very young or almost of school age, for in the former case it is he, essentially, who controls the reinforcing stimuli for the parent's behavior, and in the latter case he has access to reinforcing stimuli (upon which the efficacy of the generalized reinforcing stimulus is based) in other environments.

11. Outcomes 4 (*a*), 4 (*b*) and 4 (*e*) of a change in reinforcing setting can highlight an interesting paradox for us. They indicate that there may be a high rate of behavior for conditioned reinforcing stimuli, initially, in a new setting, as would be involved in a move to a new home, or into therapy. For on the basis of the analysis I present elsewhere in this paper of the hunger-like drive model for reinforcing stimuli, which seems to be held by many, a high rate of behavior for such reinforcing stimuli could indicate that the child was 'hungry' for them, in the sense that he had not received them in sufficient quantity in his recent or distant past. One consequence of this interpretation might be for the reinforcing agency to dispense reinforcing stimuli on a correlated, abundant schedule, which would maintain the high rate of the child's behavior for the reinforcer class until a change were made to a thinner schedule of reinforcement. Alternatively, if the appropriate reinforcer class were not dispensed at all to the child in the new setting, outcome 4(*c*) might be the consequence.

12. While the effects on stimulus functioning of deprivation-satiation operations are emphasized in this analysis, there would seem to be other background conditions which also control the effectiveness for the organism of stimuli in their different roles, but particularly as reinforcers. These may include such experimental manipulations as are involved in the following examples: From the field of perception we know that there are ways of manipulating (along one or more dimensions) the background stimulus conditions in order to diminish (as might be accomplished also by satiation) or to heighten (as might be accom-

plished also by deprivation) the discriminability of a stimulus figure, and hence to determine its effectiveness as a discriminative or a reinforcing stimulus. Further, the condition of reappearance after removal of a familiar, yet unimportant, background stimulus could function (at least for a time) as an effective discriminative stimulus, and as a positive reinforcing stimulus as well. Thus, for example, it is the rare person who ordinarily would attend to the walls of a room in which he spends much time. Yet his behaviors might be strongly reinforced if, after a wall were removed, its reappearance were made contingent upon them, and he might respond at a regular rate to keep the wall from disappearing. This notion would be compatible with conceptions of the importance of an accustomed environment for normal functioning (see, e.g., Hebb, 1958b). A last example involving quite different phenomena may be useful here also. If on one or more trials an individual's performance is not up to his expectation, the reinforcing stimulus provided by a subsequent performance which is up to expectation may be raised in effectiveness relative to those provided by each of a set of performance trials all of which are in keeping with his expectation.

13. This general possibility, that deprivation-satiation operations control the reinforcing effectiveness of a wide variety of stimuli, is supported by a growing body of research from diverse sources: the work of Hinde (1954), with a variety of species but particularly with the mobbing behavior of the chaffinch, on factors in short-term response habituation and recovery from habituation is especially relevant, as is the work of Glanzer (1953) on simple instances of stimulus satiation in the rat. Further, several studies have shown that limiting the availability of diverse stimuli which would not seem relevant to the biological needs of the organism, increases systematically their reinforcing effectiveness. Thus, Premack, Collier and Roberts (1957) have found that the effectiveness of the onset of a light as a reinforcing stimulus for an instrumental response in the rat was an increasing function of time spent in darkness, i.e. deprivation of light. And, similarly, Butler (1957) has found that an opportunity briefly to observe diverse events through an observation window was effective as a reinforcing event for an instrumental response in the Rhesus monkey as an increasing function of time in a confinement box, i.e. of deprivation of observation opportunity. Finally, two partially replicating studies that Baer and I carried out (Gewirtz and Baer, 1958a, 1958b) with children of different ages are relevant to this issue. They were on the reinforcing effectiveness for instrumental behavior of an adult's approval, and of social contact with her, both of which we assumed function as conditioned reinforcing stimuli. We found that the effectiveness of those stimuli as reinforcers was enhanced by an immediately preceding 20-minute period of (what we judged to be non-anxious) social isolation (deprivation), and lowered after an immediately preceding 20-minute period of intensive social contact (satiation), both relative to a preceding (intermediate) condition of normal classroom contact.

14. This conception of the importance early in the child's life of complete habituation of many of the diverse emotional behavior complexes present in the child's innate or initial hierarchy of responsiveness to the environment would seem to be generally consistent with Ribble's (1943, 1944) loosely supported contention about the importance of 'plentiful fondling' for the infant's development. This is based on what she labels the 'need for contact' with a mother-person, which requires ample opportunity for the infant to suck at the breast, to be held, rocked or stroked, especially when excited. Specifically, the implications of the concept of complete habituation in early development would be parallel

to those of Ribble's fondling notion to the extent that: (*a*) the fondling would provide the basis for the possibly complete habituation of a large variety of potentially negative-emotion-laden responses of the infant to his environment; and (*b*) the possibility that the child's excitement response would involve those innate emotional responses, and that habituation would be facilitated through the occurrence of incompatible relaxation responses brought about by being held, rocked and stroked. It is of course possible also that handling (and even noxious stimulation) may determine aspects of organic maturation and development, and reduce organic reactions to stress, as Levine (1960) has shown in the infant rat.

15. The essence of *instrumental* dependence is that some response of another person is required by the child to attain a reinforcing stimulus which is otherwise independent of the characteristics of either the helping response (e.g. attention) or the appearance of the helping agent. Examples would be getting food when hungry or legitimate help in attaining an important object which is out of reach. I have proposed in this paper that this type of interaction constitutes the basis for the development through learning of both non-instrumental, social dependence on people generally and attachments to particular people. Thus, it receives ample emphasis in this analysis, and hence requires no further special mention here. On the other hand, the essence of social dependence is that the reinforcing stimulus maintaining the child's behavior is provided through a positive social response, such as attention or approval, from any one of the members of a large class of persons, adults for example; and apart from a gross limit like this one the reinforcing stimulus would otherwise be independent of the appearance characteristics specific to the person making the reinforcing response to the child.

In this connection, it is of interest to note that in his provocative paper on the nature of the earliest human attachment Bowlby (1958) appears to differentiate only between instrumental dependence on, and attachment to, the mother-figure. He does not there attend to the possibility of an unspecific, social dependence on people generally, as I have done here (unless that would be implied, perhaps on such a basis as that of the principle of stimulus generalization; i.e. responses of the class made to the attached person would be made to other persons with a frequency and amplitude that is proportional to the distance separating those other persons from the attached person along relevant dimensions of similarity). However, this omission simply may be due to the fact that he meant his analysis to deal only with the origin and the quality of the child's first attachment, to his caretaker-mother, and not with social motivation and attachment generally (as is our purpose here), nor even with later developing attachments as that of the child to its father (which we also omit).

16. It is on a basis very much like this one that Mowrer (1950) conceives of the development of an attachment of the 'talking' bird to its trainer. Mowrer holds that the conditioned generalized reinforcing stimuli which are provided by the presence and attention of its trainer are the most important conditions for bringing out (i.e. maintaining) the best talking performance of the bird, in that the bird appears to find talking one of the best ways to attain such reinforcing stimuli from the trainer.

17. To facilitate this analysis, I shall eliminate from consideration the consequences of the availability in the family setting of both a father (-figure) and siblings, which would seem to introduce considerations different from those encountered in the institution. In effect, as Anna Freud (1951) has suggested,

the child's underlying relationship to his siblings is determined by his relationship to his parents and hence is a negative one, which is far less likely to be the case in the institution. Thus, such factors as the birth of a younger sibling, who inevitably displaces the child in the finite attentions of the single constant caretaker-mother, can play a special role, as does the greater likelihood that children in the family will cover a wider age range than the usually more homogeneous institutional groups.

18. The speculations in the immediately preceding sections were advanced with an eye to suggesting bases for some of the differences between home babies and institutional babies reported in the literature. I rush to point out, however, that institutions could provide relatively good environments for children (in terms of various of the assumptions emphasized in my analysis), while ordinary families may provide relatively poor caretaking environments. In short, there would be no necessary correlation between institution and 'bad', and between family and 'good'.

19. In this connection, it is interesting to note that even those (e.g. Hess, 1959) who are skeptical of the thesis that imprinting is a learning process, and think that it must constitute a most atypical learning process if it involves learning at all, assume that imprinting results only in the appreciation by the animal of the rough class characteristics of the imprinted object; and that the appreciation of the special stimulus characteristics of the particular object is acquired through normal learning.

20. Drive concepts have sometimes been employed to order phenomena through long time spans, for example, 'learned drive' and 'conditioned fear'. In such cases, typically, the term drive has been added gratuitously, as only learning operations are involved. In most instances, this is explained by the requirement of particular theoretical approaches (for the sake of internal consistency according to key assumptions) that certain habits, i.e. where behavior may be explained in terms of acquired stimulus control alone, be labelled (learned) drives. Alternatively, this usage sometimes seems due simply to labelling conventions that are long (if unsystematically) established in some conceptual areas.

21. Further, it is in keeping with the preceding analysis that, if we do *not* think it plausible to assume (*a*) that the infant is born into the world with fully developed social needs, (*b*) that certain environmental conditions are necessary for the blossoming or unfolding of biologically determined social behavior patterns, or that other non-learning processes (like imprinting, as some have thought of it) account for his social tendencies, then we must necessarily look to the learning contingencies present in recurring environmental conditions provided the infant by the behavior of his caretaking agency for the basis of the acquisition by him of patterns of social behavior and reinforcing stimuli.

Discussion following Paper by Dr Gewirtz

ROSENBLATT *May I make a rather general comment on the theory presented by Dr Gewirtz. Perhaps the best way I can put it is to say that he has presented an 'animal-free' behaviour theory much as those who create intelligence tests have attempted to make 'culture-free' intelligence tests. It no longer applies to any particular animal but rather it deals with all animals and with all forms of behaviour. Moreover, it is based on a single factor, that of reinforcement, which may not even be called a mechanism as it is used in the present discussion. It is not a mechanism since it refers to the outcome of selection by the environment from the available behaviour of the animal by whatever mechanism may be responsible for the selection. I would wonder whether at this stage this type of theory is helpful to use.*

GEWIRTZ *I don't see how you can say that. Feathers fall at different rates than do stones in some atmospheres. Yet, we would not be content to have one theory for the behaviour of feathers and another for that of stones. According to experience in science, it has been the most fruitful approach generally to build 'object-free' theories, which would cover both feathers and stones, and other events as well. Specifically, such a theory would include statements about the special effects of atmospheres and statements about the more general effects of gravity. The response and reinforcement emphasis of the theoretical approach I have outlined would be roughly parallel to general statements about gravity in the preceding example. In that sense, it would be 'object-free'. In my presentation, I attempted to show (and to illustrate for the human case) how, for instance, reinforcing stimuli might operate on different bases, and how different species of animals might each pass through stages in which different responses, or reinforcing stimuli, might be pre-potent. Thus, I attempted to tie the theory to a particular animal species (human), to developmental levels in the species, and the like. In this way, I was putting the object back into the theory, as it were, by providing more specific statements that would parallel those about atmosphere in the 'falling bodies' example cited.*

HARLOW *I certainly think Jay Rosenblatt's comment is correct when applied to the original Hull-Spence type of theory. Such a theory is 'animal-free' and also 'capacity-free'; and no attempt is made to show how the theory would account for differences between species, and developmental differences within a species.*

HINDE *We seem to be contrasting developmental ideas with formal explanations, but I think there is no real dichotomy. When people talk about physiological needs, the fact that these needs are important for reinforcement is a consequence of development. And this applies also to 'needs' like tickling, contact and so on which John Bowlby talks about, and the 'Need for Affection' which clinicians talk about. This is a useful language for them because they are concerned with the total responses of one individual, which have acquired their unique pattern during the development of that individual. But there is no incompatibility with a language of drives and reinforcement.*

GEWIRTZ *You have put the matter well. However, if I may move a bit from this last point, there are sometimes emphases in what would otherwise be molar behavioural approaches in which 'under the skin' explanations, in terms of physiological or chemical variables, are sought for molar behaviour. Apparently there is an assumption here that such explanation is more fundamental than would be explanation in terms of environmental variables which lie 'outside the skin'. Of course, what is the most fundamental explanation would depend on the requirements in the definition of the problem under study. Explanation in terms of environmental variables is surely the most fundamental in a molar approach. As a result, our problems are phrased and our explanations are sought in those terms. With respect to the issues of human social development with which I have been concerned in my paper, I and most others would be content for now with explanation in terms of such environmental variables. I do not mean to imply that 'goings-on' under the skin are not important. Of course they are. It would be as if we believed in ghosts if we thought otherwise. However, such events would be reflected in environmental input variables on the one hand, and would be reflected in turn by the molar behaviours which provide our dependent variables on the other. In this sense, account is taken of 'under the skin' variables in a molar analysis, just as, in the same sense, account is taken of molar variables in a physiological or biochemical analysis.*

HARLOW *What you are saying is that you won't consider in the theory any dependent variables that are not overt responses or the outcome of responses?*

GEWIRTZ *Exactly. I suppose a critical case for my point would be one like the following: Let us suppose that a 'habitscope' were invented which, when attached to an appropriate portion of a subject's body, could index relevant events under his skin. While the 'scope' could*

Discussion

generate dependent variables, many of which might be useful, these would still be far removed from the classes of overt behaviour we would ordinarily be interested in predicting in a molar approach, to social behaviour for instance. In this example, it would remain necessary to look for the relationship between these overt behaviours and the behaviour of the 'habitscope'. Hence, it would be more parsimonious to relate the independent variables directly to the overt behaviour variables.

BOWLBY *The big problem for many of us with such a theory is to see how it copes with those situations where an overt response is the result of something that happened a long time ago. What about dreams and thoughts and fantasies and all those other things that go bumbledozing along, and have power to influence our behaviour?*

FOSS *Isn't it just because Hebb's theory tries to include continuing internal processes that it has proved so attractive to many?*

BLAUVELT *Several times during this symposium we have talked about the importance of analysing the behaviour of infant and mother not separately but as a sequence of complicated interactions. It seems quite possible that it is the interaction itself which has high selective value here. If so, the study of this interaction should prove a profitable source of hypotheses regarding the capacities of infant and mother, including the capacity for changes in behaviour, whatever we call them. Such changes in the newborn have been defined in a variety of ways, such as – changes in one phase of a reflex response; the waning of the response; conditioning, and imprinting. Would you be open to the possibility that imprinting is a very special and rapid kind of learning in interaction which exists because of its selective value?*

GEWIRTZ *In keeping with what has been proposed in my paper, it is not a simple matter for those who think of imprinting as a case of learning under rather special circumstances to specify with confidence the nature of the learning contingencies that would be involved. Still, at the present time it seems plausible for us to suppose that the object-following behaviour-pattern of imprinting is due to a very rapid kind of learning under the unique interaction conditions which hold in earliest life for the young of certain species. Thus, the following-pattern might be frequently and potently reinforced in a short span of time in the complete absence of competing response systems. Further, whether or not imprinting is proved*

293

ultimately to be an instance of special, early learning, it seems reasonable to use a similar learning model to approach the case of early attachment learning in human infants. In this context, it would seem impossible for the young of avian species which exhibit the following behaviour-pattern of imprinting to survive for any length of time if they did not acquire that pattern. Nevertheless, I would doubt whether this process or any similar one could play such a critical role for the human infant. Under normal circumstances, he would receive reasonable care under almost all conditions. Hence, it would not seem to be as critical for his effective survival (even if it were possible) that he follow his caretaker by locomoting in space in his earliest months, or even that he be responsive to her, or form an attachment with her. Of course, I imagine we would all agree that the infant who is responsive to and orients towards his caretaker mother would be likely to turn out better in the long run than would the infant who is not.

FOSS *I wonder if I could underline Dr Blauvelt's point, not so much with respect to imprinting, as to try to show how interaction can be a vital factor in the development of discriminations? I think I could put this best by means of a story which is rather freely adapted from one by Hayakawa. There were three neighbours, Smith, Jones and Robinson, whose neighbourhood was invaded by small furry animals. Smith was a gardener, and soon discovered that these animals ate his cabbages, so he tried to chase them away. Some of them ran off emitting high metallic noises (and these he called 'pings') whereas others – and he noticed incidentally that they had longer tails – tended to bite him, so he called them 'pangs'. Jones wasn't a gardener, but he had a wife who complained that the animals smelled, and she was allergic to them. So Jones called them 'pongs'. One day the three men saw one of these animals run across the road. 'Look,' said Smith, 'that's either a ping or a pang.' 'No,' said Jones, 'it's a pong.' But Robinson, who was a bachelor, with no garden and no sense of smell, said, 'Nonsense. It's just one of those things.' The moral of this story is that the more commerce or interaction a person has with a class of objects, the finer will be his discrimination among these objects. And it seems to me that the analysis of this in terms of interactions is more realistic than an analysis in terms of reinforcement. After all, Smith, who had the finest discriminations, was reacting to the animals, and they were reacting to him. I would guess that some of the most intense discrimination learning that goes on is between a mother and infant.*

GEWIRTZ *I hasten to say that the elements of the illustration you have just presented are quite compatible with conventional learning approaches. As I have attempted in my paper, one can analyse the interaction both among persons, and between persons and environmental events, in terms of learning concepts, with reinforcement playing a central role. For instance, one could think of Smith as having learned to discriminate readily between the noisy 'pings' and the biting 'pangs' simply because of the different negative (reinforcing) consequences they involved: 'pings' pirated his cabbages while 'pangs' bit him. Given an identical problem for analysis, I don't see how you think you could approach it more effectively using what you have called 'realistic' interaction terms. To say this differently, I can't imagine that for the level of complexity of your example you could emphasize concepts that would be different from conventional learning concepts, except that you might assign different labels for them, for example labels with a cognitive flavour. Thus, in attending to the interaction between the person and the object, you are bound to focus on more than just the 'amount' of commerce between them. Surely you would single out for emphasis the interaction which leads to consequences that are important for Smith or for Jones. These consequences would be the reinforcing stimuli of an operational learning analysis. In Smith's case the consequences of having his cabbages eaten and being bitten would constitute negative reinforcing stimuli. Further, the events associated with these consequences, noises and the word 'ping' or long tails and the word 'pang', could readily acquire cue or sign value for Smith.*

FOSS *I agree that one would want to analyse the interaction in terms of its consequences. What I wanted to emphasize was the to-and-fro quality of the interaction. Each participant is emitting a continuous flow of behaviour. At any moment, what he does will depend on what he was doing a moment before, what he anticipates doing next, what the other participant had been doing, and what he anticipates the other participant will do next. Because of this complexity, I think it is inevitable that one must start with a molar analysis – as David and Appell have suggested in their paper – and the analysis will have to include measures which can only roughly be quantified,* such as the amount of interaction. Indeed it might be profitable to use concepts 'with a cognitive flavour'.

Can I make a general comment on why I think learning theories are not at present very fruitful when applied to human development? This is aimed at learning theories in general, and may come from the fact that most learning theorists use rats for their experiments. Those psychologists who have concentrated on human personality, rather than rat behaviour, always incorporate in their theories some concept such as 'identification', and Freudian theory in particular leans very heavily on this concept. Now I should think that one of the main behavioural clues that identification is occurring would be that the identifier imitates; and I want to suggest that learning theory must tackle the explanation of imitation before it can claim to be helpful in elucidating how humans develop. I should like to ask two questions: can personality theory do without a concept of identification? And, assuming that imitation is a behavioural concomitant of identification, can imitation learning be explained in terms of reinforcement?

GEWIRTZ *I shall first attempt a reply to your first question. In one sense, every theory could do without any given concept. This is because a concept is essentially a labelled abstraction which stems, if loosely, from the empirical relationships to which the theory attends in the area of study. A concept is intended to order the relationships currently known in the area, and to focus those to be sought in the future. However, there is another sense in which it is not possible to dispense with a concept. That is when the relationships the theory holds important, between present and past environmental variables and behaviours of the organism, are reflected in the concept (e.g. 'identification'). It is in this latter sense that the reply to your first question must be that, in general, the personality theories held currently could not do without the concept of identification. This is because the definition of the problem of personality of the standard theories places emphasis on the phenomena the identification concept has been evolved to cover. Before attempting a reply to your second question, I should like for a moment to consider your general comment. There are theories (e.g. the psychoanalytic theory of personality) which employ certain central concepts to deal with important and complex problem areas to which they have directed their main attention for a long time. This fact*

Discussion

in itself cannot be taken to indicate that those theories are handling well the problems on which they focus. There are also general approaches to behaviour, and here I have in mind learning theories in particular, which in both early and later stages of their development attempt to use stripped-down, basic and simple paradigms and settings to facilitate their analyses of important problems. It does not seem constructive to demand that these latter approaches immediately handle most articulately and subtly all the nuances of such complex problem areas as, for instance, might be indexed by use of the 'identification' concept. Finally, it does not seem useful to hold against such theories this quality which reflects their systematic nature more than their inadequacy, unless it is shown that by doing this, they omit from consideration certain important and relevant aspects of the problem.

FOSS *But learning theorists have applied their theories to the explanation of concept formation, which is complex.*

GEWIRTZ *Let me now reply to your second question, about whether imitation learning could be explained in terms of reinforcement. Various experimental demonstrations of imitation have accrued on rats, children, and adults where the response of copying or following another individual is acquired through reinforcement. Some 20 years ago, Miller and Dollard illustrated in a series of experiments that through reinforcement rats could learn to follow leader-rats. Since then, quite a few experiments with children and adults have shown that the response of copying the behaviour of another person (the model), with or without awareness, could be acquired according to the instrumental response paradigm. At this juncture, however, if I might backtrack for a moment to the concept of identification proper of which imitation controlled by reinforcement may be taken to be the initial basis, I think I can illustrate what may be involved for a reinforcement learning approach to identification. It is possible that the first stage in the identification process is one where in each of numerous settings, various of the child's behaviours which are similar to those of his identification model (e.g. the parent of the same sex) have been and are regularly reinforced. In the next stage, the child could generalize to exhibit behaviours like those of his model which were never reinforced before, as well as responses he had witnessed in his model, and others he has guessed his model would make in the circumstances.*

297

Some of these responses of the child would now be reinforced by the classes of reinforcers which have been operating for him all along. In the last stage, modelling behaviours themselves might acquire reinforcer value for the child, which, together with the various other reinforcers which continue to operate for him, would strongly support his modelling behaviour. What I have just outlined would represent one aspect of identification-through-reinforcement to which a learning approach might attend.

HARLOW *I think imitation is a really important problem; and it's likely to be particularly important in primates where vision plays such a dominant part. It's particularly noticeable between monkeys where there's a strong affectional bond.* .

FOSS *This suggests that identification comes before imitation, but isn't there the possibility of a mechanism of imitation as a basic part of behaviour? I'm thinking of the contagion of yawning. Are we in love with all the people who facilitate our yawning by yawning themselves?*

HINDE *I'm confused at this point as to what is meant by imitation. Following responses I should not call imitation; nor yawning when others yawn. The term is usually kept for describing the production of a novel pattern of behaviour as a result of seeing another animal perform it.*

FOSS *I don't see how these things are categorically different. Surely they are on a continuum?*

HARLOW *You certainly find imitation in Robert Hinde's sense, in monkeys and apes. Crawford and Spence have shown that a chimpanzee can learn a discrimination by watching another chimp do it.*

ROSENBLATT *In cats it has been shown that something resembling imitation in Hinde's sense occurs. However, after a developmental, experimental analysis a rather different explanation of imitation was proposed by the investigator (Adler). He suggested that the activity of one cat that is able to perform the behaviour draws the attention of the second cat to the situation and that this animal in turn, develops its own responses independently in a way which resembles the behaviour of the first animal.*

GUNTHER *Isn't it true that monkeys may not know how to feed their babies if they have been taken into captivity so young that they never had a chance to see feeding happen?*

RHEINGOLD *Yerkes in his book states that sometimes a chimpanzee*

Discussion

infant fails to face its mother, and in none of these instances does the mother turn the infant round even though she has seen other chimps feeding. It continues to carry the infant facing outwards, so that in some cases it has perished. I'm just stating this so that we don't forget those occasions when an animal fails to learn by imitation.

HINDE *There is an interesting case of what might be called imitation in passerine birds. At an early age before they start singing they listen to adults singing and apparently learn the characteristics of the species song. Months later they produce a variable babbling themselves from which they select out the sounds which approximate to the species song. To be fanciful, one might say that they first learn what they want to be like, and they then learn to be like it.*

Comment on Paper by Dr Gewirtz

JOHN BOWLBY

For a decade or more there has been a lively debate between ethologists and learning theorists regarding the roles of unlearnt and learnt components in the behaviour of a given species. In emphasizing the role of the component in which they are most interested, members of each discipline have tended to underestimate the role of the other component. Jack Gewirtz and I are no exceptions. However, I believe we are both alive to the problem.

In my own paper on the nature of the child's tie to his mother (Bowlby, 1958), I deliberately left as an open question the extent to which learning processes entered into the development of the tie, but made it clear that I believed them to play a very significant part. Towards the end (page 369) I wrote: 'In this exposition I have emphasized the endogenous aspects of these instinctual responses. Their development in the individual, however, can never be free of change through processes of learning.' It is therefore a serious misunderstanding of my position for Jack Gewirtz to suppose that I had any desire 'to show decisively that learning is *not* involved in any important way in the development of attachment' (page 254).

I am naturally very glad that in his paper Jack Gewirtz leaves open the extent to which unlearnt social releasing stimuli or species-specific behaviour patterns may be involved in parent infant interaction. Nevertheless, I believe the *prima facie* evidence that they probably play a major role to be such that his theoretical model is the poorer for their omission. Indeed, it is in the complex interaction between the gene-determined elements and the environment that most of our problems seem to lie. This viewpoint can be illustrated by reference to maternal responses. There can be no doubt whatever that learning plays a major role in the development of a mother's responses to her baby. The very fact that she quickly comes to focus all her feelings and behaviour on one particular baby must be the result in part of a process of learning. On the other hand, the sudden-

301

ness with which maternal feelings often make their appearance and the overwhelming compulsion they bring to attend to and care for the baby seem to require some other explanation. Since species-specific behaviour patterns are so clearly at work in other mammalian species, why need we baulk at postulating their presence in man? It is only by postulating them, I believe, that clinicians will understand their patients' feelings and that research workers will be oriented to ask the right questions.

The strength of Jack Gewirtz's paper lies, of course, in his detailed examination of the many ways in which learning probably enters into the processes leading to attachment and also into processes provoked by privation and deprivation. As such it represents a great advance on anything that has yet appeared. He has got away from the over-simple hypotheses of need-reduction and recognized that a great variety of stimuli can play an evoking and/or a reinforcing role in infant behaviour and that the precise conditions in which they occur are probably of much consequence. His work should in the long run be of great help both in planning new research and in interpreting findings. Furthermore, I welcome the way it emphasizes afresh the grave limitations that are inherent in any study of infant development, whether in settings favourable or unfavourable to it, which is dependent on second-hand data.

Moreover, unlike many who base their work on learning theories, Jack Gewirtz has given careful attention to the tendency of human infants (like those of other species) to become attracted to particular mother figures, a tendency I have termed 'monotropy', and to the disorganization of behaviour that commonly follows separation from the preferred figure. Even so, I do not regard his discussion of this as adequate. For instance, on p. 268 he emphasizes that how a child behaves to the new caretaker will be determined in part by 'whether the new caretakers learn from the child's behaviour what the appropriate reinforcing stimuli are for him and then provide those stimuli'. Although so far as it goes this formulation is valid, no reference is made to the possibility that the unique characteristics of his own mother-figure, her appearance, facial expressions and gestures, may not only be significant but may even be the most significant reinforcing stimuli. Were this to be so, and since the new caretaker can hardly mimic these things, it would be inevitable that she could never be wholly adequate. Furthermore, Jack Gewirtz's schema does not appear to take sufficient account of the fact that for a long time after separation the child continues to yearn for his absent mother and to search for her (Burlingham and Freud, 1942; Bowlby, Robertson and Rosenbluth, 1952; Heinicke, 1956), a psychological condition which I have shown is in all major respects the same as mourning in adults (Bowlby, 1960). There is reason to think that much of the pathogenic potential of such experiences is due to the fact that these mourning processes in young children rather frequently take a pathological course, the essence of which is that a part of the psychic apparatus remains fixated on and searching for the lost figure.

Finally, I fully agree that the experiences which in the earlier studies were lumped together as deprivation are very heterogeneous and I welcome Jack Gewirtz's discussion of them. A few years ago Mary Ainsworth and I attempted a similar analysis (Ainsworth and Bowlby, 1954), and I notice that his definitions of privation and deprivation are not dissimilar to those we proposed. Future research in this field, if it is to bring new understanding, must be planned to take account of these complexities and must rely on first hand, not retrospective, data. Fortunately, now that the major hypotheses are ceasing to be controversial, it should be easier to obtain support for more refined studies.

REFERENCES

AINSWORTH, M. D., & BOWLBY, J. (1954) 'Research Strategy in the study of Mother-Child Separation' *Courrier*, Centre International de l'Enfance, IV, 3

BOWLBY, J. (1958) 'The Nature of the Child's Tie to his Mother' *Int. J. Psychoanalysis*, **39**, Part V, 350-373

BOWLBY, J. (1960) 'Grief and Mourning in Infancy and early Childhood' *The Psychoanalytic Study of the Child*, vol. XV

BOWLBY, J., ROBERTSON, J., & ROSENBLUTH, D. (1952) 'A Two-year-old goes to Hospital' *The Psychoanalytic Study of the Child*, vol. VII

BURLINGHAM, D., & FREUD, A. (1942) *Young Children in War-time* London: Allen & Unwin

HEINICKE, C. M. (1956) 'Some effects of separating two-year-old children from their parents: A comparative study' *Human Relations*, **9**, 105-176

Index

Figures in *italic* indicate references

Acquired drive, 215
Age, response change with, 29, 204, 205
Aggression in infant, 105, 110
  in monkey, 84, 85
  in cat, 210
Ahrens, R., *180n*, 181
Allport, G. W., *277*, 186
Anoxia in feeding baby, 38f
Areola, 40
Armatruda, C., *26*
Attachments, 80f, 213f, 234ff, 250f
Attention, 223, 225, 229
Aubry, J., 101n

Baer, D. M., 213n, *279*, 288
Bakwin, H., 256, *277*
Baldwin, J. M., *277*, 284
Banks, E. M., *74*
Barnes, R. M., 6, 11, *25*
Beach, F. A., 278, *284*
Behaviour problems in babies, 47, 101f
  compared with monkeys, 89f
  disturbances in kittens, 64, 72f
Benjamin, J., 134n
Benjamin, L. S., *89n*
Berlyne, D. E., 167, *170*, *278*, 284
Bingham, H. C., 23n, *25*
Bligh, A., 38n
Bolwig, N., 23n, *25*
Bowlby, J., 24, *25*, 167,ᵗ168, *170*, 216,
  232, 236, 248, 253, 254, 256,
  257, 274, *278*, 289, 301, *303*
Brackbill, Y., *190n*, 192, 200
Breast feeding, 30f, 37-44
Breech birth, 45f
Bridges, K. M. B., 249, *278*
Buhler, C., 168, *170*
Bullis, G. E., *170*
Burlingham, D., 242, *279*, 303
Butler, R. A., *278*, 284, 288

Caldwell, B. M., *26*
Cannon, D. J., 55, *74*
Caretaker, new, 238, 269f
Caretaking, 121-141, 151, 172
Carpenter, C. R., 23n, *25*
Cathexis, 215
Cats, 51f
Chaffinches, 203
Chicks, 204
Clinging, 82, 91f, 96, 174f, 216, 285
Cohn, R., 58n, *74*
Collier, G., *282*, 284, 288
Conditioning, leg withdrawal, 55
  hormone, 42
  instrumental, 191, 217ff
Contact, 75-97, 175
Critical period, 54f, 73, 80, 94f
Crosby, E. C., *26*
Crying, 34, 129, 218, 232
Cultural differences, 43, 175
Cup-feeding, 44
Curiosity, visual, 76, 145

Dann, S., 236, *279*
Dean, R. F. A., *175n*
De Beer, G., 24, *26*
Dember, W. N., 167, *170*
Dennis, W., 168, *170*
Deprivation, 101-120, 209, 213f, 266f
  (*see also* Isolation, Separation)
  contrasted Privation, 260
  in children, 89f, 144-5, 255-6
  in monkeys, 86f, 89
  meaning of, 205
  short-term, 164, 265
Discrimination, 139, 191f, 197, 207,
  221, 294
Dollard, J., 215, 218, 253, *278*, *281*
Drive, 215ff
Ducker, G., *28*
Dynamogenesis, law of, 284

U   305

Index

James, H., *97n*, 243, 246, *281*
James, W., 243, *281*
James, W. T., 55, *74*
Jaynes, J., 243, 245, *281*

Kaila, E., *179n*
Kanner, L., 263, *281*
Keller, F. S., 217, *281*
Kids, 30
Kittens, 51f
Kluckhohn, C., 215, 253, *281*
Knol, A. R., *45n*
Kohlberg, L., 213n

Lambs, 30
Learning, 207, 213ff
  critical periods in, 94
  difficulties, 46
  earliest record, 42
  learning sets, 207
  socialization, 55f
Levine, S., *281*, 289
Levy, D. M., 256, 257, 271, *281*
Lips, stimulation near, 11f, 30
Lipton, E., 25
Lorenz, K., 24, *27*, 31, 37, 243, *281*
Love, mother's love discussed
  behaviourally, 225f

Macgregor, F., 24, *27*
McKenna, J., 25
Magnus, R., *27*
Manipulation, 76, 96, 145, 163
Mason, W. A., *96n*
Matarazzo, R. G., *26*
Maturation, 55f
Mead, M., 24, *27*
Medication of mother, 29f
Meyer, D. R., *280*, 284
Meyer-Holzapfel, M., 23n, *27*
Milk let-down, 42f
Miller, N., 215, 218, 253, *278*, *281*
Mimicry, 221
Minkowski, M., *27*, *28*
Monkeys, 75-97 (*see also* Primates)
Monotropy, 302
Montgomery, K. C., *281*, 284
Moro response, 46
Mother, medication of, 29f
  orientation to baby, 4
  response to child's movements, 34

Mother love, 251
  impact on infant, 225
Mother-infant interaction. *See* Inter-
  action
Motivation, 114, 214ff, 229
Movements, interpretation of, 32f
Mowrer, O. H., 215, 253, *281*, 289
Myers, J. L., *282*, 286

Need, physiological, 215
Neurological abnormalities, 45-48
Neurosis, experimental, 83
  first, 42
Nipple, 40
Nissen, H. W., 23n, *28*
Nolte, A., 23n, *28*
Nursing, 121-141
  monkeys, 77, 81f

Object tests, 148f, 159
Olszewski, J., 5, *28*
Operant conditioning. *See* Condition-
  ing, instrumental
Orientation, of neonate, 3-35
  of kittens, 65

Parents' attachment to infant, 250
Pavlov, I. P., 167, 204, 217
Piaget, J., 168, 169, *170*, 220, *282*, 284
Play, 91
  in kittens, 58
  in monkeys, 85f
Pocock, R., 23n, *28*
Prechtl, H. F. R., 5, *28*, *45n*
Premack, D., *282*, 284, 288
Primates, mother-infant interaction,
  23f (*see also* Monkeys)
Privation, 213f
Psychotherapy, 11f
Puppies, 244

Rand, A. L., 23n, *28*
Reflex, abnormal, 45f
  contact clasp, 75
  response of neonate, 4f, 21f
  righting, 75
Reinforcement, 43, 93, 114, 163, 192,
  200, 214, 219ff, 272
  self-reinforcement, 89, 96, 114
Response strength variation, 179f, 203f
Response varying with age, 29

307